James G. March
Stanford University

Roger Weissinger-Baylon
Director, Center for Strategic
Decision Research

with the collaboration
of Pauline Ryan.

Ambiguity and Command

Organizational Perspectives on Military Decision Making

Pitman Publishing Inc.

A Longman Inc. Company

Pitman Publishing Inc.
1020 Plain Street
Marshfield, Massachusetts 02050

Longman Inc.
95 Church St.
White Plains, N.Y. 10601

Library of Congress Cataloging-in-Publication Data
Main entry under title:

Ambiguity and command.

"Based on presentations at a workshop on decision making in military organizations held in January 1984 at the Monterey Naval Postgraduate School"—Acknowledgments.
    Includes index.
    1. Leadership—Decision making—Congresses.
2. Command of troops—Decision making—Congresses.
3. United States—Armed Forces—Organization—
Congresses.   I. March, James G.   II. Weissinger-Baylon,
Roger.
VB203.A48   1985   355.3'3041   85-16875
ISBN 0-582-98831-4
ISBN 0-582-98833-0 (pb)

Manufactured in the United States of America
10 9 8 7 6 5 4 3 2 1

Contents

Acknowledgments

The papers in this volume are based on presentations at a Workshop on Decision Making in Military Organizations held in January 1984 at the Monterey Naval Postgraduate School. The workshop and the subsequent preparation of this volume were supported by the Office of the Assistant Secretary of the Navy, the Defense Communications Agency, Lockheed Missiles and Space Corporation, the Naval Electronic Systems Command, the Office of Naval Research, the Office of the Secretary of Defense/Net Assessment, MITRE Corporation, Boeing Aerospace Company, and SRI International. We are grateful for the support of these organizations, and particularly for the personal support of key people in them: Harold Kitson, Bev Daly, David Israel, John Kirzl, Mark Sher, David Signori, Walter LaBerge, Joel Lawson, Frank Deckelman, Romulus Fratilla, James Valentino, Paul Girard, Bert King, Andrew Marshall, Robert Everett, Bud Ekas, Larry Low, and Ray Leadabrand.

The Naval Postgraduage School was a gracious and efficient host for the workshop, and we would like to thank Commodore Robert Schumaker, the superintendent of the school, Richard Elster, chairman of the Department of Administrative Sciences, and Captain Glen Gaddis, controller of the school, for their support. The local arrangements team of Bruce Johnsen, Susan Woods, and Paulette Lynch managed the many details with delicacy and grace.

Computer demonstrations at the workshop were the work of Dan Dolk. We owe a debt to each of these, as well as to Robert Penn, who continued his assistance after returning to his responsibilities at the Naval Personnel Research and Development Center.

The workshop would not have been possible without the encouragement and support of senior military officers, not only the contributors to this volume but also Admirals Arleigh Burke, Ronald Hays, Isaac Kidd, Julian Lake, Paul McCarthy, Jr., Wesley McDonald, and William Small, Commodore C. E. Armstrong, and Generals Robert Gard and David Jones. We want to record here a special debt to Ike Kidd, who helped substantially in developing support for the workshop and goaded both military and academic participants in the workshop to listen to the others.

Pauline Ryan assisted the authors in editing several of the papers. The manuscript was typed by Ilse Dignam, Gloria Parks, and (through the wonders of modern word processing) several of the individual contributors. Anne Weissinger-Baylon coordinated the documents' final preparation. We are especially grateful for the persistent tolerance and good humor of all these good people displayed in dealing with our imperfections.

Anyone familiar with the naval research community will recognize the origins of the workshop in the foresight of Joel Lawson. Sooner than most, he realized the need to understand the military decision process. This judgment was based on his long experience in naval systems research, culminating in his role as Technical Director of the Naval Electronic Systems Command and its C3I Systems and Technology Directorate, and on his belief that better understanding would lead to improved systems for the command and control of military forces. We hope that the workshop, and the papers collected here, represent a small step in that direction.

James G. March
Roger Weissinger-Baylon

1

Introduction

JAMES G. MARCH

and

ROGER WEISSINGER-BAYLON

This book is about military decision making under conditions of ambiguity. By decision making under ambiguity we mean decision making in situations where objectives, technology, or experience are unclear, where solutions and problems are joined together partly because of their simultaneous availability, and where the attention of decision makers is attenuated by the existence of multiple simultaneous demands on their time. Our intent is to explore whether theories of decision making under ambiguity, developed through observations of nonmilitary organizations, might contribute to understanding and improving some aspects of command decision making in the navy.

It is clear that the idea of ambiguity is alien to ancient military traditions. Although observers of warfare have often noted the confusions of battle, the ideology of military decision making emphasizes the imposition of order through organization and command and the importance of clarity, coherence and comprehensiveness. As a result, examining ambiguity in military decision making is a little like examining the sexual habits of Victorian England. It requires a willingness to accept the possibility that things may not be exactly what they appear to be, or are supposed to be. At the same time, it also requires a recognition that the fact that things are not exactly what they appear to be does not imply that they are necessarily exactly the opposite.

Thirteen years ago, Cohen, March, and Olsen outlined a set of ideas about decision making under ambiguity. Their original paper (Cohen et al. 1972) is reproduced as an appendix to this volume. The model they developed, called the garbage can model, was originally used to describe university decision making, then subsequently extended to other kinds of organizations, including public bureaucracies. Since navies, like other military services, are large public bureaucracies, it seems natural to ask whether their peacetime decision making processes might appropriately be described in terms of garbage can ideas; and some of the papers in this book consider that question. However, limiting attention to bureaucratic decision making in a peacetime military organization would ignore situations of central concern to military commanders and to the understanding of military organizations. Decision making in Washington is important for the navy, as is understanding how that decision making may differ from operational decision making at sea, particularly during hostilities. But it is also important to understand operational decision making and to see to what extent the concepts developed for dealing with decision making under ambiguity can be used to illuminate naval decisions at sea.

Attending to the complications of operational decision making in the navy is also important for theories of organizations. Although there are enough elements of ambiguity in warfare to make assumptions of clarity problematic, operational decisons within the navy seem different from the kinds of decisions on which most research on ambiguity has been conducted. The garbage can model and related ideas of loose coupling were originally developed to describe educational organizations. They have proven to be relatively robust across other kinds of organizations, but they have never been thought to be characteristic of all kinds of decisions in all kinds of organizations. Decisions at sea provide an opportunity to examine the limits of garbage can concepts and to develop some modifications.

The papers collected here were originally given at a workshop held at the Naval Postgraduate School in Monterey and have been revised for this volume. Without committing either to the usefulness of the other, the workshop brought together organizational theorists interested in garbage can decision processes and military commanders expert in naval operational decision making. Participants were encouraged to reflect on their own research or their own experience, to use the research and experience of others as a base for further reflection, and to say what they thought was true. The papers in this book are the result. Some are written by flag officers of the United States Navy, some by academic students of organizations. We have not attempted to impose a standard language or form on them. Professors write like professors, and admirals write like admirals.

The first section of the book contains chapters written by academics. In Chapter 2, March and Olsen review research on the garbage can model, setting a theoretical background for what follows. Weissinger-Baylon, in Chapter 3, argues that naval warfare satisfies the preconditions of the garbage can model and explores the implications of a garbage can interpretation of information overload for the design of command and control systems. Crecine (Chapter 5) and Bromiley (Chapter 6) consider applications of garbage can processes to the peacetime navy. Crecine looks at the procurement of C3 systems as a prototype of military resource allocation decisions, particularly the elements of loose coupling that are revealed by an empirical investigation of such decisions. Bromiley's focus is on budgeting and planning systems (PPBS), which he describes as a "chain of garbage cans with structure on the connections among the cans." Like Weissinger-Baylon, Bromiley and Crecine, Cohen (Chapter 4) is concerned with effective organizational design in the face of ambiguity. He treats the problem of design as an abstract problem in specifying a structure of organizational relations and incentives that facilitates adaptation to a changing and ambiguous environment. Anderson and Fischer (Chapter 7), Carley (Chapters 8 and 9), and Gray (Chapter 10) present explorations of the formal garbage can model. Anderson and Fischer make an explicit representation of solution flows within the Cohen, March and Olsen model and detail some of the resulting implications. Carley focuses on the influence of hiring and firing rules for the efficiency of garbage can hierarchies. Gray examines the impact of movement from staff positions to decision making positions.

The second section of the book is devoted to contributions by experienced naval commanders. In Chapter 11, Hughes discusses the relevance of the garbage can model to fleet operational decision making, particularly under conditions of extreme time penalties, as in battle. Hayward (Chapter 12) compares naval decision making in three contexts: a major war at sea, tactical decision making in more limited settings, and peacetime investment decisions. He draws upon his experience at a high level of command during the Gulf of Sidra incident, the Iranian hostage rescue attempt, and planning for force levels during the Carter administration. In Chapters 13 and 14, Rowden and Metcalf report recent command experiences in the navy. Rowden discusses three crises that faced the United States Sixth Fleet during his command: the Gulf of Sidra incident, the assassination of Sadat, and the invasion of Lebanon by the Israeli army. Metcalf describes the invasion of Grenada from the point of view of the Joint Task Force Commander in that operation and against the background of his previous experience as surface warfare commander during the evacuation of Saigon. Finally, Train (Chapter 15) reflects on problems in the management of political-military crises, including not only the ambiguities in recognizing and defining crises, but also the problems of changing from peacetime to wartime modes (and back again) and the problems of balancing centralized control with decentralized authority.

Neither we nor our colleagues at the workshop made any attempt to develop a joint summary of the papers; it was an opportunity for thinking about decision making, not an occasion for forming conclusions. Consequently, the papers have not been shaped to produce a single, tight line of argument. There is no "party line," and the variation in observations is as large as the variation in style of presentation. Nevertheless, the papers in this volume expose some convergences, and it may be useful to anticipate them slightly here. They can be summarized in terms of three propositions:

Proposition 1: In order to accommodate important features of military organizations and situations, garbage can models need to include significant elements of structure that are absent from most discussions of the model in the theoretical literature.

As March and Olsen point out in their paper, much of the discussion of the garbage can model has emphasized a special case of the model in which both access and decision structures are completely open. This unsegmented version of the model has been useful and provocative, but the idea of temporal garbage can processes in decision making need not be restricted to such situations. In particular, applications to many organizations will probably require more specification of constraints on access of problems, solutions and decision makers to choice opportunities. As Bromiley and Hayward note, and several of the case studies make clear, navy organization and procedures place restrictions on the free flow of problems, solutions and decision makers.

In addition, there are several indications that garbage can models fail to capture the extent to which there are linkages among choices. It is a contextual theory, but it does not seem adequate to deal with what Hughes calls the "sequential, correlated, cumulative and climactic" nature of warfare. In a more formal way, Bromiley calls for specifying linkages between choice opportunities; and several of the case studies reveal ties among decisions that are not fully explained by the flows of problems, solutions and decision makers that are central to garbage can models.

The limitations on time (or energy) that are a major feature of garbage can models seem important to military decision making, but the models do not reflect the compelling deadlines that seem characteristic of many of the situations of interest in the case studies. The model as usually specified treats time as scarce but does not impose time pressure in the way that it arises in hostilities. This limitation of the models has been noted before, but it becomes particularly salient in application to operational decisions in the navy.

Finally, several writers, most notably Hughes, note the static nature of the assumptions underlying most discussions of garbage can models. Ambiguity, as reflected in unclear objectives and technologies and in fluid participation, is implicitly treated as a stable property of an organization. Frequently, experience tends to transform ambiguity into clarity (though not necessarily into accuracy). Over the course of a battle or a war, experience changes a relatively unstructured garbage can situation into a relatively structured one.

These observations are important. If a theory of temporal order in decision making is to be extended beyond the unsegmented special case, it will have to include some explicit attention to constraints on the flows of problems, solutions, and decision makers; to linkages between choices; to deadlines and their impact; and to changes in ambiguity over time. Some efforts in these directions have been made both in the papers in this volume and elsewhere (Weiner, 1976; Olsen, 1983), but they are incomplete.

Proposition 2: Although military decision making is rarely, if ever, a pure case of unsegmented garbage can decision making, there are significant garbage can elements even in the most operational decisions.

In military decision making, as in decision making within other types of organizations, there is a persistent tendency for problems and solutions to be linked by their simultaneous availability—a key feature of garbage can models. Thus, several authors have noted the frequency with which problems and solutions are connected in resource allocation decisions with only modest relevance of the latter to the former. Operational decisions in developing plans for the Iranian rescue mission were solution driven, as were some of the decisions in the Grenada invasion. In a similar vein, Lake (1984) described the way in which the development of the Tactical Command Center was a history of solutions looking for problems to which they might become attached.

A second key feature of garbage can models is the extent to which attention to any particular choice depends on the array of choices (garbage cans) currently available. Similarly, in descriptions of naval decision making, response to one decision situation depends on the time and energy claims of other situations. In formal discussions of garbage can models, decisions are described as being made by oversight when a choice opportunity arises but decision makers are busy attending to other choices. Thus, for example, a situation that has the potential of being defined as a "crisis" is treated routinely when problems and solutions are being attended to somewhere else. Train suggests that Angola represents such a case—a potential crisis that was not so defined, in part because the system was busy with other things. At the same time, problems, solutions and decision makers tend to track one another as they move from one choice opportunity to another. Problems associated with American resolve and prestige have linked a series of otherwise rather distinct political-military operations: Iran, Lebanon, Grenada.

The garbage can character of decision making is observable in naval training exercises intended to simulate battle conditions. Without the structures and pressures imposed by war, exercises tend to become collections of problems, solutions and decision makers. This becomes even more obvious as naval commanders with battle experience retire, and the problems and solutions of maintaining a peacetime navy subject to multiple, not necessarily consistent, internal and external political, professional and economic demands come to dominate operational decisions. Although, as Hughes argues, it seems reasonable to assume that hostile actions at sea will transform such a decision process, it is not clear that the transformation will be either instantaneous or complete. Descriptions of naval engagements, even those written by commanders in the glow of postbattle rationalization, seem replete with occasions on which decisions reflect relatively arbitrary mixes of problems, solutions and participants.

> Proposition 3: Although military decision making cannot be managed effectively by assuming a pure garbage can, significant insights into managerial problems and possibilities can be obtained by combining a more traditional view with some elements of garbage can thinking.

It has been argued in parts of the organizational literature that the temporal linkage between problems and solutions described in the garbage can model is often a more sensible approach to managing complex organizations in changing environments than are the procedures of classical planning. That argument is not addressed significantly in the present volume. Rather, the emphasis is on how a manager might cope intelligently with a process that contains substantial garbage can elements.

One set of recommendations suggests managing garbage cans through organizational design. The basic idea is that garbage can processes occur within access and decision (as well as other) structures and that managers can exercise control over the processes by manipulating the structures. This point of view is most explicit in the work of Carley, who considers the effectiveness of alternative structures, but it also drives some of the work by people like Bromiley and Cohen. The perspective is also implicit in comments by naval commanders, particularly those dealing with the delegation of authority. It is striking to observe the extent to which the classical argument for delegation (i.e., that the manager at the operational level has a better view of the local terrain) is supplemented by an argument that delegation shields an operational manager from garbage can dumps of miscellaneous problems and solutions.

A second set of recommendations focuses on improving the inventory of solutions. One clear vulnerability of a garbage can process is the arbitrary nature of temporal links between problems and solutions. As several naval commanders point out, this awkwardness can be ameliorated somewhat by an opportunistic exploitation of available resources, such as the masking of a rescue operation behind a prior location of a fleet in the Indian Ocean or the transformation of a senior army liaison officer into a deputy commander. An alternative management technique is proposed explicitly by Weissinger-Baylon, but it is implicit in almost all of the cases studies of naval operations and in the discussions of decision making by naval commanders. The strategy is to develop an inventory of potential solutions, so that the mix of problems and solutions generated at some future moment is more likely to include relevant solutions. The idea is somewhat in the spirit of contingency plans, but it emphasizes the prior development of multiple flexible competences more than it does planning and the multiplication of possible scenarios for the future.

These three propositions are consistent with the thrust of the papers in the volume. They do not summarize them. As we observed at the outset, the papers have a general theme and converge on a few broad points; but they are individual contributions with the specific insights of individual perspectives and experiences. An introduction cannot adequately anticipate the richness of those chapters, nor tell a meaningful story that will observe the differences in the ways the contributors describe the elephant. But we will record our own surprise and pleasure at the remarkable phenomenon of professors and admirals, neither group noted for tolerance or diffidence, each finding something of value buried in the other's funny language. It is a rare event when military commanders and academic scholars talk to each other, and an even rarer one when they show modest signs of having listened.

REFERENCES

Cohen, Michael D., March, James G., and Olsen, Johan P. "A Garbage Can Model of Organizational Choice." *Administrative Science Quarterly* 17(1972): 1–25.

Lake, Julian. Unpublished remarks, Conference on Decision Making in Military Organizations, Monterey, California, 1984.

Olsen, Johan P. *Organized Democracy.* Bergen, Norway: Universitetsforlaget, 1983.

Weiner, Stephen S. "Participation, Deadlines, and Choice." In *Ambiguity and Choice in Organizations,* edited by James G. March and Johan P. Olsen, pp. 225–250. Bergen, Norway: Universitetsforlaget, 1976.

THE ACADEMIC
PERSPECTIVE

2

Garbage Can Models of Decision Making in Organizations

JAMES G. MARCH

and

JOHAN P. OLSEN

ABSTRACT

Classical theories of choice in organizations emphasize decision making as the making of rational choices on the basis of expectations about the consequences of action for prior objectives, and organizational forms as instruments for making those choices. Empirical studies of actual decision-making processes seem to show something that is considerably more confusing. Those studies have led to the development of a set of ideas emphasizing the ambiguities of decision making, loose coupling within organizations, and considerable apparent disorder. Garbage can models are attempts to understand those phenomena within a temporal context. Rather than relying on a consequential order to form linkages within decision making, garbage can models of decision making assume a temporal order. That is, problems, solutions, and participants are assumed to be connected by virtue of their simultaneity. Garbage can ideas are discussed, along with some

James G. March is Fred H. Merrill Professor of Management, Political Science, and Sociology at Stanford University. Johan P. Olsen is a professor at the Institute for Public Administration and Organization Theory at the University of Bergen, Norway.

This paper is based on research supported by grants from the Norwegian Research Council for Science and the Humanities, the Norwegian Ministry of Consumer Affairs and Public Administration, the Naval Postgraduate School, the Mellon Foundation, the Spencer Foundation, the Stanford Graduate School of Business, Batelle Columbus Laboratories, and the Hoover Institution.

We are grateful for the comments of Pauline Ryan.

related efforts to define alternative temporal contexts within which to understand the empirical confusions of decision making. Since temporally ordered decision processes have implications for improving decision making as well as for describing it, some possibilities for intelligent action within garbage can structures are identified.

INTRODUCTION

The study of ambiguity and loose coupling in organizational decision making has a long history. There was, however, a resurgence of interest in such ideas about 10 to 15 years ago (Cohen et al., 1972; Cohen and March, 1974; March and Olsen, 1976; Weick, 1976); and subsequent work has extended the understanding of decision making under conditons in which goals, technologies and participation are changing and ambiguous and in which problems, solutions and participants are joined together more by the timing of their arrivals than by other attributes. This paper is intended to provide a short introduction to such ideas as they have developed in the study of organizational decision making, with particular reference to garbage can decision processes.

Concepts of ambiguity, organized anarchy, and loose coupling have been applied to organizations ranging from schools to navies, from firms to courts of law. Since the complexity of decision making in an organization is unlikely to be captured by a single model, any more than by the reports of a single participant or historian, the role of garbage can ideas is limited. They seek to identify and comprehend some features of decision making that are not well treated in other contemporary perspectives and yet are important. Thus, they are efforts to extend, rather than replace, understandings gained from other perspectives.

The garbage can model has been specified at several different levels of precision. In fact, the garbage can metaphor has been sufficiently evocative to have become, itself, a kind of garbage can. It has been used as a general frame within which to describe almost any choice situation in which there are complicated flows of participants, problems and solutions. It has been used as a lens to look at decision processes and to guide the collection of empirical observations. It has been used as the basis for a specific class of simulation models.

In order to understand the ideas, it is probably helpful to have them located within a more general picture of theories of organizational decision making as they have evolved over the past 30 years. We do that briefly in the first sections of this paper. Then we show how the garbage can notion is related to some of the complications and puzzles associated with earlier efforts to develop behavioral theories of decision making in organizations. It is an extension of those efforts rather than a contradiction. Finally, we discuss some recent and possible future directions for theoretical and empirical work in this field.

THEORIES OF ORGANIZATIONAL DECISION MAKING

Most theories of organizational decision making are theories of willful choice. They presume that choices are made intentionally in the name of individual or collective purpose and on the basis of expectations about future consequences of current actions. Within such theories, choice is assumed to depend on four things: (1) a knowledge of alternatives—decision makers have a set of alternatives for action, and these alternatives are defined by the situation and are known unambiguously, (2) a knowledge of consequences—decision makers know the consequences of alternative actions, at least up to a probability distribution, (3) a consistent preference ordering—decision makers have objective functions by which alternative consequences of action can be compared in terms of their subjective value; and (4) a decision rule—decision makers have rules by which to select a single alternative of action on the basis of its consequences for the preferences.

In the most familiar form of the model, we assume that all alternatives, the probability distribution of consequences following from each alternative, and the subjective value of each possible consequence are known; and we assume a choice is made by selecting the alternative with the highest expected value. Subject only to variations attributable to variations in preferences, therefore, such theories assume that choice is dictated by environmental conditions and is predictable from them. Heterogeneity in preferences tends to be denied, ignored or assumed away by some kind of natural selection argument. Within such a framework, the details of organizational processes involved in decision making cannot affect decision results. These details may vary from one organization to another, and they may appear to differ substantially from the assumptions specified explicitly in the theory, but the decisions are uniquely determined by environmental constraints.

The longevity of this framework is impressive. Simple choice models permeate contemporary theories of individual and collective behavior. The durability of the model is also understandable. Choice is a faith as well as a theory; it is linked to the ideologies of the Enlightenment and associated with definitions of the nature of the species. On a more practical level, models based on rational theories of choice capture some truth. Demand curves for consumer products generally have negative slopes, and labor unions usually are more resistant to wage cuts than to wage increases. Moreover, the core ideas are flexible. When the model seems not to fit, it is often possible to reinterpret preferences or knowledge and preserve the axioms. The prevalence of willful choice models of behavior in economics, political science, psychology, linguistics and anthropology attests to the attractiveness of choice as a vision of human behavior.

Such attraction extends to ordinary discourse and journalism. A reading of the leading newspapers or journals of any Western country will show that the primary interpretive model used by individuals in these societies is one of willful choice. The standard explanation provided for the actions of individuals or institutions involves two assertions. First, someone decided to have something happen. Second, the decision was made because it was in the self-interest of the decision maker to make it. In cases involving multiple actors, a third assertion may be added: different people, in their own self-interest, wanted different things and got what they wanted in proportion to their power. Ideas of willful, rational choice are the standard terms of discourse for answering the generic questions: Why did it happen? Why did you do it?

The same basic structure underlies modern decision engineering. Operations analysis, management science, decision theory and the various other analytical approaches to improving choices are variations on a theme of rational choice, as are standard ideas for determining the value of information and the design of information systems. Systematic rational analyses of choice alternatives have improved the blending of aviation fuel, the location of warehouses, the choice of energy sources, and the arrangement of bank queues, in addition to providing solutions to many other decision problems. And, although it is also possible to cite examples in which the consequences of decision analysis have been less benign, these modern technologies of choice have probably done more good than harm.

Over the past 30 years, this basic theory of choice has been considerably extended through the elaboration of computational procedures for making complicated calculations and the development of various more specific models within the general frame. Parallel to these developments, empirical research on the ways in which decisions are actually made by individuals and organizations has identified some problems in fitting the standard theory of choice to observed decision behavior.

EMPIRICAL OBSERVATIONS OF ORGANIZATIONAL DECISION MAKING

The theoretical ideas outlined above have guided most modern empirical efforts to observe how complex organizations make decisions. Many of the empirical observations, however, have proven to be inconsistent with a relatively pure theory of rational choice. Thirty years ago, empirical observations led students of organizations to make two major criticisms of the existing theory of organizational decision making. The first criticism was that the theory made excessive time and information demands on organizations (Simon, 1957a, 1957b; March and Simon, 1958). Information and time were treated as freely available resources. To ask that all consequences of all alternatives be known precisely seemed unreasonable given the empirical evidence that organizations considered only a small number of alternatives, examined only a small number of consequences related to only a subset of organizational goals and made relatively imprecise estimates.

The second criticism was that the theory assumed that all participants in an organization shared the same goals, or that, if they did not, conflict among them could be managed readily through the terms of some prior negotiated agreement (March, 1962; Cyert and March, 1963). In the case of a political organization, the agreement consisted of a coalition contract, or constitution, by which all members of a coalition, or polity, agreed to be bound by the policies specified through bargaining or legislation. Hence the familiar distinction between politics and administration. In the case of an economic organization, or other Weberian bureaucracy, the agreement consisted of an employment contract by which employees, in return for the payment of wages, agreed to act as though they had the same goals as the owner or other legitimate policy-maker. Empirical studies, however, seemed to indicate that conflict was endemic in organizations and tended to be interminable rather than settled by prior agreements.

These two criticisms led to considerable interest in the ways in which norms, rules and standard operating procedures are used by organizations to control the consequences of limited rationality and conflict. Rules and procedures might be seen as deliberately chosen by a person in formal authority as part of an employment contract (Simon, 1951). Alternatively, they might be seen as evolving through some kind of selection and diffusion process by which ineffective rules are gradually eliminated (Nelson and Winter, 1982). In either case, the actions of individual organizational members are protected from the potential perversities of bounded rationality and conflict of interest. Rather than being primarily a choice among alternatives on the basis of expectations, action involves the search for appropriate rules within established normative structures.

These criticisms of decision theory were well-known and widely accepted for some time before they penetrated formal theories of choice; but ultimately they were translated into acceptable theoretical statements through the development of information economics and theories of agency. Such theories consider information as a scarce resource subject to strategic manipulation in a world populated by self-interested rational actors. Ideas drawn from organizational studies of bounded rationality and internal conflict permeate modern economic theory in the form of discussions of moral hazard, asymmetric information, agency, signaling and optimal information strategies (Hirschleifer and Riley, 1979). Increasingly, this attention has been extended to a concern for the normative rules and institutions within which choice takes place (Shepsle, 1983). Although most behavioral students of organizations would argue that these theories are also incomplete and to some degree perversely inattentive to the way organizations operate, the earlier empirical criticisms have reformed theoretical thinking.

More recently, increased theoretical attention has been given to difficulties with conventional assumptions about organizational goals. Theories of rationality assume that organizations have preferences and that preferences will drive action. Indeed, in the revealed preference form of the theory, preferences are deduced from action. Theories of conflict assume that preferences are knowable and known by participants in an organization, although the mutual inconsistency of personal preferences makes it impossible to talk about an organizational goal with the orderliness required of classical preference functions. Individual preferences are expected to be stable. Decisions are made now in the name of preferences under the assumption that preferences will remain unchanged when the consequences of action are realized. Preferences are expected to be consistent. Any possible inconsistency is removed through the specification of trade-offs. Preferences are expected to be precise. Whether a particular outcome is consistent with a particular taste must be clear. Preferences are expected to be exogenous. In particular, they are presumed to be unaffected by choices made in their name.

All these theoretical features of preferences seem incongruent with empirical observations of choice behavior by individuals and organizations. Preferences, even individual preferences, do not seem to have the properties assumed by a willful theory of action. In fact, preferences are expressed but not followed. Preferences change; and they change as a result of choice. Preferences are inconsistent and imprecise. From the point of view of standard decision theory, it seems clear that organizations routinely and habitually make decisions without the kind of preferences that would satisfy the axioms of rational choice. Corwin (1981,p.270), observing that most empirical studies support the idea of loose coupling as a pervasive feature of decision making in organizations, argued that "if goals were not so prominent in our portrayals of organizations, we would be less surprised to learn that they are nonrational and only loosely coupled."

Limited rationality, conflict and preference ambiguity are major phenomena in organizations, but they do not exhaust the problems of matching theories of choice with observations of organizations. As early as 15−20 years ago, it was observed that theories of decision making underestimate the confusion and complexity surrounding actual decision making. Observations of decision making suggested that the link between problems and solutions was often tenuous. Many decisions were made by default. Decision processes frequently seemed to exercise problems rather than solve them. And the attention of participants was difficult to predict simply from properties of choices being considered. The instrumental linkages between means and ends, between action today and action tomorrow, between action in one part of the system and action in another, between plans and decisions and between decisions and implementation all tended to be obscure. The generic observation was that organizations could be viewed as relatively loosely coupled systems. Although this notion was used in a variety of not entirely consistent ways, it often seemed to describe real organizations.

Numerous empirical observations of organizations have confirmed a relatively confusing picture of decision making. Many things seem to be happening at once, technologies are changing and poorly understood; alliances, preferences and perceptions are changing; solutions, opportunities, ideas, people and outcomes are mixed together in ways that make interpretation uncertain and leave connections unclear (Kingdon, 1984).

It has been observed that individuals fight for the right to participate in decision making and then do not exercise that right with any vigor (Olsen, 1976a). Organizations ignore information they have, ask for more information and then ignore the new information when it is available (Feldman and March, 1981; March and Sevon, 1984). Organizations buffer processes of thought from processes of action (March, 1980; Brunsson, 1982). Managers spend substantial amounts of time in activities that appear to have few consequences beyond acknowledging the importance of others, as well as themselves (Cohen and March, 1974). Minor issues create governmental crises and unexpected patterns of political activation, then fade away again (Olsen, 1983, Chapter 3). Organizational participants contend acrimoniously over the adoption of a policy, but once that policy is adopted the same contenders appear to be largely indifferent to its implementation, or the lack of it (Christensen, 1976; Baier et al., 1982; Saetren, 1983). Although any one of the observations above could be explained in a number of ways, it is hard to consider the ensemble without seeing support for a perspective that views decision making as an occasion for exercising problems and solutions more than connecting them, for displaying decision making more than profiting from it and for exhibiting virtue more than using it.

March and Romelaer (1976) described this process in terms of a funny soccer game: "Consider a round, sloped, multi-goal soccer field on which individuals play soccer. Many different people (but not everyone) can join the game (or leave it) at different times. Some people can throw balls into the game or remove them. Individuals while they are in the game try to kick whatever ball comes near them in the direction of goals they like and away from goals they wish to avoid." (p.276)

THE GARBAGE CAN MODEL

The apparent disorderliness of many things in decision making has led some people to argue that there is very little order to organizational decision making and that it is best described as bedlam. Since the origin of the confusion may lie in the inadequacy of the theoretical ideas by which we try to order the observed events, rather than in the phenomena themselves (Glassman, 1973, p. 85; Weick, 1976, p. 9), a more conservative position is to assume that the ways in which organizations bring order to disorder differ somewhat from those anticipated by conventional theories. The garage can model is an effort to define an alternative way for discovering order in decision-making processes.

In most theories of action, we assume things are ordered by their consequential connections. Deviations from consequential order are viewed as aberrations. They are disturbances of a system otherwise held together by the way wanting something leads to doing something connected to the want, and doing something leads to consequences related to the intention. The central idea of garbage can models is the substitution of a temporal order for a consequential order. In a culture with a strong sense of monthly or yearly cycles, or of birth cohorts, we should not be overly surprised by the idea of a decision process affected by timing. In many human situations the most easily identified property of objects or events is the time subscripts associated with them. Thus, students of time allocation in organizations have observed the ways in which attention to problems seems to be determined as much by the time of their arrival as by assessments of their importance (Cohen and March, 1974; Olsen, 1976c).

In pure form, the garbage can model assumes that problems, solutions, decision makers and choice opportunities are independent, exogenous streams flowing through a system (Cohen et al., 1972). They are linked in a manner determined by their arrival and departure times and any structural constraints on the access of problems, solutions and decision makers to choice opportunities. In the absence of structural constraints within a garbage can process, solutions are linked to problems, and decision makers to choices, primarily by their simultaneity.

A garbage can process in such an unsegmented structure exhibits phenomena not entirely unfamiliar to empirical students of organizations (Cohen et al., 1972). Resolution of problems is not the most common decision style, except where load is very light or problems and decisions makers are severely restricted in movement. Decision making by flight (i.e., by the departure of problems from a choice arena) or by oversight (i.e., by action before problems become activated) is a major feature of the process. The process is thoroughly and generally sensitive to load. An increase in the number of problems, relative to the energy available to work on them, makes problems less likely to be solved, decision makers more likely to shift from one arena to another more frequently and choices longer to make and less likely to resolve problems. Decision makers and problems tend to track one another through choices. The process makes it hard simultaneously to reduce problem activity, problem latency and decision time. Some structures reduce one or two but at the cost of increasing the others. The process is frequently sharply interactive. Many of the outcomes are produced by distinct consequences of a particular timing of choices, problems and participant availability. Important problems are more likely to be solved than unimportant ones. But important choices are much less likely to resolve problems than are unimportant choices. And although a large proportion of the choices are made, the choice failures that do occur are concentrated among the most important and least important choices.

This unsegmented structure has attracted most of the attention in the literature; and empirical studies have revealed decision processes that appear to approximate such an open structure (March and Olsen, 1976). However, not all organizations are quite so unstructured. Garbage can choice situations have been characterized in terms of two structures. The first is the access structure, a relation between problems (or solutions) and choice opportunities. The access structure may require, allow or not allow a particular problem, if activated, to be attached to a particular choice. The second is the decision structure, a relation between decision makers and choice opportunities. This structure may require, allow or not allow that a particular decision maker participate in the making of a particular choice.

Access and decision structures can be imagined in any kind of arbitrary configuration, but two in particular have received formal consideration. The first, a specialized structure, is a structure that is decomposable into substructures that are open. Thus, a specialized decision structure is one in which it is possible to divide choice opportunities and decision makers into subgroups and match the two sets of subgroups so that every decision maker in a particular subgroup of decision makers has access to every choice opportunity in the matched set of choice opportunities, but to no other. The second, a hierarchical structure, is a structure in which access rights expand as a function of hierarchical rank. For example, in a hierarchical access structure, problems and choices are ordered; and each problem has access to choices of the same or lower rank.

Events within a garbage can decision process are understandable and, in some ways, predictable, but those events are not dominated by preferences. Typically, neither the processes not the outcomes appear to have a close relation with the explicit intentions of actors. In situations in which load is heavy and the structure is relatively unsegmented, intention is lost in context-dependent flows of problems, solutions, people and choice opportunities. Indeed, outcomes are frequently sufficiently dependent on elements of exogenously determined timing as to make the differences between what happens and what does not happen deceptively significant.

In their original article, Cohen, March and Olsen (1972) showed how garbage can processes within differing structures produced different problem-solving performance (i.e., effectiveness, efficiency) and resulted in different organizational climates (i.e., problem latency). Attention to such structural features of garbage can processes has characterized several more recent discussions. Anderson and Fischer (1985) introduced solutions explicitly, associated problems and solutions with decision makers and changed the rules for allocating decision makers to choices in order to reflect an individual focus on solving problems important to that individual. They obtained the same general results as were reported from the original but observed that the alternative assumptions had the effect of spreading decision makers among choice opportunities more evenly than did the original, thus reducing the consequences of bunching. Other theoretical analyses of garbage can processes in hierarchies have identified conditions for their relative efficiency (Carley, 1985).

Similarly, empirical students of decision making in organizations have noted how garbage can processes are affected by structural features of organizational life. March and Romelaer (1976) pointed out that the drift of decisions within a garbage can situation is not random but occurs in a context of beliefs, norms and institutions that produce a systematic bias, or "slope" to the soccer field. Powell (1978) found that timing was important to publishing decisions, but so was the structure imposed by company traditions, by the academic status of the author, and by whether the initiative was taken by the author or the publisher. Rommetveit (1976) showed that moving a decision from one arena with certain structural features to another with different characteristics apparently changed the outcome. Weiner (1976) explored the consequences of having flows of problems and participants interconnected and showed that deadlines made a difference in a garbage can process. The effect of belief structures and normative duties was observed by Enderud (1976) and Olsen (1976a). Various studies have examined the structural constraints imposed by demographic orders (March and March, 1977, 1978; Pfeffer, 1981b), symbolic orders (Meyer and Rowan, 1977; Pondy, 1978; March, 1981a; Pfeffer, 1981a; March and Olsen, 1983), historical orders (Etheredge, 1976; Olsen, 1976b; Levinthal and March, 1982), normative orders (Christensen, 1976; Kreiner, 1976; Olsen, 1976c; Rommetveit, 1976; Stava, 1976), formal organizational charts (Egeberg, 1981; Olsen, 1983) and accounting systems (Cooper et al. 1981).

The garbage can model has received considerable professional attention. Reviews of March and Olsen (1976) have been extensive (Moch and Pondy, 1977; Nystrom, 1977; Perrow, 1977; Becker, 1978; Bregnsbo, 1978; Mohr, 1978; Seashore, 1978; Enta and Jung, 1981). Garbage can concepts have been suggested as a framework for studying such relatively clear organized anarchies as educational organizations (Clark et al. 1980) and planning activities (Bromiley, 1985), but also for relatively less obvious candidates like defense resource allocation (Crecine, 1985) and naval warfare (Hughes, 1985; Weissinger-Baylon, 1985). The original ideas are now reflected in standard textbooks on organization theory (Weick, 1979; Scott, 1981; Miner, 1982; Pfeffer, 1982). They have been linked to a major shift in theoretical models used in the study of formal organizations (Scott, 1981, pp. 131–132; Mohr, 1982) and administrative science (Thompson and Vidmer, 1983). They have contributed to discussions of the uses of metaphor in explaining organizational behavior (Pinder and Bourgeois, 1982; Bourgeois and Pinder, 1983; Morgan, 1983) as well as to commentary on differences between case studies and ethnography (Lutz, 1982). They have even reached the exalted status of receiving an examination of their epistemological and ideological bases (Willower, 1979).

GENERALIZED GARBAGE CAN PERSPECTIVES

Discussions of garbage can models have initiated a search for more general forms of temporal orders. Observers of decision making in organizations usually assume that the primary results of a decision process are decisions, that decisions can be understood by an analysis of the process and that the centrality of a particular decision for an observer assures its centrality for participants. Such an exclusive focus on results, and the implicit projection of their theoretical importance onto a belief in their subjective centrality and unity, can be contrasted with the contextual perspective provided by the assumption of some general form of garbage can process.

Two elaborations of this view have been suggested. The first emphasizes the context of intertwined individual lives. Any specific decision-making process involves a collection of individuals and groups who are simultaneously involved in other things. It is hard to understand the way decisions are made in one arena without understanding how those decisions fit into the lives of participants. Each participant is involved in a life with a variety of changing demands. The meaning, importance and accessibility of any decision to any one participant depend on the mosaic of demands on that individual at that time.

From this perspective, decision processes are cross-sections of the lives of individual participants and cannot easily be understood without embedding them within those lives. The context is an intermeshing of the vagaries of demands on the lives of the whole array of actors. In this mosaic, any particular decision, however important to the observer, is likely to be substantially less important to many participants. Consequently, it seems likely that theories of choice in organizations, following the Weberian norm of a strict separation between bureaucratic office and personal life, may err in assuming a decision process abstracted from the complexities of ordinary lives.

To understand the course of a decision in full cross-sectional detail requires us to fit a decision, and the process that generates it, into the life of each participant. Then we can describe organizational action as the more or less fortuitous consequence of combining different moments of different lives. It is an old vision, but the requirements of scholarship are such that it has rarely been attempted seriously (Krieger, 1979, 1983).

A less comprehensive form of the multiple-lives perspective focuses on the allocation of attention. The idea is simple. Each potential participant in a decision process is faced with a personal decision problem—how to allocate scarce attention across various demands for attention. Individual decisions are made in the context of the array of opportunities presented. Individuals attend to some things and thus do not attend to others. Individual decisions to participate determine the collection of individuals involved in any specific decision and thus the outcome of the process. There are structural constraints on attention. Some people are not allowed to participate in some things; some people are required to do so. But within those structural limits, attention is allocated to a particular decision in a way that depends not only on properties of that decision but also on the variety of other demands that face various possible actors.

The most powerful part of the idea is also the most elementary. The attention given to a particular decision will depend both on attributes of that decision and on alternative claims on the attention of possible decision participants. Since those claims are not homogeneous across participants and do change over time, the attention that any particular decision will receive can be both quite unstable and remarkably independent of the properties of the decision. The same decision will attract more attention or less, depending on the other things that possible participants might be doing. As a result, participation in the process can be quite difficult to understand within a narrow focus on a single decision arena.

The importance of attention allocation is derived from a notion that attention is a scarce resource. In pure form, we can imagine each participant as having a fixed amount of time to allocate to organizational and other concerns and each unit of time as being allocated to one and only one activity. Such a pure form is useful as an initial metaphor, but it clearly requires some modification. It is possible to conserve attention by simultaneously attending to more than one activity, and it is possible to augment attention through purchase, barter, representation or threat. As a result of individual variations in capabilities for attention conservation and augmentation, some people have considerably more time than others to devote to decisions of importance to them.

The assumption of attention scarcity, however, does not depend on the simple metaphor. All that is required to make decision results highly contextual is that attention be a scarce resource among individuals, that changes in the array of demands on potential participants be neither homogeneous nor synchronous, and that decision outcomes depend on the pattern of attention.

The second elaboration of decision contexts emphasizes the symbolic aspects of decision making. Decision processes are sacred rituals, and decision making is linked to important symbolic concerns of organizations and society (Olsen, 1970; Edlefson, 1978; Bartunek and Keys, 1979; Roos and Hall 1980).

As a result, many of the phenomena within a decision process are better understood as part of a symbolic process than as a way to produce substantive decision results (Pfeffer, 1981a).

The symbolism of decision making reflects two interrelated phenomena. At a simple instrumental level, organizations and the individuals in them need to communicate to their observers that the decisions they make are legitimate (Meyer and Rowan, 1977). Legitimacy is established by showing that the decisions accomplish appropriate objectives or by showing that they are made in appropriate ways. The first demonstration is often difficult. It is hard to show the linkage between decision and outcome. Thus, legitimacy often depends as much on the appropriateness of the process as it does on the outcomes. Both for the organization and the observer, process measures are possible surrogates for outcome measures. It is a story familiar to students of organizational control and should not be surprising in this context.

Organizations establish that they are good decision makers by making decisions in a way that symbolizes the qualities that are valued. They consult relevant people, consider alternatives, gather information and act decisively but prudently. Decision making is, in part, a performance designed to reassure decision makers and others that things are being done appropriately. Good decision makers are those who do what good decision makers do, and as organizations and decision makers compete for legitimacy and reputations, decision processes are ways in which they attempt to signal competence at decision making. Where, as is often the case, decision quality is difficult to measure directly, the competition for reputation is likely to lead to an emphasis on displaying process attributes. Plans, information gathering, analysis, consultation and other observable features of normatively approved decision making are thus explicable less in terms of their contribution to decision outcomes than as symbols and signals of decision-making propriety (Feldman and March, 1981).

The symbolism of decision process is not limited to the tactics of competition among organizations and decision makers. The idea of intelligent choice is a central idea of modern ideology, and organizations are institutions dedicated to that vision of life. Consequently, activities within organizations, and particularly decision activities, are part of a set of rituals by which a society assures itself that human existence is built around choice. Such rituals confirm that human institutions are manifestations of the intelligent control of human destiny through rational action. The decision process is a ritual by which we recognize saints, socialize the young, reassure the old, recite scripture and come to understand the nature of our existence (Olsen, 1970; March and Sevon, 1984).

To recognize the symbolic significance of decision making is not to denigrate it. Symbols and social ritual may be a way of concealing the reality of outcome perversities. Unquestionably, symbols sometimes mask realities (Edelman, 1964). However, the converse can also be true. Students of decision making probably have a systematic tendency to exaggerate the significance of the explicit substantive results of decisions and to underestimate the significance of the symbolic contributions that decision making gives to organizations and society. For such students, symbols obfuscate outcomes. Yet it is hard to imagine a society with modern Western ideology that would not require a well-elaborated and reinforced myth of organizational choice, both to sustain a semblance of social orderliness and meaning and to facilitate change. We may quarrel with the ideology and seek a different set of symbols; but, by most reasonable measures, the symbolic consequences of organizational decision processes are at least as important as the substantive consequences. In many respects, decision results are minor embellishments of a life of symbols, rather than the other way around.

The contexts of multiple lives and symbols, like the garbage can, are alternative ways of ordering the confusions of an apparently disordered world. It is undoubtedly true that both organizations and the individuals in them often act in the name of consequences and in pursuit of objectives and that organizational decision making can often be understood in terms of intentional, consequential choice. However, where environments and organizations are relatively complex and objectives and history are relatively ambiguous, the decision processes that have been observed seem inadequately comprehended within such a frame. In such situations, alternative visions of how decisions happen in organizations lead to an emphasis on rule-bound decision making and the adaptation of rules over time, temporal linkages between problems and solutions, and the symbolic and ritual aspects of choice in organizations.

INTELLIGENT ACTION IN A DISORDERLY WORLD

Research on temporally ordered decision processes in organizations has pursued two tacks. The first is behavioral. It explores the ways in which organizations make decisions without clearly defined preferences and where problems and solutions seem loosely coupled. The second tack is normative, concerned with the engineering of better decision making. The engineering of choice has been preeminently a domain for decision theorists. The conventional dogma of modern decision engineering requires that decision outcomes be the focus of decision processes and that such outcomes represent willful choices made on the basis of prior expectations and prior preferences. Garbage can decision processes seem patently inconsistent with such dogma. Nevertheless, a number of analysts have concluded that there are possibilities for intelligent action within the context of loosely coupled organizations, ambiguous preferences and temporally ordered processes.

Different reactions to the disparity between the garbage can realities of decision processes in organizations and decision theory utopias lead to three prototypic responses: (1) some analysts recommend changing organizations in order to make them conform to the normative ideals of decision theory; (2) some analysts recommend accepting the reality of garbage can processes and adopting strategies for adaptation to such processes in the name of individual rational actors; and (3) some analysts recommend examining the good sense of decision theory, seeing elements of intelligence in the ways in which actual organizations deviate from decision theory norms.

Reforming Garbage Can Processes

It is easy to view garbage can processes as muddleheaded, to accept the general idea that, although *actual* decision processes involve unclear goals and temporal orders, *proper* decision processes should be based on more classical visions of choice—clear goals, understood technologies, orderly participation. Such a view leads to efforts to convert organizational processes into more systematically rational ones through reorganization or efficient organizational design. For instance, some students of military (Thompson, 1980; Sabrosky et al.,1982) as well as other organizations (Lutz, 1982) accept organized anarchy descriptions as relevant to organizational decision making. They argue that garbage can processes inhibit efficiency and responsiveness and greatly increase the likelihood of failure.

The argument is that reform is necessary and possible and that it consists in transforming the existing processes into others more nearly in conformity with classical ideas of optimal choice behavior and efficient organization. Such an argument follows the tradition of interpreting reorganization in instrumental terms (Mosher, 1967). It defines the primary task of organizational leadership not as the making of decisions but as the creation of an organizational environment and framework that makes the organization function well (Thompson et al., 1959; Simon, 1960). This tradition is echoed in recent treatises on the importance of establishing an organizational culture (Deal and Kennedy, 1982; Peters and Waterman, 1982). Efforts in this vein to modify garbage can processes through organizational design are, for the most part, efforts to eliminate the temporal order of a garbage can and its effects. They embrace an instrumental vision of formal organization and a perspective on decision making that emphasizes willful choice.

The history of reorganization, however, indicates the problematic roles of intention, reflection and choice in the development of institutions (Hamilton et al.,1787; Mill, 1861; Scott, 1981). Organizations change continuously (March, 1981b), but hopes for a firm theoretical basis for organizational design remain mostly unfulfilled (Fox, 1974; Seidman, 1974, 1980; Szanton, 1981). The long-range development of formal organizations and institutions is less a product of intentions, plans and consistent decisions than of incremental adaptation to changing problems with available solutions within gradually evolving structures of meaning (March and Olsen, 1983, p.292). Prescriptions for organizational redesign tend to be contradictory (Simon, 1957a; Kaufman, 1977); and no matter which principles of organization are followed, it seems to be inevitable that administrative problems persist (March and Simon, 1958). While organizations sometimes follow predecided plans (Roness, 1979; Egeberg, 1984), major reorganizations often become typical garbage cans themselves. They evoke metaphors of gardening rather than engineering, of gathering rather than hunting (Szanton, 1981; March and Olsen, 1983).

Consider, for example, our recent description of decision making with respect to administrative reorganization in American national government:

"Although some features of political trading are fairly stable over the history we have examined, political bargaining over reorganization is sensitive to contextual fluctuations and to short-run changes in political attention. Reorganization is an ecology of games in which attention is problematic. Access rules for participants and issues change over time in response to experience, conscious attempts to control reorganizations, and the cumulative twists of history, but the general absence of precise rules controlling access makes it likely that reorganizations will become . . . highly contextual combinations of people, choice opportunities, problems, and solutions. Thus the course of events surrounding a reorganization seems to depend less on properties of the reorganization proposals or efforts than on the happenstance of short-run political attention, over which reorganization groups typically have little control. . . . . Any particular reorganization proposal or topic for discussion is an arena for debating a wide range of current concerns and ancient philosophies. Since there are few established rules of relevance and access, reorganizations tend to become collections of solutions looking for problems, ideologies looking for soapboxes, pet projects looking for supporters, and people looking for jobs, reputations, or entertainment. The linkages among these concerns seem to be testimony more to their simultaneity than to their content, and administrative reform becomes associated with issues, symbols, and projects that sometimes seem remote from the initial impetus behind the effort. (March and Olsen, 1983, pp. 285–287)

Despite the difficulties involved in understanding and controlling the structure of social organizations and institutions, attention to the institutional factors in human behavior and to organizational design has increased in recent years (Nystrom and Starbuck, 1981; Starbuck and Nystrom, 1981; March and Olsen, 1984). Thus, it is probably important to distinguish situations in which organizations may be susceptible to deliberate willful reorganization from situations in which the process of change more nearly resembles a garbage can process. Current literature provides little help with such distinctions, although it seems likely that different considerations may be involved in designing acounting systems for organized anarchies (Cooper et al., 1981), designing an organizational structure for a single agency (Olsen, 1976d; Sproull et al., 1978) and designing a comprehensive reorganization of a nation's public bureaucracies (March and Olsen, 1983).

Adapting to Garbage Can Processes

An alternative to eliminating or modifying garbage can processes and loose coupling through reorganization is to adapt to the processes intelligently in the name of individual or group preferences. Some suggestions for such adaptation call for changes of thinking about decision making and organizational forms. For example, it is argued that educational planning (Clark, 1980) is likely to fail because it is built on a bureaucratic, rather than a loosely coupled, conception of an organization. It seems necessary to reconsider some central mechanisms of organizational intelligence in organized anarchies, including coordination (Strand, 1977; Corwin, 1981), control (Hofstede, 1981), evaluation (Cameron, 1980; Lotto, 1982, 1983) and transfer pricing (Swieringa and Waterhouse, 1982). In such a spirit, McCaskey (1979, p. 47) notes that "we need alternatives to goal-directed approaches for how a manager can act in a rational way. We need broader, more complex ways of thinking about planning, deciding, management, and organizing that do not depend on pre-existing specific goals."

A few suggestions of that sort have been made (March, 1973, 1978b; Cohen and March, 1974)—for example, that goals be treated as hypotheses subject to experimentation and doubt, that intuition be treated as real, that tolerance be extended to certain kinds of transitional hypocrisy, that judicious ability to forget past experience and to reinterpret past experience be encouraged, that management be viewed partly as upsetting preconceptions of what the organization is doing, that planning and evaluation be used as places for reinterpreting past behavior and that playfulness in organizations be accepted.

Guidelines for less heroic rational action within organized anarchies have also been suggested. For the most part, these involve ideas of how the confusion of garbage can processes can be relatively unobtrusively managed or exploited (Cohen et al., 1972; Cohen and March, 1974; Weiner, 1976; Padgett, 1980). There are some features of garbage can processes that are particularly relevant to an individually rational actor (Cohen and March, 1974). For example, most substantive issues most of the time have low salience for most people. Symbolic issues are likely to be important. Attention is a scarce good. At the same time, almost any decision is capable of becoming a garbage can for almost any problem. As a result, the processes are easily subject to overload.

From such features, Cohen and March (1974) derive eight basic rules for use in influencing the course of decisions in a garbage can process:

1. Spend time. Since time is a scarce good, someone who is prepared to spend time is offering a valuable resource.

2. Persist. Losses and victories are partly fortuitous, due to the particular pattern of attention generated on a particular occasion (March and Romelaer, 1976; Baier et al. 1985).

3. Exchange status for substance. Symbolic issues are likely to be more important to many participants than the substantive issues (Pondy, 1978; Pfeffer, 1981a). Thus, someone willing to trade in the opposite direction is in a favorable trading position (Carnegie, 1936).

4. Facilitate opposition participation. The frustrations of garbage can decision processes tend to reduce aspirations.

5. Overload the system. Any individual proposal may easily be defeated in a garbage can, but someone with a large number of projects will find some

fraction of them being successful. Deadlines can also be used to manage the flow of problems (Arvedson, 1974; Weiner, 1976).

6. Provide garbage cans. Deflect potentially irrelevant problems and solutions into innocuous choice situations—for example, discussions of long-term plans and organizational objectives (Christensen, 1976; Sproull et al. 1978; March and Olsen, 1983).

7. Manage unobtrusively. Sail the organization, rather than powerboat it, through the use of high-leverage minor interventions.

8. Interpret history. Control definitions of what is happening and what has happened to take advantage of the changing patterns of participation.

Embracing Garbage Can Processes

Not all analysts see garbage cans and ambiguity as a pathology. For example, Cohen (1984) has discussed the relation between garbage can processes and the flexibility needs of an adaptive system and jointly with Axelrod (Cohen and Axelrod, 1984) has shown some of the advantages of ambiguity for organizational efficacy. Indeed, much of the modern literature on decision making in organizations finds substantial normative attractiveness in this special kind of disorder. It questions classical visions of decision making in organizations not only in terms of their descriptive accuracy but also as guides to action. It is argued that ambiguous goals, loose coupling and garbage can processes are not only common phenomena but frequently also forms of intelligence.

With respect to ambiguity, the argument is that ambiguous preferences have sensibility that is obscured by the conventional model of consequential rationality (March, 1971). In particular, it is argued that ambiguity allows preferences to develop through action, that ambiguity reflects an intelligent modesty about the adequacy of guesses about future wants, that ambiguity is part of a sensible effort to manage the tendency for preferences to become inappropriate and that ambiguity is a way of building protection from the political use of rational argument (March, 1978a).

Loose coupling and temporal ordering can be seen partly as the natural consequence of the fact that organizations not only are decision-making institutions but perform many other functions. An organization designed to optimize decision capabilities would presumably not be optimal from other important points of view. Thus, a less than perfect decision procedure should be expected. The argument goes further than that, however, and asserts that loose coupling does, in fact, contribute to adaptability. It buffers inconsistencies (Weick, 1976; Enderud, 1977, 1980; Pfeffer and Salancik, 1978, p. 13; Scott, 1981, p. 108; March, 1981a; Lotto, 1982), including the inconsistent demands of effective thinking and effective acting (March, 1980; Brunsson, 1982). It facilitates change by making it less decisive (Hagan et al. 1979); it legitimates controversies, fosters self-evaluation and stimulates exploration of new environmental niches (Hedberg et al., 1976); and it provides the vitality of sensible foolishness and playfulness that is likely to be threatened by managerial stringency (West, 1979). In general, Moch and Pondy (1977) describe loosely coupled organizations as "all-terrain" vehicles, having parts that are able to function relatively autonomously and to absorb and internalize variety and the capability of responding successfully to environmental variation and unpredictability.

CONCLUSION

The modern history of research on organizational decision making can be written in terms of the gradual relaxation of rigid assumptions in classical theories of choice. Garbage can models of decision making, together with other ideas of temporal context reviewed in this paper, belong to that history. Theories of limited rationality relaxed the assumptions about cognitive capacities and knowledge. Theories of conflict relaxed the assumptions about the unity of objectives. Theories of ambiguity and temporal order relax the assumptions about the clarity of objectives and causality, as well as the centrality of decisions to the process of decision making.

Garbage can phenomena are pervasive. They can be observed in many different kinds of organizations and under many different circumstances. Understanding any particular decision process will probably be made easier by an awareness of temporal contexts. But such ideas are only a part of a collection of ideas about decision making, all of which are required for a full appreciation of the phenomenon. Just as it is necessary to identify features of an organization or a choice situation that make ideas of limited rationality, ambiguity or conflict more or less salient to an understanding of decision making, it is necessary to identify factors that make garbage can processes more or less likely to be conspicuous. At the same time, there exists a family of garbage can models, not just a single one. Variations in the model may be obtained by varying several different features of that model.

First, the structural limits on movement of problems, solutions and participants to and from choices can be verified across wide ranges. Thus, the model can be used to explore the consequences of garbage can processes in relatively tightly coupled systems, containing hierarchies and division of labor, as well as in less tightly coupled systems that have been the primary focus of attention so far. Exploration of temporal contexts in highly structured organizations has hardly begun.

Second, the model may be varied by altering assumptions about the way in which participants, problems and solutions move from one choice to another, and the extent to which problems and solutions are associated with particular participants and move with them. It is possible to imagine various rules by which problems are initially attached to choices and by which they move. The original model assumed movement to the accessible choice closest to decision, but it is possible to explore the implications of assuming various forms of inertia in movement or to increase random elements in movement.

Third, assumptions about energy (time) and deadlines can be modified. The model assumes that there are both energy demands (carried primarily by problems) and energy resources (carried primarily by participants or solutions) and that choices are made when adequate resources are available. Alternative assumptions about how energy enters the system and the requirements for choices can also be made.

Fourth, the model can be varied by changing assumptions about the degree to which participants are conscious of garbage can processes and temporal orders, and the degree to which arrivals and interconnections among problems, solutions, participants and choice opportunities can be controlled. As participants become more self-conscious actors in a recognized garbage can, the system becomes more subject to explicit gaming.

This family of models, nested in a larger family, represents one set of theoretical ideas within which to explore fundamental issues about the ways in which deterministic structures, chance and willful choice interact in organizational contexts. It is not the only such family; it is a possibly useful one. By emphasizing temporal orders within organizations, the models provide a framework for considering how decisions happen with only loose means-ends linkages but without disorderliness.

REFERENCES

Anderson, Paul A., and Fischer, Gregory W. "A Monte Carlo Model of a Garbage Can Decision Process." In *Ambiguity and Command: Organizational Perspectives on Military Decision Making*, Edited by James G. March and Roger Weissinger-Baylon. Marshfield, Mass.: Pitman, 1986.

Arvedson, Lennart A. "Deadlines and Organizational Behavior." Ph.D. Dissertation, Graduate School of Business, Stanford University, 1974.

Baier, Vicki E., March, James G. and Saetren, Harald "Implementation as a Doubtful Metaphor." Mimeographed. Stanford, Calif.: Stanford University, 1985.

Bartunek, Jean M., and Keys, Christopher B. "Participation in School Decison Making." *Urban Education* 14(1979): 52−75.

Becker, Bernd. "Ambiguity and Choice in Organizations" (review). *Die Vervaltung. Zeitschrift fur Vervaltungswissenschaft* 11(1978): 255−256.

Bourgeois, V. Warren, and Pinder, Craig C., "Contrasting Philosophical Perspectives in Administrative Science: A Reply to Morgan." *Administrative Science Quarterly* 28(1983): 608−613.

Bregnsbo, Henning. "Ambiguity and Choice in Organizations" (review). *Statsvetenskaplig Tidsskrift* 4(1978): 296−298.

Bromiley, Philip. "Planning Systems in Large Organizations: Garbage Can Approach with Application to Defense PPBS." In *Ambiguity and Command: Organizational Perspectives on Military Decision Making*, edited by James G. March and Roger Weissinger-Baylon. Marshfield, Mass.: Pitman, 1985.

Brunsson, Nils. "The Irrationality of Action and Action Rationality: Decisions, Ideologies, and Organizational Actions." *Journal of Management Studies* 19(1982): 29−44.

Cameron, Kim. "Critical Questions in Assessing Organizational Effectiveness." *Organizational Dynamics* 9(1980): 66−80.

Carley, Kathleen. "Measuring Efficiency in a Garbage Can Hierarchy." In *Ambiguity and Command: Organizational Perspectives on Military Decision Making*, edited by James G. March and Roger Weissinger-Baylon. Marshfield, Mass.: Pitman, 1986.

Carnegie, Dale. *How to Win Friends and Influence People.* New York: Simon & Schuster, 1936.

Christensen, Søren. "Decision Making and Socialization." In *Ambiguity and Choice in Organizations*, edited by James G. March and Johan P. Olsen. Bergen, Norway: Universitetsforlaget, 1976.

Clark, David L., and others, eds. "New Perspectives on Planning in Educational Organizations." San Francisco: Far West Laboratory for Educational Research and Development, 1980.

Cohen, Michael D. "Artificial Intelligence and the Dynamic Performance of Organizational Designs." In *Ambiguity and Command: Organizational Perspectives on Military Decision Making*, edited by James G. March and Roger Weissinger-Baylon. Marshfield, Mass.: Pitman, 1986.

Cohen, Michael D. and Axelrod Robert, "Coping with Complexity: The Adaptive Value of Changing Utility." *American Economic Review* 74(1984): 30–42.

Cohen, Michael D., and March, James G. *Leadership and Ambiguity: The American College President.* New York; McGraw-Hill, 1974.

Cohen, Michael D., March, James G., and Olsen, Johan P. "A Garbage Can Model of Organizational Choice." *Administrative Science Quarterly* 17(1972): 1–25.

Cooper, David J., Hayes, David, and Wolf, Frank, "Accounting in Organized Anarchies: Understanding and Designing Acounting Systems in Ambiguous Situations." *Accounting, Organizations, and Society* 6(1981): 175–191.

Corwin, Ronald G. "Patterns of Organizational Control and Teacher Militancy: Theoretical Continuities in the Idea of 'Loose Coupling.' " *Research in Sociology of Education and Socialization* 2(1981): 261–291.

Crecine, J. Patrick, "Defense Resource Allocation: 'Garbage Can' Analysis of C3 Procurement." In *Ambiguity and Command: Organizational Perspectives on Military Decision Making*, edited by James G. March and Roger Weissinger-Baylon. Marshfield, Mass.: Pitman, 1986.

Cyert, Richard M., and March, James G. *A Behavioral Theory of the Firm.* Englewood Cliffs, N.J.: Prentice-Hall, 1963.

Deal, Terry E., and Kennedy, A. A. *Corporate Cultures.* Reading, Mass.: Addison-Wesley, 1982.

Edelman, Murray. *The Symbolic Uses of Politics.* Urbana, Ill.: University of Illinois Press, 1964.

Edlefson, Carla J. 'Participatory Planning for Organizational Change: The Case of Project Redesign.'' Ph.D. Dissertation, School of Education, Stanford University, 1978.

Egeberg, Morten. *Stat og organisasjoner.* Bergen, Norway: Universitetsforlaget, 1981.

Egeberg, Morten. *Organisasjonsonsutforming i offentlig virksomhet.* Oslo, Norway: Aschehoug, 1984.

Enderud, Harald. "The Perception of Power." In *Ambiguity and Choice in Organizations*, edited by James G. March and Johan P. Olsen. Bergen, Norway: Universitetsforlaget, 1976.

Enderud, Harald. *Four Faces of Leadership in an Academic Organization.* Copenhagen, Denmark: Nyt Nordisk Forlag, 1977.

Enderud, Harald. "Administrative Leadership in Organised Anarchies." *International Journal of Institutional Management in Higher Education* 4(1980) 235–253.

Enta, Yuji, and Jung, Allison. "Ambiguity and Choice in Organizations" (review). *Keiei Shirin*, Faculty of Business Administration, Hosei University (Japan) (March 1981): 169–176.

Etheredge, Lloyd S. *The Case of the Unreturned Cafeteria Trays.* Washington, D.C.: American Political Science Association, 1976.

Feldman, Martha S., and March, James G. "Information as Signal and Symbol." *Administrative Science Quarterly* 26(1981): 171–186.

Fox, Douglas M., ed. "President Nixon's Proposals for Executive Reorganization." *Public Administration Review* 34(1974): 487–495.

Glassman, Robert B. "Persistence and Loose Coupling in Living Systems." *Behavioral Science* 18(1973): 83–98.

Hagan, John, Hewitt, John D., and Alwin, Duane F. "Ceremonial Justice: Crime and Punishment in a Loosely Coupled System." *Social Forces* 58(1979): 506–527.

Hamilton, Alexander, Jay, John, and Madison, James. *The Federalist Papers*. New York: Pocket Books, 1787/1964.

Hedberg, Bo L.T., Nystrom, Paul C., and Starbuck, William H. "Camping on Seesaws: Prescriptions for a Self-Designing Organization." *Administrative Science Quarterly* 21(1976): 41–65.

Hirschleifer, J., and Riley, J.G. "The Analytics of Uncertainty and Information—An Expository Survey." *Journal of Economic Literature* 17(1979): 1375–1421.

Hofstede, Geert. "Management Control of Public and Not-for-Profit Activities." *Accounting, Organizations, and Society* 6(1981): 193–211.

Howell, Jon P., and Wall, Larry C. "Executive Leadership in an Organized Anarchy: the Case of HSOs." *Health Care Management Review* 8(1983): 17–26.

Hughes, Wayne P. "Garbage Cans at Sea." In *Ambiguity and Command: Organizational Perspectives on Military Decision Making*, edited by James G. March and Roger Weissinger-Baylon. Marshfield, Mass.: Pitman, 1985.

Kaufman, Herbert "Reflections on Administrative Reorganization." In *Setting National Priorities: The 1978 Budget*, edited by J.A. Pechman. Washington, D.C.: Brookings, 1977.

Kingdon, John W. *Agendas, Alternatives, and Public Policies*. Boston, Mass.: Little, Brown, 1984.

Krieger, Susan. *Hip Capitalism*. Beverly Hills, Calif.: Sage, 1979.

Krieger, Susan. *Mirror Dance*. Philadelphia: Temple University Press, 1983.

Kreiner, Kristian, "Ideology and Management in a Garbage Can Situation." In *Ambiguity and Choice in Organizations*, edited by James G. March and Johan P. Olsen. Bergen, Norway: Universitetsforlaget, 1976.

Lincoln, James R., Hanada, Mitsuyo, and Olson, Jon "Cultural Orientations and Individual Reactions to Organizations: A Study of Employees of Japanese-Owned Firms." *Administrative Science Quarterly* 26(1981): 93–115.

Levinthal, Daniel, and March, James G. "A Model of Adaptive Organizational Search." *Journal of Economic Behavior and Organization* 2(1982): 307–333.

Lotto, Linda S. "Revisiting the Role of Organizational Effectiveness in Educational Evaluation." Paper presented at the annual meeting of the American Educational Research Association, New York, 1982.

Lotto, Linda S. "More on Loose Coupling."*Aministrative Science Quarterly* 28(1983): 294–296.

Lutz, Frank W. "Tightening up Loose Coupling in Organizations of Higher Education." *Administrative Science Quarterly* 27(1982) 653–669.

March, James C. and March, James G. "Almost Random Careers: The Wisconsin School Superintendency, 1940-1972." *Administrative Science Quarterly* 22(1977): 377–409.

March, James C., and March James G. "Performance Sampling in Social Matches." *Administrative Science Quarterly* 23(1978): 434–453.

March, James G. "The Business Firm as a Political Coalition." *Journal of Politics* 24(1962): 662–668.

March, James G. "The Technology of Foolishness." *Civiløkonomen* 8(1971): 4–12.

March, James G. "Model Bias in Social Action." *Review of Educational Research* 42(1973): 413–429.

March, James G. "Bounded Rationality, Ambiguity, and the Engineering of Choice." *Bell Journal of Economics* 9(1978a): 587–608.

March, James G. "American Public School Administration: A Short Analysis." *School Review* 82(1978b):217–250.

March, James G. "How We Talk and How We Act: Administrative Theory and Administrative Action." Champaign-Urbana, Ill.: David D. Henry Lecture on Administration, University of Illinois, 1980.

March, James G. "Decisions in Organizations and Theories of Choice." In *Assessing Organizational Design and Performance*, edited by Andrew Van de Ven and William Joyce. New York: Wiley Interscience, 1981a.

March, James G. "Footnotes to Organizational Change." *Administrative Science Quarterly* 26(1981b): 563–577.

March, James G. "Theories of Choice and Making Decisions." *Transaction/SOCIETY* 20(1982): 29–39.

March, James G., and Olsen, Johan P. *Ambiguity and Choice in Organizations*. Bergen, Norway: Universitetsforlaget, 1976.

March, James G., and Olsen, Johan P. "Organizing Political Life: What Administrative Reorganization Tells Us about Government." *American Political Science Review* 77(1983): 281–296.

March, James G., and Olsen, Johan P. "The New Institutionalism: Organizational Factors in Political Life." *American Political Science Review* 78(1984): forthcoming.

March, James G., and Romelaer, P. "Position and Presence in the Drift of Decisions." In *Ambiguity and Choice in Organizations*, edited by James G. March and Johan P. Olsen, Bergen, Norway: Universitetsforlaget, 1976.

March, James G. and Sevon, Guje "Gossip, Information and Decison Making." In *Advances in Information Processing in Organizations*, Vol. 1, edited by L.S. Sproull and P.D. Larkey, Greenwich, Conn.: JAI Press, 1984.

March, James G., and Simon, Herbert A. *Organizations*. New York: Wiley, 1958.

McCaskey, Michael B. "The Management of Ambiguity." *Organizational Dynamics* 7(1979): 31–48.

Meyer, John W., and Rowan, Brian. "Institutionalized Organizations: Formal Structure as Myth and Ceremony." *American Journal of Sociology* 83(1977): 340–363.

Mill, John S. *Considerations on Representative Government*. South Bend, Ind.: Gateway Editions, 1861/1962.

Miner, John B. *Theories of Organizational Structure and Process*. Chicago, Ill.: Dryden Press, 1982.

Moch, Michael K., and Pondy, Louis R. "The Structure of Chaos: Organized Anarchy as a Response to Ambiguity." *Administrative Science Quarterly* 22(1977): 351–362.

Mohr, Lawrence B. "Ambiguity and Choice in Organizations" (review). *American Journal of Sociology* 84(1978): 765–767.

Mohr, Lawrence B. *Explaining Organizational Behavior*. San Francisco: Jossey Bass, 1982.

Morgan, Gareth. "More on Metaphor: Why We Cannot Control Tropes in Administrative Science." *Administrative Science Quarterly* 28(1983): 641–652.

Mosher, Frederick C. ed. *Government Reorganization: Cases and Commentary*. Indianapolis: Bobbs-Merrill, 1967.

Nelson, Richard R., and Winter, Sidney G. *An Evolutionary Theory of Economic Change.* Cambridge, Mass.: Harvard University Press, 1982.

Nystrom, Paul C. "Rummaging Through Organizations' Garbage Cans." *Contemporary Psychology* 22(1977): 643–645.

Nystrom, Paul C., and Starbuck, William H. eds. *Handbook of Organizational Design.* New York: Oxford University Press, 1981.

Olsen, Johan P. "Local Budgeting: Decision Making or a Ritual Act?" *Scandinavian Political Studies* 5(1970): 85–118.

Olsen, Johan P. "University Governance: Non-Participation as Exclusion or Choice." In *Ambiguity and Choice in Organizations*, edited by James G. March and Johan P. Olsen. Bergen, Norway: Universitetsforlaget, 1976a.

Olsen, Johan P. "The Process of Interpreting Organizational History." In James G. March *Ambiguity and Choice in Organizations*, edited by James G. March and Johan P. Olsen. Bergen, Norway: Universitetsforlaget, 1976b.

Olsen, Johan P. "Choice in an Organized Anarchy." In *Ambiguity and Choice in Organizations*, edited by James G. March and Johan P. Olsen. Bergen, Norway: Universitetsforlaget, 1976c.

Olsen, Johan P. "Reorganization as a Garbage Can." In *Ambiguity and Choice in Organizations*, edited by James G. March and Johan P. Olsen. Bergen, Norway: Universitetsforlaget, 1976d.

Olsen, Johan P. *Organized Democracy.* Bergen, Norway: Universitetsforlaget, 1983.

Padgett, John F. "Managing Garbage Can Hierarchies." *Administrative Science Quarterly* 25(1980): 583–604.

Perrow, Charles. "Ambiguity and Choice in Organizations" *Contemporary Sociology* 6(1977): 294–298.

Peters, Thomas J., and Waterman, Robert. *In Search of Excellence.* New York; Harper & Row, 1982.

Pfeffer, Jeffrey. "Management as Symbolic Action: The Creation and Maintenance of Organizational Paradigms." In *Research in Organizational Behavior*, edited by L. Cummings and B.M. Staw. Greenwich, Conn.: JAI Press, 1981a.

Pfeffer, Jeffrey. "Some Consequences of Organizational Demography: Potential Impacts of an Aging Work Force on Formal Organizations." In *Aging: Social Change.* edited by Sara B. Kiesler, James N. Morgan, and Valerie K. Oppenheimer, New York: Academic Press, 1981b.

Pfeffer, Jeffrey. *Organizations and Organization Theory.* Marshfield, Mass.: Pitman, 1982.

Pfeffer, Jeffrey, and Salancik, Gerald R. *The External Control of Organizations: A Resource Dependence Perspective.* New York: Harper & Row, 1978.

Pinder, Craig C. and Bourgeois, V. Warren "Controlling Tropes in Administrative Science." *Administrative Science Quarterly* 27(1982): 641-652.

Pondy, Louis R. "Leadership as a Language Game." In *Leadership*, edited by M.W. McCall, Jr, and M.M. Lombardo. Durham, N.C.: Duke University Press, 1978.

Powell, Walter W. "Publishers' Decision-Making: What Criteria Do They Use in Deciding Which Books to Publish?" *Social Research* 45(1978): 227–252.

Rommetveit, Kåre. "Decision Making under Changing Norms." In *Ambiguity and Choice in Organizations*, edited by James G. March and Johan P. Olsen. Bergen, Norway: Universitetsforlaget, 1976.

Roness, Paul. *Reorganisering av departementa: Eit politisk styringsmiddel?* Bergen, Norway: Universitetsforlaget, 1979.

Roos, Leslie L., Jr., and Hall, Roger. "Influence Diagrams and Organizational Power." *Administrative Science Quarterly* 25(1980): 57–71.

Sabrosky, Alan Ned, Thompson, James Clay, and McPherson, Karen A. "Organized Anarchies: Military Bureaucracy in the 1980s." *Journal of Applied Behavioral Science* 18(1982): 137–153.

Saetren, Harald. *Iverksetting av offentlig politikk: Utflytting av statsinstitusjoner fra Oslo*. Bergen, Norway: Universitetsforlaget, 1983.

Scott, William R. *Organizations: Rational, Natural, and Open Systems*. Englewood Cliffs, N.J.: Prentice-Hall, 1981.

Seashore, Stanley E. "Ambiguity and Choice in Organizations" (review). *American Journal of Sociology* 84(1978): 765–767.

Seidman, Harold. "Remarks." In "President Nixon's Proposals for Executive Reorganization," edited by *Public Administration Review* 34(1974): 487–495.

Seidman, Harold. *Politics, Position and Power: The Dynamics of Federal Organization*. 3rd ed. New York:, Oxford University Press, 1980.

Shepsle, Kenneth A. "Institutional Equilibrium and Equilibrium Institutions." Paper presented at the annual meeting of the American Political Science Association, Chicago, Ill., 1983.

Simon, Herbert A. "A Formal Theory of the Employment Relationship." *Econometrica* 19(1953): 293–305.

Simon, Herbert A. *Administrative Behavior*. 2nd ed. New York: Macmillan, 1957a.

Simon, Herbert A. *Models of Man*. New York: Wiley, 1957b.

Simon, Herbert A. *The New Science of Management Decisions*. Englewood Cliffs, N.J.: Prentice-Hall, 1960.

Sproull, Lee, Weiner, Stephen, and Wolf, David. *Organizing an Anarchy: Belief, Bureaucracy, and Politics in the National Institute of Education*. Chicage, Ill.: University of Chicago Press, 1978.

Starbuck, William H., and Nystrom, Paul C. "Why the World Needs Organizational Design." *Journal of General Management* 6(1981): 3–17.

Stava, Per. "Constraints on Politics of Public Choice." In *Ambiguity and Choice in Organizations*, edited by James G. March and Johan P. Olsen. Bergen, Norway: Universitetsforlaget, 1976.

Strand, Torodd. "Samordning som Administrasjonsproblem." *Tidsskrift for Samfunnsforskning* 18(1977): 193–213.

Swieringa, Robert J., and Waterhouse, John H. "Organizational Views of Transfer Pricing." *Accounting Organizations and Society* 7(1982): 149–155.

Szanton, Peter, ed. *Federal Reorganization: What Have We Learned?* Chatham, N.J.: Chatham, 1981.

Thompson, James Clay. *Rolling Thunder. Understanding Policy and Program Failure*. Chapel Hill, N.C.: University of North Carolina Press, 1980.

Thompson, James Clay, and Vidmer, Richard F. *Administrative Science and Politics in the USSR and the United States*. New York: Praeger, 1983.

Thompson, James D., Hawkes, Peter W., Junker, Buford H., and Tuden, Arthur, eds. *Comparative Studies in Administration*. Pittsburgh, Pa.: University of Pittsburgh Press, 1959.

Weick, Karl E. "Educational Organizations as Loosely Coupled Systems." *Administrative Science Quarterly* 21(1976): 1–19.

Weick, Karl E. *The Social Psychology of Organizing*, 2nd ed. Reading, Mass.: Addison-Wesley, 1979.

Weiner, Stephen S. "Participation, Deadlines, and Choice." In *Ambiguity and Choice in Organizations*, edited by James G. March and Johan P. Olsen, Bergen, Norway: Universitetsforlaget, 1976.

Weissinger-Baylon, Roger. "Garbage Can Decision Processes in Naval Warfare." In *Ambiguity and Command: Organizational Perspectives on Military Decision Making*, edited by James G. March and Roger Weissinger-Baylon. Marshfield, Mass.: Pitman, 1985.

West, Richard R. "Will Playfulness be Possible in University Management?" *College Board Review* 112(1979): 14–15.

Willower, Donald J. "Ideology and Science in Organization Theory." Paper presented at the annual meeting of the American Educational Research Association, San Francisco, 1979.

3

Garbage Can Decision Processes in Naval Warfare

ROGER WEISSINGER-BAYLON

ABSTRACT

The command of large naval forces can be better understood, and perhaps improved, by the application of Cohen, March and Olsen's (1972) garbage can model of organizational choice. Garbage can decisions can occur in any organization but are more likely to be found in "organized anarchies," where decisions are made under ambiguity and fluid involvement of participants.

Naval warfare creates an organized anarchy of a special class, which will require extensions to the classic garbage can model. In particular, the decision procedures of operational naval commanders may be interpreted as adaptations to ambiguity under extreme loads with deadlines. These adaptations include such time honored approaches as standard operating procedures (SOPs), plans and

Roger Weissinger-Baylon is Director of the Center for Strategic Decision Research. During the 1985 academic year, he was a visiting scholar at Stanford University and a consultant at the Navy Personnel Research and Development Center.

Grants from the Assistant Secretary of the Navy (Research, Engineering, and Systems), Boeing Aerospace Company, the Defense Communications Agency, Lockheed Missiles and Space Corporation, MITRE Corporation, the Naval Electronic Systems Command, the Naval Personnel Research and Development Center, the Office of Naval Research, the Office of the Secretary of Defense (Director of Net Assessment), and SRI International have supported this research.

The author appreciates the comments of Joel S. Lawson, Pauline Ryan, and James G. March.

organizational design. The process of shifting decisions backward in time, or within the organization, moves decision loads from peak areas to those of relative slack.

An extended garbage can model also has normative implications: senior commanders should recognize and operate within limits of their influence and act to improve the decision-making capabilities of the organizations they command.

INTRODUCTION

Cohen, March and Olsen (1972) have suggested that in certain organizations decision making may be characterized by a threefold ambiguity: in technology, in preferences and in participation. According to their model—known as the garbage can model—ambiguity of technology results when organizations do not understand their own processes. Ambiguity of preference results when decision-maker preferences are unclear, heterogeneous, changing or discovered as the decision unfolds. Ambiguity of participation results when decision makers move in and out of individual decision arenas or vary their allocated energies and attention.

Organizations that experience these three elements of ambiguity are called "organized anarchies" (Cohen et al., 1972), and their decision-making processes may differ significantly from the classical rational model. In fact, decision making in organized anarchies may be so difficult as to permit only extreme forms of satisficing. These ad hoc decision processes are likely to be driven by the relative timing of largely independent flows of problems, solutions, participants and choice opportunities. In addition, the rules that govern access of problems, solutions and participants to available choice opportunities may significantly influence the effective flows.

Given the three elements of ambiguity in the model, this paper examines the issue of naval warfare in order to show that it does, indeed, reflect the model but that the ambiguities arise in somewhat special circumstances. Since these ambiguities directly influence naval decision making, this approach is valuable in that it demonstrates the practical relevance of a garbage can model in understanding the structure of decision making in wartime. However, knowledge of the particular, unusual forms of organized anarchy that appear in naval operations should guide the development and extension of the garbage can theory and its application to war at sea.

This paper suggests that naval garbage cans may be usefully described as organized anarchies under heavy load and deadlines. The military approaches of standard operating procedures, planning and structured organizational design are adaptations to ambiguity, load and time-critical decision making. They mitigate certain effects of ambiguity by clarifying which decisions are likely to be approved by the organization; and they help shift load to time periods (usually before the engagement with the enemy) and to parts of the organization (usually lower in the hierarchy) where relative slack is more likely to be found.

The improved understanding of naval operational decisions, which the extended garbage can model provides, is vital to the naval systems commands and other shore activities because these organizations are required to support naval operations at sea, with which they are not adequately familiar. Similarly, the extended garbage can model should help guide commanders' efforts to improve force readiness and their prospects for operational success.

GARBAGE CANS, ORGANIZED ANARCHIES AND NAVAL WARFARE

Naval warfare is usually described as an "organized anarchy" because of unavoidable ambiguities in technology, preference and participation. In various forms, these conditions occur in peacetime and prewar tension, transition to hot war, and during warfare itself. In addition, these ambiguities seem to arise from fundamental characteristics of war at sea, including the "fog of war" that originates in the limitations of information and communication. Of the sources of ambiguity in sea war, technological ambiguity may be the most important.

Ambiguity of Technology

Ambiguity of technology describes an organization's ignorance as to the options that are available to its decision makers and the linkages between these alternatives and their likely consequences or outcomes.

In times of peace, a commander faces ambiguity because he usually cannot know how his forces will perform in combat, and he cannot properly evaluate his doctrine or tactics. This difficulty is often aggravated by inexperience in particular roles, because all commanders and their subordinates rotate rapidly through new jobs (Hughes, 1985). When a carrier force begins its predeployment workup, for example, many of its officers or men may never have been to sea. Even experienced commanders, however knowledgeable and qualified, are likely to be assigned to geographic areas with which they are unfamiliar or where the political climate is subject to rapid changes.

During periods of peacetime or prewar tension, a commander must realize that force postures likely to deter aggression require that his ships and aircraft be seen by the enemy. This creates a delicate situation: his forces are then vulnerable to enemy attack. Of course, the outbreak of war presents even greater difficulties. Unless he is completely confident of his prospects for success, the enemy will not normally start a war. Therefore, it is almost certain that future wars will occur at times, in geographic locations or in forms for which our forces are not prepared. Like Poland or Pearl Harbor in World War II, early battles of a future war will be confused and ambiguous for the defending forces. During such a war, the enemy will adapt to weapons or tactics that are successful against him. Worse yet, he will repeatedly develop new threats that will be difficult to anticipate or counter.

Other sources of technological ambiguity arise from tactical information that is unavailable, unreliable or deceptive, or that simply overloads decision makers. These effects may be the result of enemy actions, natural phenomena, such as atmospheric conditions, or a commander's own decision to restrict communications. Finally, the force-on-force characteristics of naval war make its outcomes inherently unstable and unpredictable with respect to organizational decisions. In fact, many of the soundest of tactical principles are mutually contradictory. For example, achievement of surprise is a fundamental principle, but its successful implementation may mean reduced surveillance of the enemy. This makes the force itself vulnerable to surprise.

Ambiguity of Preference

Ambiguity of preference is coupled with ambiguity of technology in at least one sense: decision makers cannot impose their preferences when technological ambiguities prevent the association of decision alternatives with their likely consequences. In naval war, however, ambiguity of preference takes on important characteristic forms. Ambiguity of preference contributes to organized anarchy by interfering with rankings of alternatives and their outcomes.

Until a military crisis arrives, policymakers at the top levels may be isolated from naval operations. For example, a fairly recent chief of naval operations had about ten minutes a year with the president in order to present the Navy's budget. Obviously, interaction between senior commanders and the president was quite limited. This suggests the following: (1) that commanders do not have enough access to civilian leaders to learn their values and policy preferences; (2) that top civilian policymakers are probably unaware of their own values, which they are likely to discover incrementally as a military crisis develops (they may lack the military policy experience that is necessary for stable values); and (3) that in a rapidly developing situation, top-level preferences cannot be quickly communicated to commanders at sea.[1] Finally, preferences in military operations are likely to be heterogeneous in the extreme.

Ambiguities of technology and preference are both influenced by part-time, fluid or ambiguous participation. For example, when policymakers are heterogeneous in their values, participants' fluid movement among decision arenas is likely to alter coalition structure and make dominant preferences unstable.

Ambiguity of Participation

Ambiguity of participation results when participants are part-time, or shift their energies among decision situations within the organization or across organizational boundaries. Examples include military officers and defense officials who contribute to technological ambiguity through job rotation; also included are those same top-level decision makers who create preference ambiguities by entering military choice arenas in times of crisis.

In military organizations, fluidity of participation has two important causes that are less significant elsewhere: (1) battle losses of key specialists or forces; and (2) communication limitations that effectively isolate potential participants from decisions.

From the ambiguities outlined above, it is clear that naval warfare corresponds with the model of an organized anarchy but that in addition it exhibits a number of unique features. In particular, it is the extreme unpredictability and uncertainty of decision outcomes in naval warfare that distinguish it from other garbage can organizations. Other unique features include ambiguities arising from equipment and tactics that cannot be tested during prolonged periods of peace or limited-scale military actions. Military garbage cans are also unique to the degree to which their vital information is deceptive—or just plain wrong, delayed, missing or in such volume as to overload the receiver.

In addition to these features, naval operations are subject to both heavy decision loads and stress. This suggests that naval commanders' decisions can be analyzed as adaptations to a garbage can process under heavy load and deadlines.

ORGANIZED ANARCHIES UNDER HEAVY LOAD AND DEADLINES

In developing an extended garbage can theory for naval operations, it seems clear that commanders' decisions are often made under conditions of organized anarchy, possibly of a special class. Therefore, a number of naval decisions might resemble garbage can processes. Unfortunately, a growing body of work by Cohen, March, Olsen and their co-workers (March and Olsen, 1976) suggests that such decisions are likely to have undesirable properties: for example, garbage can choices are usually made by flight[2] (migration of problems away from choice opportunities) or oversight rather than by resolution. Moreover, problems are likely to be solved only when they are especially important or discovered early in the process. In addition, both empirical studies and computer simulations demonstrate that these kinds of processes are very sensitive to the extreme load conditions of naval combat.

In naval warfare, even relatively limited operations, as, for example, the Iranian hostage rescue mission or the Grenada rescue mission, have national consequences. On account of this, certain adverse characteristics of garbage can processes should be unacceptable to commanders. Consequently, a first step in developing an extended garbage can theory of naval war might be to analyze naval decision making in terms of adaptations to the management of organized anarchies under heavy load and deadlines. Figure 3.1 depicts a preliminary representation of this theory. For this approach to managing a garbage can process under load and deadlines the basic elements are the following:

- *Decision load can be shifted in time to earlier periods of reduced activity.*
  There are at least two approaches: (1) standard operating procedures (SOPs), which are rehearsed, organizationally approved decisions of broad applicability; and (2) operational plans, which are tailor-made for specific tactical objectives and therefore have narrow applicability. Both SOPs and plans are equivalent to prematching in time of problems and solutions.

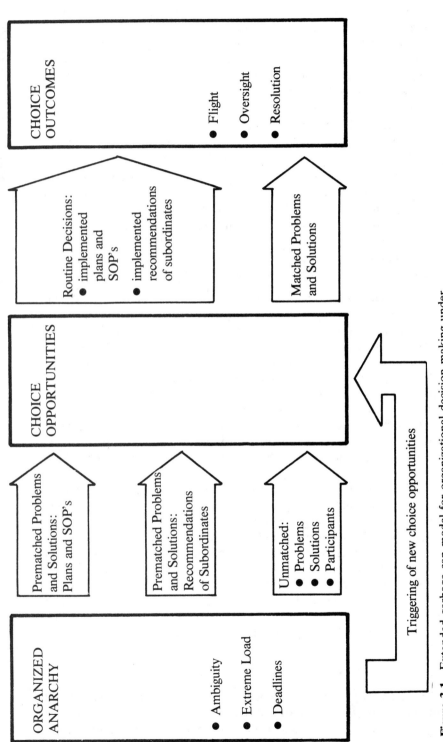

Figure 3.1 Extended garbage can model for organizational decision making under ambiguity, extreme load and deadlines.

- *Decision load can be shifted within the organization, usually to lower hierarchical levels.* This can be achieved through appropriate organizational design, including the relatively new concept of command by negation (composite warfare commander, or CWC) of the U.S. Navy. This approach is equivalent to prematching of problems and solutions at lower levels of the hierarchy.

- *Decision loads can be dynamically shifted to participants enjoying temporary slack.*[3] This process enables heavily loaded actors to narrow the scope of their attention for short periods. Other participants can expand their responsibilities to temporarily fill the void.

- *Multiple concurrent decisions can be processed by time-sharing.* Small time slices of participant energies can be sequentially allocated until priority choices are finally disposed of or disappear.

- *Decision loads can be reduced by providing information.* For example, surveillance information (Feldman and March, 1981) may not directly contribute to decisions, but it allows discussion of choice options in a way that reduces load on communication channels.

These strategies for load management and redistribution have additional advantages. Plans, for example, are generally presumed to be mechanisms for resource allocation and coordination of organizational activities (March and Simon, 1958). In naval operations, however, it is now argued that plans shift decision loads to periods of reduced activity, prior to engagement of the enemy. Plans also improve prospects for operational success during periods of communication difficulty or restriction. In the absence of communications, plans at least tell commanders where their forces should be and what they are supposed to be doing. In addition, certain tactical objectives, such as achievement of surprise or concentration of forces against weaker enemy units, can be remarkably difficult. Plans may be the only means by which these objectives become possible.[4]

Finally, in an extended garbage can model, prematching through planning, SOPs and organizational designs have important additional interpretations. According to the theory of organizational choice under ambiguity (Cohen et al., 1972), decisions in organized anarchies are normally by flight or oversight. But in an extended model, plans, SOPs and command by negation provide vital backup options. Thus, in naval warfare, a commander under pressure to decide by flight has additional possibilities. He can implement his operational plan or SOP, or he can accept the recommendations of his subordinates. Any of these possibilities should be better than the flight or oversight options provided by the classic model. In military operations, such improvements are vital.

WAR GAMES AND WARFARE

The extended garbage can model can be illustrated through an example based on a computerized war game. In times of relative peace, war games are especially important. They are one of the principal means for training naval decision makers and evaluating equipment, tactics and strategies.

Many of the Navy's war games are conducted in "seminar" form, without computer support. However, small-scale computerized war games are now available as training aids on the Navy's larger ships and a large-scale computerized gaming system (Naval War Gaming System, or NWGS) supports the various objectives of the Center for Naval Warfare studies at the Naval War College. The NWGS is being further enhanced for operation at additional remote sites; it will become the Navy's primary war-gaming system for the operational planning of fleet commanders-in-chief and training of battle group staffs.

All data presented in this paper have been adapted from a single, week-long war game at the Naval War College. The participants included admirals with both extensive operational command and war-gaming experience. For example, one of these flag officers was accompanied by key members of his staff who had previously served with his battle force in the Indian Ocean. Participants in the game comprised several hundred naval officers, Defense Department officials, and civilian engineers or other specialists from the various defense industries. These included players who assumed the various command and subordinate command roles and staff positions for both friendly (blue) and enemy (orange) forces. Other participants served as umpires on the game floor, monitoring and managing computerized routines that ranged from damage assessment to the generation of meteorological or intelligence information. Costs for the one-week game, including salaries, travel, pregame preparation and postgame analysis were several hundred thousand dollars.

In order for the game to achieve its organizers' objectives, the participants were guided by the following scenario. The orange army invades a Middle Eastern nation. In order to assist the defenders, the blue commander assembles a large battleship and aircraft carrier task force in the Indian Ocean, as well as amphibious forces, maritime prepositioned forces and aircraft of the rapid deployment joint task force. As the blue commander prepares to move his forces north into the Arabian Sea, the orange naval commander feigns an amphibious attack on a blue client state. The purpose of the feint is to draw blue naval forces into a guided missile trap and prevent blue from interfering with the orange navy's invasion.

Although all examples in this paper are drawn from the war game, interpretation of the data was facilitated by drawing on other, additional sources of background information:

- *Interviews* with nearly 30 admirals and general officers, both active and retired, as well as other senior officers and Department of Defense officials; the interviews ranged from one hour to visits of several days in Monterey, California.
- *Observations* of a naval commander at sea aboard the destroyer U.S.S. *Rogers*; observations of decision making by a flag officer in command of a naval force. These latter observations were aboard the aircraft carrier U.S.S. *Enterprise*.

- *Studies of historical accounts* with special attention to the role of sea power in recent crises: the Mayaguez incident, the Iranian hostage rescue mission, the Falklands war, and the Grenada invasion.

CHOICES

The war-gaming data show heavy loads of flag-level decision makers, suggesting that operational commanders may experience still greater loads of extraordinary intensity. Moreover, near peak loads may even occur during periods of international tension. While relatively little action is apparent to outsiders, commanders and their staffs are stressed by requirements to position their forces for battle, to strike before the enemy and to avoid accidental or premature triggering of a conflict.

Choices by naval commanders are also characterized by high risk. Ambiguity in technology, preference and participation implies uncertainty. In addition, the stakes of naval warfare are likely to be high. However, flag decision making differs from other processes with high loads and risk. Compared to the Cuban Missile Crisis decision (Allison, 1971; Anderson, 1983), for example, flag decision making seems more intense. During the three-and-one-half-day war game described in this paper, the game historians recorded several hundred operational decisions: for example, aircraft launches or prosecutions of enemy submarine contacts. Furthermore, each decision required information gathering, planning and, often, approval by the flag officer or his staff. Despite this intense load, flag-level coordination is too vital to completely delegate many of these decisions to subordinate commanders or staffs.

In order to illustrate the heavy loads on the war game decision makers, Figure 3.2 presents the first ten choices of one commander and his staff. These choices, selected from four days for which data is available, occupied approximately the first 60 minutes of the game.

The figure gives the information that triggered each choice, the decision-making activities that occurred, an estimate of the time allocated and the decision outcomes. For decisions that ended in flight, F is shown in the right-hand column. In these choices, all participants migrated to a temporarily more attractive choice situation, and no significant problems were solved by the choice. For decisions ending in resolution, R appears in the right-hand column; each of these choices led to a clear decision, such as launching a reconnaissance flight or assigning targets to submarines. This data suggests that resolution (50 percent of choices) is not a more likely outcome than flight.

In the war game, flag decision makers and their staffs responded to intense load and time pressure by attending to those choices that were temporarily more attractive. This leads to behavior more like a computer time-sharing system than like "fire fighting."

Decision makers successively allocate small blocks of time to an important choice. This continues until the choice is resolved or its problems have migrated to other arenas. Figure 3.3 shows a somewhat typical time pattern of this behavior.

Choice Number	Choice Trigger	Choice Activity	Estimated Time (in minutes)	Decision
1	Enemy sonar ships on flag officers' geographical plot	Generate alternative tactical responses that will not start a war	18	F
2	Intelligence report on location of enemy sonar detection systems	Evaluate tactical implications; chart required for full message interpretation	4	F
3	Reconnaissance flights reported launched	Evaluate tactical implications of possible reconnaissance information	4	F
4	Higher authority requests delay in bomber feint	Bomber feint delayed	4	R
5	Higher authority objects to planned amphibious landing feint	No change in planned landing feint	12	R
6	Request to clear bombers for launch	Bombers cleared for launch	4	R
7	(Trigger unclear— possibly flag officer's geographical plot)	Submarines assigned to targets	4	R
8	(Trigger unclear— return to choice #1)	Generate additional alternatives	4	F
9	Arrival of chart required for return to choice #2	Update geographical plot; intelligence staff not responsible for chart delay	2	F
10	(Trigger unclear)	Decision to prepare for war; but do not start war	2	R

Figure 3.2 Flag choices during the war game's first 58 minutes. F indicates decision by flight; R indicates decision by oversight or resolution.

In Figure 3.3, the flag officer's allocation of time is shown for the war game's first 60 minutes. (Figure 3.3 presents, in different form, the same data as Figure 3.2.) Choice number one, involving sonar ships, initially received 18 minutes of attention. Choice number two, on the sonar barrier, was then investigated for approximately four minutes. Choices four, five, seven and ten ended in resolution and are labeled R. For two of the three choices that were not resolved, the flag officer and his staff returned to a related choice, once time became available.

Athens and Weissinger-Baylon (1983) have studied this behavior by adapting the Cohen et al. (1972) FORTRAN simulation model of garbage can decision making. According to Athens and Weissinger-Baylon, in some respects the decision making of the flag officer and his staff resembles the

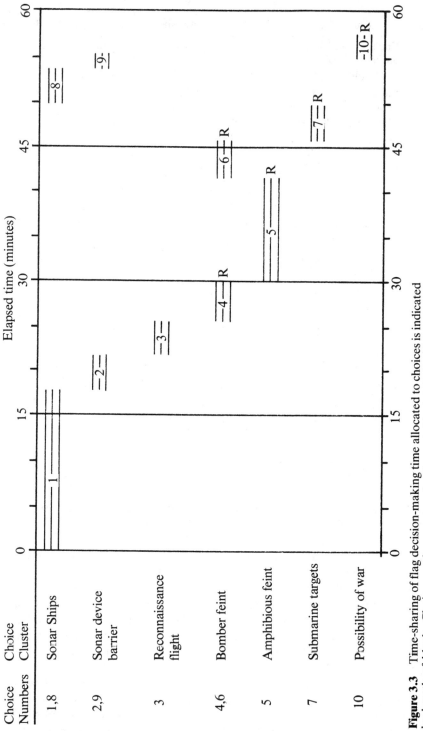

Figure 3.3 Time-sharing of flag decision-making time allocated to choices is indicated by length of block. Choice number appears inside each block; choices by oversight or resolution are labeled R.

exhibitions of world class chess experts playing several games simultaneously. On account of their expertise and training, the flag officer and staff can move from choice to choice without rebriefing delays or other obvious cognitive or organizational costs. This allows the flag officer and staff to coordinate effectively the decisions of their subordinate commanders without delaying their tactical actions or responses.

MATCHING

Cohen et al. (1972) describe largely independent flows of problems, solutions and participants as fundamental characteristics of the garbage can decision-making process. During choice situations, problems and solutions are matched by satisficing in order to produce decisions by flight or oversight rather than by resolution.

In naval combat, low-quality decisions either by flight or oversight are likely to have adverse consequences. Therefore, naval commanders and their organizations have devised unique mechanisms for matching problems and solutions during the organized anarchy of naval warfare. These approaches reduce the decision-making load on commanders either by prematching problems and solutions at lower levels in the organization or by planning, which prematches problems and solutions before peak loads actually occur.

The war game data provide examples of both kinds of prematching for problems and solutions. They also illustrate an additional matching phenomenon, sometimes called the *boxcar effect*, which will be discussed later.

Prematching by Subordinate Commanders

The flag officer's decision-making process must be adapted for extremely heavy loads (i.e., very low slack). Under such conditions, the rational approach to decision making is an unsatisfactory prescriptive model: the flag officer and his immediate staff must achieve the vital coordination advocated by proponents of "rational" decision making but simply do not have time to generate and fully evaluate decision alternatives.

In order to adjust to these heavy decision loads and coordination requirements, the Navy has developed an approach called the "composite warfare commander" (CWC) concept. It leads to a process strikingly different from what might be expected:

- Flag choices tend to be triggered by subordinate commanders, since these officers are often closest to information and can effectively identify problems and propose solutions.
- Solutions and problems are matched by subordinate commanders themselves. Problem-solution matches are then presented to the flag officer as decisions recommended for his approval. On account of time pressures on the overall commander and his subordinates, as well as communications limitations, neither alternative courses of action nor justification for the decision are necessarily provided.

- The flag officer and his staff examine the decision recommendation and search for the problems which it will solve: (1) if the problem-solution match appears appropriate, the decision is approved as recommended; (2) if the flag officer's broader view suggests that the proposed problem-solution match is not desirable, an alternative decision will be approved by the flag officer and his staff; and (3) if the flag officer does not respond, the subordinate commander may implement the decision he himself recommended.

This approach to decision making is illustrated by an example from the war game. In order to permit two submarines to operate radars, the submarine force commander requests a change in the electronic emissions plan. This would draw enemy antisubmarine forces in their direction, away from other submarines more vital to the battle plan. The flag officer and his staff check the position of the two submarines on the plotting display. The submarines are too far from the battle area to participate in any way other than the proposed diversion. The flag officer approves the request.

This decision-making process is especially appropriate under the following conditions: (1) heavy load on the flag decision maker limits his opportunities for generation and evaluation of alternatives; (2) deadlines further limit most flag decisions to flight or oversight; (3) ambiguity of participation restricts opportunities for participant interaction; and (4) impossibility of communication (or extremely short deadlines) may require a subordinate to act without specific approval by superior commanders.

The CWC process is especially desirable, moreover, if the organization can be designed to group key specialists appropriately. Information, problems and solutions can then be analyzed and prematched before submission to the flag officer as decisions proposed for his final approval.

However, the process also has several weaknesses. It requires a flag officer to have considerable confidence in his subordinate commanders who, in order to earn this trust, must have previously proven themselves. This type of confidence is necessary because the flag officer does not receive enough information during operations to learn immediately from experience; the flag officer does not know all the alternative problem-solution matches considered by his subordinates; nor does the subordinate commander immediately learn why the flag officer accepts, modifies or denies his decision recommendations. (Of course, this information is likely to be available *after* the exercise is debriefed.)

Prematching by Plan

A central problem of flag-level decision making is the preparation of an operational plan. According to some flag officers, in fact, the principal function of the overall tactical commander is to develop the plan and implement it as far as joining his forces in battle. At this point, the commander's role may be complete; the battle will then be fought by his subordinate commanders and the ships and aircraft that they control.

The role of the plan is partially illustrated by another example from the war game. The orange commander planned a trap for blue aircraft carriers that were to be lured within range of orange missile-launching submarines. This was to be achieved by feigning an amphibious landing against an important blue client state. The blue force's strategy was to lure orange submarines through a barrier of submarine detection devices—greatly simplifying blue's antisubmarine warfare problem. On account of the interaction between these two plans, as the game progressed, tactical separation of the two forces tended to increase. Each commander was eager to implement his own trap and unwilling to fall into the trap established by the opposing commander. Ultimately, the game managers intervened to bring the two sides into combat.

Analysis of the plan's role in naval force control suggests that it has a number of features in common with the "plan" in the theory of human problem solving (Newell and Simon, 1972). In other words, the plan is a somewhat abstract outline description of how a problem is to be solved. As with individual human problem solving, the plan helps the flag officer and his staff to do problem solving in a simplified "problem space" (Newell and Simon, 1972) that does not include or fully consider all the details and eventualities involved in actual control of friendly forces, enemy reactions or the effects of physical, political and other environments.

However, the operational plan is also a unique adaptation to the requirements of naval warfare. A plan is necessary to coordinate the action of large numbers of men and ships (despite ambiguities of technology, preference, and participation) in a situation where vital commanders, technical specialists and ships may be lost, cut off or unable to communicate with each other adequately but must, nevertheless, work toward realizing the desired objective. Only through a careful plan, moreover, is it possible to achieve certain time-honored and proven tactical principles, such as surprise or the concentration of a large force against a smaller portion of enemy forces. Finally, preparation of the plan is an occasion for the National Command Authority and other senior commanders to express preferences and values, and to ensure that the plan implements them. In garbage can terms, the plan permits advance matching of problems and solutions. This has the effect of shifting problem solving and decision making from the peak loads to the lighter, prebattle load periods.

Further examination of the earlier example may suggest that operational plans do not work. However, a more mature tactical notion is that they are indispensable. In the example, each commander's plan had a realistic chance for success. If successful, each plan would have yielded great military advantage to that side. Moreover, such potential advantages could not be achieved without the force coordination that plans provide.

Boxcar Effect: Rematching Problems and Solutions

The "boxcar effect," as a phenomenon of organizational decision making, has been previously observed in the context of large-scale computer system acquisitions by the U.S. Navy. Purchases of multiple complex systems, for various independent and unrelated applications, are ordinarily analyzed and planned over more than a decade. On account of these lengthy delays, however, requirements change drastically before the systems are actually delivered. After years of delay, railroad boxcars of computer mainframes arriving for System A, and storage devices, terminals and other equipment ordered for System B, are invariably rerouted in the freight yard to meet the unanticipated requirements of System C. The term *boxcar effect* owes its origin to this metaphor. To sophisticated observers, the vast rational effort required to justify Systems A and B is only useful if it ultimately contributes to the successful implementation of unanticipated or unplanned future requirements such as those of System C.

On the war game's third day, a similar boxcar effect occurred in the context of naval operational decision making. The orange national command authority ordered an already airborne, long-range bomber force to strike an airfield, instead of the blue surface group it was originally directed to attack. A separate long-range bomber strike had been previously planned against a small group of acoustic towed-array ships. It was, consequently, redirected against the blue surface force originally targeted by the first bomber strike. Finally, intelligence ships and a submarine were reassigned to attack the acoustic towed-array ships.

In order for the boxcar effect to occur, the following conditions seem necessary: (1) changes in preferences, (2) delays in the creation of new solution possibilities, and (3) deadlines. In the above example, changes in the tactical environment induced a shift in preferences of the orange national command authority. The preference shift then caused this authority to enter the choice. It subsequently offered—and imposed—its own solution: a redirected strike. Since long delays are required to rearm or reposition long-range bombers for a possible strike, additional bomber attacks cannot be mounted in the short run. Commanders must, therefore, adapt to changes in their preferences by rematching a temporarily fixed supply of bomber strike "solutions" with the "problems" created by enemy targets. The rematching is imposed by the physical threat presented by enemy forces that are not brought under timely attack. This threat forms a kind of "soft" deadline that does not allow time to create additional bomber strike "solutions."

"Boxcar" rematching is distinctly nonrational in character. Normally, solution-problem matches are highly nonoptimal and only make sense in terms of the preference changes, delays and deadlines facing decision maker participants.

SUMMARY AND CONCLUSIONS

Garbage can models of organizational choice, or Weick's (1973) loosely coupled systems, describe aspects of combat decision making experienced by senior naval commanders. In particular, the conditions of naval warfare closely approach the organized anarchies of Cohen et al. (1972). In naval organizations, however, ambiguities of technology, preference and participation occur for quite different reasons, and in quite different forms, than those found in the types of organizations to which garbage can models have previously been applied. In particular, organized anarchies interfere with fundamental tactical principles that depend on tight control and coordination, such as achievement of surprise or concentration of forces. In the face of these ambiguities, adaptations employed by naval commanders include the use of SOPs, operational plans, strong centralized authority acting through a chain of command and promising recent innovations such as the CWC concept.

NOTES

1. These three factors may explain the tendencies of the National Command Authority to intervene directly in military operations, often with imperfect results (Hayward, 1985; Metcalf, 1985; Train, 1985).

2. On the other hand, an explicit decision "not to decide" is often a wise and easily overlooked option. This point has been emphasized by Vice Admiral Joseph Metcalf (personal communication, September 1983).

3. The importance of this phenomenon in naval warfare was pointed out to me by David Castanon, based on our joint observations for the Naval Electronic Systems Command of war gaming at the Naval War College.

4. This contrasts with the classic "plan or no plan" debate in the field of economics, where the benefits of planning are not always clear (March and Simon, 1958, p. 200).

REFERENCES

Allison, Graham T. *Essence of Decision: Explaining the Cuban Missile Crisis*. Boston: Little, Brown, 1971.

Anderson, Paul A. "Decision Making by Objection and the Cuban Missile Crisis." *Administrative Science Quarterly* (1983): 201–222.

Athens, Arthur, and Weissinger-Baylon, Roger. "Attention Mechanisms in Garbage Can Decision Processes." Unpublished working paper, 1983.

Cohen, Michael D., March, James G., and Olsen, Johan P. "A Garbage Can Model of Organizational Choice." *Administrative Science Quarterly* 17(1972): 1–26.

Feldman, Martha S., and March, James G. "Information in Organizations as Signal and Symbol." *Administrative Science Quarterly* 26(1981): 171–186.

Hayward, Admiral Thomas B. "An Ex-CNO's Reflection on the Garbage Can Theory of Naval Decision Making." In James G. March and Roger Weissinger-Baylon. *Ambiguity and Command: Organizational Perspectives on Military Decision Making*, edited by Marshfield, Mass.: Pitman, 1986.

Hughes, Captain Wayne P., Jr. "Garbage Cans at Sea." In *Ambiguity and Command: Organizational Perspectives on Military Decision Making*, edited by James G. March and Roger Weissinger-Baylon. Marshfield, Mass.: Pitman, 1985.

March, James G., and Olsen, Johan P., eds. *Ambiguity and Choice in Organizations*. Bergen, Norway: Universitetsforlaget, 1976.

March, James G., and Simon, Herbert A. *Organizations*. New York: Wiley, 1958.

Metcalf, Vice Admiral Joseph, III. "Decision Making and the Grenada Rescue Operation." In *Ambiguity and Command; Organizational Perspectives on Military Decision Making*, edited by James G. March and Roger Weissinger-Baylon. Marshfield, Mass.: Pitman, 1985.

Newell, Allen, and Simon, Herbert A. *Human Problem Solving*. Englewood Cliffs, N.J.: Prentice-Hall, 1972.

Train, Admiral Harry D., II. "Decision Making and Managing Ambiguity in Politico-Military Crisis." In *Ambiguity and Command: Organizational Perspectives on Military Decision Making*, edited by James G. March and Roger Weissinger-Baylon. Marshfield, Mass.: Pitman, 1985.

Weick, Karl. "Educational Organizations as Loosely Coupled Systems." *Administrative Science Quarterly* 21(1973):1−9.

4

Artificial Intelligence and the Dynamic Performance of Organizational Designs

MICHAEL D. COHEN

ORGANIZATIONAL DESIGN

There has been a steady growth of interest in the special problems associated with the design of organizations. Nystrom and Starbuck's (1981) massive two-volume handbook is only one of the many contributions to this subject. While there are a great many issues that stand out in thinking about the design of organizations, I want to focus here on one cluster that seems to be extremely important, namely, the problems that arise in judging the expected performance of a proposed organizational design *over time.*

Organizational Design as Capabilities, Relations, Incentives and Change Processes

In order to pursue the topic, we will need a working definition of *an organizational design.* My preference is to take quite an abstract view of what organization is. One of the benefits of this approach is that it presents the

Professor Michael D. Cohen is a faculty member at the Institute of Public Policy Studies at the University of Michigan.

Financial support for the research has been provided by the National Science Foundation under grant SES-8213169.

opportunity to learn something from developments in fields outside the usual areas studied by social scientists—for example, computer science, where very instructive organizational design problems frequently occur. Here an organizational design is defined as a specification of (1) a set of actors, (2) the initial capabilities and (3) the incentives of those actors, (4) the relations among them, and (5) the processes by which those capabilities and incentives are expected to change. This is an intentionally broad definition, which could encompass an array of microprocessors or an extended family, for example, as well as more traditional cases, such as a county fire department or a corporate sales office.[1]

If we look at two exemplary fragments of organizational designs, it may provide some feeling for what is meant by the terms listed in the definition. Consider first a staff member in the central office of a large corporation. She has a wide range of *capabilities*, as all human beings do, but among the most distinctive are those derived from her formal training in the law and her experience in a corporate law firm before joining this company. Pay is certainly among her *incentives*, but relative to pay she is more concerned than usual about career advancement. Approval from her bosses that may lead to other posts is, therefore, among her chief objectives. She serves as staff to all three vice presidents, but her salary and personnel evaluations are formally the responsibility of the vice president for marketing. The most important *relations* defining her job are the directions she takes from these three. Working on projects which they set for her, she is rapidly developing a better understanding of the way the company's legal affairs are entangled with its overall planning process. Her interest in corporate planning is increasing, and her ability to contribute has also grown. These are the major *change processes* that have been induced by the structure of her job.

As a second example, consider a consultant who sells his public sector accounting expertise to small city and county governments in his region. His *capabilities* include a well-developed ability to explain state accounting regulations to public officials (but he has never learned to touch-type, which hinders his use of the new small computers). He has had numerous offers of government posts or positions in large accounting firms. However, he values his independence and finds it unpleasant not to control his own workflow. These are his dominant *incentives*, together with a proud sense that improving local government is a socially valuable activity. His *relations* with his numerous employers are governed by a contract that has evolved by now into a standard form. It specifies who will control his activities and how disputes about his performance are to be adjudicated. Occasionally, he negotiates variations in this contract to fit special conditions, but his position is basically one of an individual selling his services in a market with numerous buyers and sellers.[2]

In both these cases there is an organizational design. A system of actors works together. Each particular actor has special capabilities and incentives. There are characteristic change processes at work. A network of communication and control relations links the actors to make them into a larger system ("control" is used here to indicate the ability of one actor to alter the capabilities or incentives of another). And, of course, the game can be played on top of itself. There can be actors whose capabilities consist of being able to alter the control relations between sets of other actors.

Evaluating a Design—Dynamic Performance in an Environment

Now suppose that we have a pair of candidate designs. How are we to choose between them? (The logical problem we face is much the same whether these are two well-worked out and fairly final alternatives or just a preliminary idea and a possible amendment to it.) In choosing between two designs, one is making—perhaps implicitly—a judgment about their likely relative performance, over their expected lifetimes, in their intended environment.

This statement has two unavoidable consequences that can be unpleasant for a self-conscious organizational designer. The first is that a designer will have to allow for the possibility that the performance of the organization will change over time. Both incentives and capabilities may evolve. The second, is that the designer will have to have some idea about the nature of the environment—the world outside the boundaries of this piece of organization with which it will have to cope. Without a model of the environment and its requirements, meaningful statements about the performance of the design are hardly possible. And, of course, these two complicating factors may interact. The environment may drive organizational change, to some degree, by generating events that teach the organization's members "lessons," and the organization may induce changes in—even adaptive responses by—the environment (March and Olsen, 1976).

So the intellectual task facing the organizational designer turns out to be something quite formidable. Given an environment, some capabilities and some incentives, and given the power to alter or create some others, what relations should be established among which actors so as to lead to maximum performance over time?

"Maximum performance over time," itself, requires definition. There are substantial bodies of literature—particularly in economics—devoted to the difficulties of clearly defining the idea. For an organizational designer's purposes, most of the available treatments of such maximization suffer from an overemphasis on efficiency considerations. They assume that the job to be done is a well-understood deterministic or stochastic process, and they consider how to discount future time periods and choose a strategy that will maximize discounted return over some (finite or infinite) time horizon. From the bounded rationality point of view that is widespread among organization theorists, this is a very serious misemphasis. Most jobs for which an organizational design is needed change fast enough and unpredictably enough in content that an approach that concentrates solely on efficiency at well-understood tasks overlooks what may often be the larger part of the problem, which we will refer to as *flexibility*.

Consider an illustrative bit of history. In 1971 an Intel engineer working on a design for a calculator conceived the possibility of the microprocessor. The

Intel board resisted approving the resulting 4004 project, in part because the marketing department foresaw that no more than a few thousand units per year could be sold. The project carried by a single vote. Within a few years, Intel was making microprocessors by the hundreds of thousands (Morgan, 1982). This example illustrates two interconnected arguments about organizational design. The first is that it was difficult to foresee the consequences of something that now seems monumentally obvious. This reminds us of the great uncertainty that always plagues organizational decision making. The second point is that Intel's subsequent success depended only in part on its short-run efficiency. In a case like this, the principal issue was not the ability of the organization to do a well-understood job (e.g., making and selling its existing chip line efficiently). Instead, it was the ability of the organization to repeatedly modify existing capabilities and routines in order to do a sequence of rapidly emerging, and often poorly understood, new jobs.

It is this property of an organizational design, its ability to transform existing capabilities into new ones, suited to new tasks required by the environment, that we will call *flexibility*. One often sees organizations investing in it, as when, for example, they sacrifice interest income to maintain relations with a potential source of credit, or when a liberally educated employee is chosen over one with more specialized training appropriate to the problems of the moment. Flexibility might be regarded as the potential of a system to *become* efficient at tasks related to its current capabilities. Unfortunately, it has been a difficult concept to study with existing mathematical tools, so it is not so commonly discussed in the economic treatment of maximization over time. But it has been noticed by some economists:

> The prime need in organizational design is increasing capacity to handle a large agenda. To the extent that information and its handling are accumulations of personal capital, what is needed is what Pareto called "the circulation of elites," the turnover of decision makers. More generally, what is needed is a "circulation of information and decision rules." Shortrun efficiency and even flexibility within a narrow framework of alternatives may be less important in the long run than a wide compass of potential activities. (Arrow, 1974, p. 59)

This view of the evaluation of design alternatives leads to a different way of thinking about the quality of an organizational design. A major question to be asked is, in the environment in which this design is expected to function, how important is it to employ existing capabilities efficiently on relatively well-understood problems? Or, is there a significant need to maintain flexibility, the potential to do new things in new ways? In realistic design settings, there will be a mixture of these requirements. You may have to produce current products efficiently to meet prices of competitors, but you may also have to be able to switch production rapidly to new product variations in order to respond to innovations. In some markets, the former requirement might predominate heavily. In others, it could be the latter that is most important.

This approach to evaluation imposes severe demands on designers. They need to know how well different possible organizational designs can be expected to perform in different classes of environments. If you have to make frequent product innovations, should your firm have functional or product-line subdivisions? If it is essential to learn how to shorten the system's response time to crises, will free-roaming trouble shooters help or hurt? Will the flow of communications lead to more innovation with a network of personal computers, or with a time-shared mainframe?

It is natural enough for people who must make design decisions to hope for help from academic students of organization on questions about the probable performance of a proposed design in a given context. Unfortunately, the available answers are not very satisfactory. The largest cluster of work on organizational design rests on theory derived from Thompson (1967). To vastly simplify his theory, he sees tasks as differing in the kinds of coordination they require between organizational members, and organizational design as a problem of matching organizational structures to these coordination requirements. Figuring out how to do something new is just another kind of task, one that often has heavy coordination requirements. The problem of flexibility in an organizational design enters his scheme mainly through the coordination that flexibility might require. Minimizing costs of coordination is the dominant idea.

There are a number of reasons why this failure to distinguish flexibility is serious, but one example may suffice here. Thompson (1967) observes that many organizations are designed with a ring of buffering structures surrounding what he called a "technical core," for example, manufacturing activities surrounded by sales, purchasing, personnel and public relations. His explanation for this common pattern is that it isolates the technical core from environmental disturbances and, therefore, permits efficient use of key resources. For example, an output inventory isolates the production line from sales fluctuations and permits long production runs that capture scale economies. Thompson, (1967, p. 20) says, "To maximize productivity of a manufacturing technology, the technical core must be able to operate as if the market will absorb the single kind of product at a continuous rate, and as if inputs flowed continuously." An approach that gives major prominence to flexibility along with efficiency (definitely *not instead* of efficiency) will bring some additional considerations to light. The buffered core structure not only makes it easier to be efficient, it simplifies the problem of *becoming* efficient. Controlling the fluctuation of extraneous variables dramatically simplifies the mysteries of learning what works and what does not. We recognize this when we say that game experience is not necessarily the best learning environment for a tennis beginner. In the same way, an output inventory may make it easier to bring on new production processes or improve old ones. This may be quite as significant as the help it gives in capturing known efficiencies.

Elsewhere in Thompson's work there is much concern for the ability of an organizational design to do new things, but it seems to be bypassed here. His original treatment of the subject is not replaced by an insistence on flexibility but merely clarified and augmented. There certainly seem to be cases where efficiency considerations generate the principal pressure for a buffered core structure. However, the augmented perspective might help to explain why one also sees the buffered core structure in factories that make relatively frequent shifts in what is being produced. If anything, the frequently shifting Japanese auto factories appear to have more heavily developed inventory buffering systems than their long-production-run American counterparts. One may say that it is "efficient" to be able to switch production quickly or to be able to bring new models to the market more rapidly. However, one is then applying the term *efficient* in a sense very different from its usual connotation of producing a well-understood product with minimum resources. This former usage means something very like *flexibility*, in that if production is organized in this way, it has a good chance of being able in the near future to make products that have, at the moment, not even been designed, and at an acceptable price.[3]

Since Thompson's work underlies so much of what has been done on organizational design, the example illustrates a number of typical shortcomings of what organization theory currently has to offer a frustrated designer. First, very little of the available theory has the kind of rigorous internal consistency one routinely expects in economics or operations research. Second, the best developed parts of what exists concentrate on efficiencies of coordination and do not really give the flexibility issue any separate, careful treatment.

At this point it will be useful to consider in detail the issue of contemporary theories and their overall contribution to the design of organizations. Two further cases are used to illustrate the argument. These cases contribute additional evidence for the proposition that organization theory will support design much more effectively if it can find a rigorous way to (1) represent alternative organizational designs, and (2) study their flexibility in addition to their efficiency. How this might be achieved is discussed in the paper's final section.

HOW WELL DO CONTEMPORARY THEORIES AID DESIGN—TWO CASES

What are Hierarchies Good For?

Hierarchy is what most of us think of first when we think of organizations. But there are clearly alternatives. Probably the most obvious of these is market organization, and the question I want to review here is the one Williamson (1975) has pressed upon both economists and organization theorists with such force, namely: "What are the relative advantages of hierarchies and markets?"

Williamson is not the only one to offer an answer to this question. It will prove instructive to look at additional answers that have been offered by Thompson and Simon on the advantages (and disadvantages) of hierarchical organization. This will permit us to acquire additional insight into the usefulness and limitations of current theories, and this may lead in turn to a better understanding of what new developments in theory would most help those who must design.[4]

OLIVER WILLIAMSON

A first step in such an investigation is to say a little more clearly what *hierarchy* and *market* refer to. Malone (1982) has pointed out an unfortunate ambiguity in Williamson's terminology, since markets can form hierarchical structures. For example, consider subcontracting relationships between two firms. Suppose A obtains subassemblies from B and C, and B obtains parts from subcontractors D, E and F, while C obtains parts from G and H. Then the network of subcontracting relations (see Figure 4.1) does form a graph-theoretic tree, but it is not at all what Williamson really means by *hierarchy*. At a number of points he uses *internal organization* as a synonym for *hierarchy*, which is another indication that one should not be too literal about the word he chose for his title.

Using our list of the elements of organizational designs, Williamson's work appears to be a study of the effects of substituting one type of interactor relation for another, holding other capabilities, incentives and change processes more or less constant. The comparison he pursues between markets and hierarchies can be rephrased as a comparison between two kinds of multiactor systems. In one, ("markets") there are many possible pairwise relations of mutual exchange between actors. In the other, every actor but one is subordinate to the authority of exactly one other actor. The single exceptional actor is subordinate to no one. This type should probably be referred to as a *hierarchical authority system* (or HAS) in order to keep it clear that the hierarchial structure under discussion is built with *authority* as its fundamental relation.

Williamson's view is that an HAS is a good design when the well-known efficiencies of a market organization cannot be realized. He calls this the "market failures" approach and believes that the most common barrier to market organization is the combination of small numbers with self-interest seeking and guile. When a job, in order to be done well, requires detailed and rare knowledge of local circumstances, either as an initial condition of doing the job or as a result of learning that occurs while on the job, then there will be very few candidates for the job who can perform it well. Williamson sees this situation as eroding competitive pressures on the job candidates and unleash-

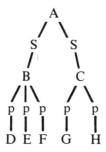

Figure 4.1

ing possibilities for extractive bargaining and various forms of deception. Under these conditions, an HAS is preferable to a market, because it is better at preventing the appropriation by individuals of the benefits of acting opportunistically, better at auditing and better at adjudicating disputes.

HERBERT A. SIMON

Williamson's treatment of hierarchy contrasts quite sharply with that of Simon in his essay "The Architecture of Complexity" (1962). In this essay, Simon places heavy stress on the effects of superordinate uniqueness and on the observation that as one descends through the levels of a hierarchy the appropriate time scale for events becomes faster. Thus, single longer lasting events at high levels form the entire context of multiple faster processes unfolding at lower levels.

Indeed, in "The Architecture of Complexity" Simon deliberately ranges over examples of hierarchies built from many kinds of relations. The authority relation is given no special place. In *Administrative Behavior* (1957) and other treatments of human organizations, he also concerns himself with authority. He simply interprets it as the right of a superordinate, within a limited range, to dictate the premises of decisions that will be made by subordinates. In Simon's view, the fact that the system is a hierarchy (one superordinate per actor) interacts powerfully with the authority relation. It helps guarantee coordination of action, because everyone in a group gets, and knows that the others get, decision premises from the same longer-time-horizon source. (Napoleon's short dictum for this view was, "One bad general is better than two good ones.")

JAMES D. THOMPSON

In the Simon view, an organizational designer should place together those capabilities that most benefit from being exercised under common premises. This design criterion for hierarchical decomposition is similar to Thompson's proposal that activities with high coordination requirements ("reciprocal interdependence" is Thompson's phrase) should be grouped together. However, while Thompson acknowledges some value to having such activities subject to a common authority, he gives that a rather secondary role. His primary stress is on lowering the costs of the requisite communication by bringing into proximity the people who need to be in contact. Thompson was one of the first organization theorists to notice the emergence of task forces, liaison men and other precursors of the modern matrix organization (Davis and Lawrence, 1977). He saw these as workable, if possibly costly, devices to provide coordination that was extremely valuable to the organization (Thompson, 1967, p. 79).

What do these three viewpoints tell interested organizational designers about when to employ an HAS? Williamson's thrust urges designers to use mutual exchange relations, rather than HASs whenever possible. One might have to resort to an HAS if small numbers give rise to a problematic level of opportunism—for example, because the tasks are nearly unique. It is not the need for coordination itself but the vulnerability of trying to achieve that coordination, using market relations in the absence of competitive pressure, that may make an HAS a more desirable alternative. Thompson's position is intermediate. He argues that one should group things together to make coordination among them easy by facilitating communication. Common authority over them could be important for adjudicating conflicts that coordination attempts will inevitably generate. Coordination is easier in an HAS because the actors share incentives more fully than they would if they were coordinating in a market setting. Simon's position is that unique superordinates, together with the authority relation, provide a profound mechanism of coordination that obviates the need for much communication which would otherwise be required in order to reconcile conflicting action premises.

Thus, all three authors agree, but for different reasons, that you are likely to want an HAS if you have high needs for coordination. Williamson thinks that the coordination may lead to *ex ante* small numbers and that opportunism will have to be controlled. Thompson (and Simon) think that a hierarchical decomposition will minimize the communication costs of the coordination. Simon will add that the HAS will give you powerful tools to achieve much of the coordination with less communication.

But they may not agree about which things should be grouped together in the HAS. Williamson's major themes suggest placing together the capabilities that will facilitate prevention of opportunism (activities with antagonistic incentives, or activities which lend themselves to easy joint adjudication and auditing). Thompson's major stress is on grouping the high coordination need capabilities together. Simon's emphasis goes beyond that of Thompson. Simon prefers grouping together the capabilities that may need to share common premises, whether or not they have high communication needs. He stresses being subject to common authority more than being physically proximate.

When comparing alternative designs, a simplified problem in business organization provides an opportunity to show how these three approaches, despite their agreement on the importance of coordination needs, pose quite different questions. Suppose company X has been obtaining parts from supplier Y and is now considering whether or not to establish its own in-house capability to make the parts or to go on buying them from Y.

Williamson's approach would focus the analysis on whether Y is, or is likely to become, the only supplier of the parts. If competitive pressures can be counted on, then he will generally expect that continuing the market relationship will be best. Thompson's approach will ask how much coordination needs to take place about the exact characteristics of the parts. If a lot is required, it might suggest sending a representative of the manufacturing process in company X to work part-time with the people in Y. If that is inadequate, then starting an in-house capability might be required. The Simon view suggests that the coordination required might be obtained by altering the incentives and general constraints operative at Y. Purchasing Y would establish the ability to say things such as, "in a crunch, these deliveries get first priority." Physical proximity or high communication volume may not be necessary.

All three approaches appear to identify pressures that are real. If one looks at an industry like semiconductor chip manufacturing, one sees insistence on second-source availability as a condition of using a vendor's parts. This rather heavily reflects Williamson. Liaison relationships between computer makers and chip makers, along Thompson's lines, are also very common. Many computer makers have some in-house chip-making capabilities, and the Commodore Corporation is a well-known illustration of a company that purchased a chip supplier, in the spirit of the Simon approach. This company's chip requirements were not especially novel, but it wanted to have priority setting ability.

Therefore, to sum up, when a designer asks, "Do I want parts supply to be on a market (voluntary mutual exchange) basis, or do I want to build that capability in the HAS already doing the assembly?", the answer he selects poses additional questions and additional design possibilities. When one looks at a case study—that is, a single, real manufacturing setting—one can see examples of all the available design alternatives.

The three approaches of Williamson, Simon and Thompson do provide some support for the designer's choice. If all three problems are present, communication need, priority setting and possible opportunism, then in-house capability might well be the preferred solution. And if the issues are "split" (e.g., priority setting is needed, but intensive communication is not, and outside competitors do exist), then one of the suggested alternatives may look good (e.g., buy the company to obtain priority setting, but retain competitive pressures on its performance by leaving it in the market.)

Despite these possibilities, however, this does not mean that the designer's problem is solved. There is another whole class of questions to be asked. Each of these designs provides a solution to a current set of problems. The designs are, in effect, efficient strategies for maximizing three different criteria. But some of the design alternatives are rather long-range in character—especially building up an in-house capability. So the designer should ask how the alternative designs might perform in the face of the problems that could arise later. What if X should have to modify its current product, or bring out an entirely new line? How would each organizational design respond to that? Suppose there were an as yet undiscovered way of improving the integration of the parts into the assemblies? Which design would have a better chance of discovering this improvement? What if the parts market were to be shaken up by new production technology? Which design would help X to make the best response? Suppose wage trends forced X to use less skilled laborers? In which design would that have the least serious effects?

It is easy to generate a large number of questions on these design issues. The sample business setting chosen here is not in any way unique. A government or nonprofit setting would present much the same daunting set of potential and confusing problems. Each problem has, at most, a moderate probability of occurring. Nevertheless, there are so many problems of this nature that it is virtually certain that some of them will appear—including some that were not even vaguely anticipated. As a result, the designer would like to know something about the *robustness* of the alternative designs, their ability to generate adequate performance when buffeted by problems that are, in effect, unpredictably drawn from a very wide range of possibilities. This amounts to asking, "How flexible are these alternative designs?"

Certainly, empirical studies of design flexibility have a value of their own, and much can be learned from further detailed observations. However, the focus of this paper is on what improvements in design are needed at the theoretical level. (Indeed, the generation of improved theory could markedly improve the quality of empirical observations. But the theoretical needs are, at present, quite substantial.) To be of much use in predicting—even very roughly—the flexibility properties of organizational designs, such new theories must be able to represent the key elements of the problem: the capabilities, incentives, relations, change processes and environment that are to be organized.

The requisite ideas can be expressed one at a time in English, but, due to their plurality, when they are interlinked, their joint logic becomes tangled— even if the complexity of each one can be greatly simplified by a theory. Mathematical tools, with which economics and operations research combat such difficulties, are useful when the issue is one of efficient choice among a few, well-defined capabilities. Such tools do not work well, by and large, when the questions are those which sensible designers should ask about the robustness or flexibility of alternative designs. The need seems to be for tools with logical power *and* richer representation possibilities than those inherent in, say, differential equations. (The last section will return to assessing the potential of computer modelling techniques for filling these needs.)

Could Garbage Can Processes Ever Be Desirable?

To give a quick account of what is meant by garbage can processes in an organization, it might be helpful to begin this section by using the list of organizational design elements. This list of design elements was developed in the course of trying to generalize the original gargage can (GC) model (Cohen et al., 1972).

The GC model elaborates the hypothesis that solutions and problems may be mobile within an organization. Rather than assuming the traditional sequence, in which a problem gives rise to a choice, which implies several alternative solutions, one of which is eventually chosen, the model views problems and solutions as each having some independent capacity to circulate in the organization. Thus, they have the potential to become attached to several different choices. The liberating effect of this assumption is to provide a place in the theory for frequently observed phenomena such as "accidents of timing." (For example, the amendment was introduced the day Jones was home with the flu, so his opposition was not registered.) It also includes the apparently erroneous process in which a solution is chosen that seems not to solve the original problem. (She *did* need to hire someone with a finance degree, but she also had to help her nephew find a job.) These and many other events that appear as homeless pathological exceptions in more conventional views of decision making can happily occupy niches of their own in the GC model.

From the point of view of an organizational designer, the GC concept of *solution* appears to be a special case of a *capability*. The former has a little more of the flavor of a single event, while the latter is a bit more general and gives the idea of the potential to produce a series of events. But they are quite similar notions. Incentives (or objectives) and the GC concept of problems are also quite closely related. A problem, after all, is equivalent to a shortfall with respect to one or more incentives or objectives. So, the processes assumed in the GC model can be described as fluid or loosely regulated relationships between capabilities and the incentives that govern their execution.

In the view offered here, organizational action occurs when incentives are mated with capabilities. Action is purposive behavior. In a classical HAS, built on the authority relationship, incentives (or, in Simon's language, "premises of decision") flow from a single, stable source to activate selected capabilities of subordinates. In a matrix organization (Davis and Lawrence, 1977), the capabilities of an actor may be subordinate to incentives coming from two stable sources (e.g., a project manager and a functional manager). The GC model describes the possibility of pairing capabilities with incentives from irregular and organizationally remote sources. It also acknowledges that capabilities may "seek out" incentives just as much as the other way around.

The absolute GC would be a situation in which a pairing of any objective with any capability would be sufficient to produce action. It is quite clear that this extreme GC design would be a nonviable disaster. Thus, we are never really talking of instituting the absolute GC but only about whether it might ever be preferable to make changes that move an organization in that direction. So our consideration of when a GC might be desirable needs to be recast into a discussion of the merits of loosening the systems in an organization that regulates the access of capabilities and incentives to each other.

In organizational life, there are an enormous number of devices that provide such regulation; these include recruitment procedures, promotion patterns, customary notifications of pending matters, reporting relationships, procedures for constituting committees, rules of order in formal meetings, informal "rules of order" and standards of germaneness in informal settings and so forth. It is appropriate, I think, to refer to all these devices as *filters*, since they function to let some capabilities and incentives come together in choice settings while keeping others out. Thus, a more careful way to state what is meant by a *GC organization* is an organization in which one or more of these filters is relatively loose, allowing wide mobility for incentives and capabilities.

But when would such loose filtration be desirable? The problem we have posed is, after all, a normative one. There is a fair amount of evidence that GC processes do occur, but that is quite a different matter from determining whether they *ought* to occur.

It has already been pointed out that an absolute GC could probably not survive. It also seems probable that—if conflict is low—an organization that really "knows what it is doing" will be relatively less efficient with relatively looser filtration. After all, germaneness rules, personnel assignment procedures and so forth are meant to bring together the combination of capabilities and incentives that the organization really needs in order to get its work done well. If it is actually quite clear who the best person is for each job, or what objectives should govern the making of a particular set of decisions, then any system that more frequently gave the jobs to less suitable individuals, or introduced extraneous objectives into the decision making, would be wasteful.

It is only when an organization really does not know what it is doing—and to a significant degree—that GC processes might be of some value. In this context, the unusual combinations of incentives and capabilities that might be generated by these processes can sometimes lead to a better performance at old tasks or the discovery of new and useful ones. Usually, when an engineer is allowed to propose new marketing strategies, the results are not encouraging. However, the proposed strategies will be likely to deviate from the standard recommendations of trained marketing people. Once in a while, such strategies might deviate in a novel and promising direction. Therefore, if there seems to be real room for improvement in marketing (the organization does not completely know what it is doing), and if it is reasonably easy to distinguish a promising suggestion from an outlandish one, then allowing the engineer to participate in the marketing decision might be a good bet.

The degree to which this strategy may be helpful is, unfortunately, a matter of comparative rates. Loosening filtration amounts to altering the organization's search strategy, moving away from considering capability-incentive pairings that are similar to what is already established and toward more novel variations. Cyert and March (1963) distinguished two principal modes of organizational search: in the neighborhood of the problem (unmet incentive or objective) and in the neighborhood of the current solution (capabilities). The introduction of GC processes allows search in the neighborhoods of new incentives that might be relevant to the current capabilities, or in the neighborhoods of new capabilities that might be relevant to the existing incentives—or possibly both.

Once an organization has had some time to become proficient at its present way of doing things, most novel variations will be inferior to its established procedures. At the same time, most really large improvements on current performance will involve capabilities and incentives substantially different from the current ones. Novelties will usually be bad, but big improvements will usually come through novelties. A change in the organization, toward a GC search strategy, will be desirable only if the increased rate of generating large improvements more than pays for the cost of the increased rate of generating inferior novelties. This cost also includes not only the wasted effort of generating inferior novelties but also the losses associated with actually implementing those inferior novelties that cannot be weeded out in advance.

It is important to note that the rate criterion is a version of flexibility, not of efficiency. The main point is, how rapidly can new and valuable capability incentive pairings be developed, not how best can existing capabilities be deployed to meet existing objectives? The rate criterion poses at least two difficulties. One is how to assess "value," if there can be new objectives or incentives. If goals are changing, against what standard shall there be measurement? This is a difficult problem, but recently some progress has been made (March, 1978; Cohen and Axelrod, 1984; Cohen, 1984). There is some reason to believe that even though incentives are changing or in conflict while the decisions are being made, decision making can be effective and contribute to survival. So it may be that some instability of standards of assessment need not constitute an insurmountable barrier to deciding when garbage cans are desirable.

The second difficulty is even more challenging: how can a designer judge whether a case under consideration is appropriate for a loosening of filtration? To help a designer make such a judgment, organization theory needs to provide a better understanding of the kinds of novelties generated by the various devices for loosening filtration that may be at the designer's disposal. Such devices for loosening filtration are interpreted in this paper as alternative types of relations among capabilities and incentives. The following section focuses on how organization theory might better represent and study these and other elements of organizational designs.

COMPUTER-ASSISTED THEORIES FOR ORGANIZATIONAL DESIGN

Our earlier examination of the two organizational design cases has revealed a number of areas in which better organization theory could help designers. This section briefly rehearses these problems and argues that one possible route to progress involves developing computerized methods for assessing the performance of alternative organizational designs. The paper concludes with a brief discussion of the strong relationships between this type of development and developments in artificial intelligence.

Initially, it should be stressed that much of what will aid organizational designers can be discovered by thoughtful observation and careful verbal theorizing. The emphasis here is on the possible contributions of more formal theoretical methods. This does not imply exclusion of the more traditional intellectual tools. All three approaches have complementary strengths and weaknesses, and the overall inquiry will benefit if they are used in a healthy mix. Formal theory, in particular, can never match the richness of the verbal style, but it can contribute to our ability to assess correctly the implications of a complex system of assumptions in a way that the verbal theoretical style often is unable to do.

The cases we have examined make it clear that organizational designers often do need to discover the joint implications of a complex system of assumptions. We saw that an organizational design can be decomposed into capabilities, incentives, relations and their change processes and that the designer's problem is to determine which of several such designs will attain higher levels of efficiency and/or flexibility. Even though this list was developed with the aim of finding a minimal sufficient set of concepts, and even though the list may be useful in its verbal form, it can give rise to problems complex enough to require the help of formal intellectual tools. It may be possible to reason verbally through a problem, such as whether a market or an HAS will prove more flexible across a range of potential environments. But with the use of formalized aids to reasoning, the chance of error is lessened. The possibilities for explaining the reasoning to others are heightened, and the ability of others to discover errors and/or make their own improvements is multiplied.

To provide such help, however, the formalisms employed must be able to represent the elements of an organizational design. This demand puts a severe strain on traditional mathematical tools, such as systems of differential or difference equations. Even small increases in realism, including a change process such as simple Bush-Mosteller operator learning, can quickly lead to a model that has no closed-form solution.

While mathematical results are preferable where possible, the computer has provided us with an alternative that can be used while we wait for the necessary mathematical tools. Careful use of simulation techniques does, at least, permit us to reason with the reliability of fastidious experimentation, if not with that of eternally consistent mathematics. And with simulation, we can extend our inquiry to somewhat more complex sets of assumptions.

Simulation has been very widely used by organization theorists ever since the pathbreaking work of Cyert and March (1963). This is not the place to review that twenty-year effort. But the preceding discussions do have one implication for the use of simulation in organization theory: in order to develop theory that would really aid design, simulation work done by organization theorists should converge to a substantial degree with work going on in artificial intelligence (AI).

It may seem that this convergence has already occurred—especially in view of Herbert Simon's founding role in both areas of research. In fact, it has not. A closer examination reveals that the overwhelming majority of organization theory simulations are composed in FORTRAN or BASIC and are internally structured as systems of equations—albeit large and nonlinear systems. They show very little of the list-based data structures and recursive function definitions that are characteristic of AI programming in that field's favorite language: LISP.

Artificial intelligence (and its psychological cousin, cognitive science) has developed a marvelous array of structures that embody the very elements of organizational design discussed in this paper. However, these structures have, for the most part, not made their way into the repertoire of organization theorists. This raises two questions: first, what is to be gained by bridging the gap between the fields, and second, why has it not happened already?

The potential gains in bridging this gap could be considerable. Consider capabilities. There are strong parallels between production systems, a major AI technique for representing skills and the notion of skills as fundamental building blocks of organizational action found in Nelson and Winter's (1982) work on change processes in firms. (Their approach is very similar to the notion of capabilities used here.) Nelson and Winter notice the similarities of their ideas to another AI representation technique: the scripts approach of Schank and Abelson (1977). An extremely important capability of individual human decision makers is planning (Miller et al. 1960). Artificial intelligence has a variety of sophisticated representations of planning processes (Cohen and Feigenbaum, 1982). None of these parallels has been exploited in formal models.

The potential for change processes is also apparent. A number of powerful representations of learning have been developed (Waterman, 1970; Sussman, 1975; Holland, 1975). Learning is widely taken to be the most significant change process in organizations, but, again, little of this has made its way into organization theory simulations. In relations between actors, AI has studied not only hierarchical control relations but also markets (Smith and Davis, 1978).

This brings us to the second question: if simulation has been plentiful in organization theory and there are relevant structures "next door" in AI, why have they not been used? There are at least four possible reasons:

1. Relative inaccessibility of AI hardware and software tools. Sophisticated people, programs and equipment were at just a very few locations.

2. High intellectual entry costs for organization theorists. Even if the tools were available, they have been expensive to learn to use.

3. Anticipation that the models would be extremely large. If the model of an organization would have multiple, possibly differentiated, actors, each as complex as a typical AI program, then it would be incredibly complex.

4. Lack of agreement within AI on best representations. If AI presents many ways to represent, say, learning, which one should the organization theorist employ?

The first two of these barriers are being eroded considerably by the diffusion and codification of AI hardware, software and concepts. The third may be partially calmed by the realization that interesting results can be obtained, even when the components of the model organization are simple, relative to a large AI program. For example, Axelrod (1984) was able to make substantial progress in understanding the peculiar effects of the "prisoner's dilemma" incentive structure by studying the interactions of many small programs that embodied intelligent but simple strategies.

In effect, it is possible to do some "miniaturization" of AI techniques, once they are well developed. Like microprocessors, the results may lack the full power of their bigger ancestors, but it may be much easier to study the behavior of systems containing many copies of these simple structures. Holland (1984) has shown that productions, which are a leading candidate structure for the formalization of capabilities, can be represented as simple strings of symbols from an alphabet of just three characters. Larger systems have been developed from these extremely simple components that learn, and they perform quite complex tasks such as managing a simulated pipeline system (Goldberg, 1983).

This leaves the fourth item in the list of barriers to AI-organization theory convergence: the existence within AI of too many possibilities. The best that can be done here is to try a number of the options. This is, in fact, what AI itself is doing. My own effort, together with that of Rick Riolo and Tom Malone, will be to employ a version of the "miniaturized productions" developed by John Holland (he calls them "classifier systems"). We are building a system of model actors that can be equipped with a wide variety of capabilities and incentives and embedded into many different patterns of organizational relations. It will make it possible to assess, on a consistent basis, the flexibility and efficiency of a wide spectrum of alternative designs in a very large variety of environments. A discussion of this work is beyond the scope of this paper.

The purpose of this concluding section has been to indicate the reasons why formal work in organization theory seems to be pointing toward AI. New theory built with AI tools is one promising avenue of response to the need for theory revealed in the earlier analysis of organizational design problems. Years ago, however, Herbert Simon anticipated these needs in pointing out that human organizations and computer programs were both fit objects for study in the "sciences of the artificial."

NOTES

1. Surprisingly, organization theorists have been slow to appreciate how many problems of organizational design occur a little farther afield than the conventional territory of corporate or governmental systems. The most striking examples, in my view, are arising in computer science, where the design of systems with many centers of intelligence is a major preoccupation, both in hardware and in software. I say "surprisingly" because Herbert Simon is a major figure both in computer science and in organization. This makes it seem natural that the connections would be well developed. However, with but a few exceptions (Fox, 1981; Malone and Smith, 1983), organization theorists trained in the social sciences have not been willing to follow the lead of Simon's essay on "The Architecture of Complexity" (1962) and extend the concepts of the field to organizations of nonhuman components. The approach taken here will try to make room for such extensions.

2. Just to illustrate the possibility of extending the ideas to nonhuman organizations, we could consider a design for a computer central processor. The CPU's capabilities might include the potential to be microcoded for execution of LISP as well as hardware required for floating-point math operations. Incentives for the processor are established by its priority interrupt management logic. This determines which incoming messages will be allowed to alter the CPU's course of action. In some computer systems, the processor is expected to control the placement and removal of data in memory. It has instructions giving it this capability. In newer systems, however, another processor executes Direct Memory Access when the job is delegated to it by the CPU. In such a system, the CPU is embedded in a more complex set of relations. In general, a CPU does not have its own processes for changing its capabilities, incentives or relations. These processes are executed by system designers who can alter its microcode, its interrupt processing routines or its relations to other processors in the system.

3. The distinction between efficiency and flexibility turns, in part, on an underlying distinction between activities that are "the same" and those that are "different." This

distinction is not always easy to make in practice. Thus, we have the proverb pair: "There is nothing new under the sun," and "You cannot step twice into the same river." Situations may be seen as varying in their similarity to each other. At one extreme, we have the problem of dealing with a stream of highly similar situations. This is the clear domain of efficiency. At the other end of the spectrum, we have streams of highly dissimilar situations. This is the realm of flexibility. In between is the realm of debate, the dialectic of generalization and differentiation that characterizes much of both individual and social learning (Holland, 1984).

4. Of course, in summarizing the major themes of these different approaches to the question, it is hard to do full justice to the minor themes and qualifications each author has presented. As a result, the account given probably overstates the contrast between the theories. The hope is that the distortion is both slight and useful.

REFERENCES

Arrow, K. *The Limits of Organization.* New York: W.W. Norton, 1974.

Axelrod, Robert. "More Effective Choice in Prisoner's Dilemma." *Journal of Conflict Resolution* 24 (1980): 379–403.

Axelrod, Robert. *The Evolution of Cooperation.* New York: Basic Books, 1984.

Cohen, Michael D. "Conflict and Complexity: Goal Diversity and Organizational Search Effectiveness." *American Political Science Review* 18 (1984): 435–451.

Cohen, Michael D., and Axelrod, Robert "Coping with Complexity: The Adaptive Value of Changing Utility." *American Economic Review* 74 (1984): 30–41.

Cohen, Y., and Feigenbaum, E. *Handbook of Artificial Intelligence.* vol. 1. Los Altos, Calif.: William Kaufmann 1982.

Cohen, Michael D., March, James G., and Olsen, John P. "A Garbage Can Model of Organizational Choice", *Administrative Sciences Quarterly.* 17, (1972).

Cyert, Richard M., and March, James G. *A Behavioral Theory of the Firm.* Englewood Cliffs, N.J.: Prentice-Hall, 1963.

Davis, S. M., and Lawrence, P. R. *Matrix.* Reading, Ma.: Addison-Wesley, 1977.

Fox, M. S. "An Organizational View of Distributed Systems." IEEE *Transactions on Systems, Man, and Cybernetics* SMC-11 (1981): 70–79.

Goldberg, D. "Computer Aided Gas Pipeline Operation Using Genetic Algorithms and Rule Learning." Ph.D. dissertation (Civil Engineering), University of Michigan, 1983.

Holland, J. *Adaptation in Natural and Artificial Systems.* Ann Arbor, Mich.: University of Michigan Press, 1975.

Holland, J. "Escaping Brittleness: The Possibilities of General Purpose Learning Algorithms Applied to Parallel Rule-Based Systems." Working Paper. University of Michigan. Department of Computer and Communications Science, 1984.

Levinthal, Daniel, and March, James G. "A Model of Adaptive Organizational Search." *Journal of Economic Behavior and Organization* 2 (1981): 307–333

Malone, T. W. "Organizing Information Processing Systems." Xerox Corp., Palo Alto Research Center (revision), August 1982.

Malone, T. W., and Smith, S. "Tradeoffs in Designing Organizations: Organizational Structures as Solutions to the Task Scheduling Problem." Working paper, Conference on Transaction Cost Analysis, Wharton School, University of Pennsylvania, 1983.

March, James G. "Bounded Rationality, Ambiguity, and the Engineering of Choice." *Bell Journal of Economics* (1978).

March, James G., and Olsen, Johan P. (eds.). *Ambiguity and Choice in Organizations.* Bergen, Norway: Universitetsforlaget, 1976.

Miller, G. A., Galanter, E., and Pribram, K. H. *Plans and the Structure of Behavior.* New York: Holt, 1960.

Morgan, C. "The Microprocessor's Tenth Birthday." *Byte* 7 (1982): 6–10.

Nelson, Richard R., and Winter, Sidney G. *An Evolutionary Theory of Economic Change.* Cambridge, Mass.: Harvard University Press, 1982.

Nystrom, P. C., and Starbuck, W. (eds.). *Handbook of Organizational Design.* Vols. 1 & 2, New York: Oxford University Press, 1981.

Schank, R. C., and Abelson, R. P. *Scripts, Plans, Goals and Understanding.* Hillsdale, N. J.: Lawrence Erlbaum, 1977.

Simon, Herbert A. *Administrative Behavior.* 2nd ed. New York: Free Press, 1957.

Simon, Herbert A. "The Architecture of Complexity." *Proceedings of American Philosophical Society* 106 (1962): 467–482.

Simon, Herbert A. *The Sciences of the Artificial.* Cambridge, Mass.: MIT Press, 1969.

Smith, R. G., and R. Davis. "Frameworks for Cooperation in Distributed Problem Solving", *IEEE Transactions on Systems, Man and Cybernetics,* SMC–11. (1981): 61–69.

Sussman, G. *A Computer Model of Skill Acquisition.* New York: Elsevier, 1975.

Thompson, James D. *Organizations in Action.* New York: McGraw-Hill, 1967.

Waterman, D. A. "Generalization Learning Techniques for Automating the Learning of Heuristics." *Artificial Intelligence* 1 (1970): 121–170.

Williamson, O. *Markets and Hierarchies.* New York: Free Press, 1975.

5

Defense Resource Allocation: Garbage Can Analysis of C3 Procurement

JOHN P. CRECINE

INTRODUCTION

Increased Importance of C3I in Modern Warfare

The increased mobility and lethality of modern military forces places tremendous demands upon the C3I (command, control, communications and intelligence) systems of military organizations during times of war. This is especially true of U.S. military forces in conventional war scenarios, where the assumed enemy forces possess a numerical superiority, are nearly equivalent technologically and will most likely be on the offensive. Under such conditions, in order to be successful, U.S. military organizations, or any defense, must be extraordinarily quick reacting and flexible. Only by properly diagnosing combat situations promptly and bringing appropriate forces to bear at the appropriate time and at the appropriate point can numerically inferior conventional forces be successful on defense. This implies a well functioning C3I system, one that performs in real time and is survivable in an environment where the physical

John P. Crecine is Senior Vice President for Academic Affairs at Carnegie-Mellon University. Much of the material reported here derives from a contract to study conventional force C3I systems from the Office of Net Assessment, OSD.

components of the system represent high priority and early targets for the enemy.

Serious Deficiencies in U.S./NATO C3I Systems

A recent assessment of the C3I capabilities of U.S./NATO air-ground forces in central Europe reveals serious deficiencies in the C3I systems necessary to support conventional war (Coulam et al., 1983; Crecine et al., 1981). At the top of the NATO command structure—NATO Council of Ministers down through the two major army groups (NORTHAG and CENTAG) and air forces (2 ATAF and 4 ATAF)—there are C3 problems involving slow reaction time, a cumbersome alliance decision process and serious doubts about the continuity of command. Major command headquarters are soft and immobile, multiple command centers are collocated and most major communication systems are vulnerable. There is little redundancy in C3 systems at the top levels of the NATO command structure and little rehearsal of ways to respond to major damage to command facilities and communication outages.

At lower levels of the NATO command structure—army corps and air force wings and below—there are similarly serious C3I deficiencies in the capacity to process information in communications, in reaction time, in the capacity to coordinate air and ground operations, in the physical survivability of command posts and communication systems and in the general robustness against attrition. Basically, C3 systems are vulnerable physically and wartime C3 systems are not exercised under realistic conditions. Rehearsals and maneuvers do not adequately reflect combat conditions. To the extent that the employment of C3 systems is tested, it is under peacetime conditions and under the U.S. command structure, not the NATO command structure that would be operative in wartime.

Intelligence systems likewise have serious deficiencies. They rely on dedicated communication circuits and sensors, without redundant communication paths. The facilities necessary for processing various intelligence information and communications are few, they are overloaded during peacetime and generally are shared with other users. Existing intelligence-processing facilities, like most time-sharing systems, degrade rapidly when overloaded. Consequently, they are not well suited to accomodate the flood of communications associated with increased military activities. With low interconnect on communications and serious bottlenecks in processing information, U.S. battlefield intelligence systems are also seriously deficient.

C3I deficiencies in U.S. military forces are especially acute at the "seams" of the organization—C3I which involves more than one combat unit, more than one different function (e.g., communications between intelligence and targeting), or two different services (air and ground forces). Generally, C3I functions, including their supporting manpower and equipment, are performed reasonably well when they are organic to an organization. For example, division-to-platoon C3I, where all communications are internal to the division, is performed quite well on relatively modern equipment that is functional and survivable. Similarly, C3I functions performed by a mixture of naval air and surface navy forces are performed with relative efficiency. This is to be contrasted with the C3I systems that support, for example, coordination between two adjacent divisions on a battlefield, or that are designed to coordinate air units providing support to ground forces, when those air units are controlled by the air force rather than the army.

There are alternate ways of organizing command and, hence, the way combat units are coordinated. For example, U.S. air-ground unit coordination is in contrast to the organization of the Soviet military, where the air forces that provide ground support to combat troops are in the same unit with, and organic to, the ground forces.

Some C3I difficulties are the product of incoherent overall military doctrine. Some are caused by quantitative deficiencies in manpower and equipment. For example, the communication linkages provided in central Europe by the Defense Communication Agency are provided and maintained by a very small manpower contingent, with a very low budget. Other deficiencies are the product of severe qualitative shortcomings of C3I systems.

In general, C3I functions are performed better when all the relevant performance units are part of a single organic whole—for example, within a division, or division and below, in the army, corp-to-division C3I, which involves only ground forces. Even with combined arms operations, those units where components of the force are organic to the organization do better than those where they are not. For example, coordination between air units and the Marine Corps ground forces (which have their own air support units), and the U.S. Navy, which similarly has its own air force, is far superior to the air-ground coordination of U.S. Air Force and corresponding U.S. Army units. By implication, the major C3I problems of the U.S. military exist in the "echelons above corp"—in the corp-to-theater, to SACEUR, and to the National Command Authority.

There are many reasons for C3I problems. There is a lack of realistic rehearsal, with the consequence that operational deficiencies in C3I systems are rarely apparent. One major problem until recently has been the generally low priority assigned to the C3I functions. Perhaps the most intractable underlying reason for deficiencies is the fact that the processes that result in the provision of C3I systems are not well attuned to, and do not generally reflect, the operational requirements of the employing forces.

Impact of Structural, Organizational Problems on C3 Procurement

On the most general level, C3I and other weapons systems which do not well support operational military requirements are to be expected from the division of responsibilities and command structure established by the amended National Security Act of 1947. In this charter for the U.S. defense establishment, the responsibility for *maintaining* military forces (including procurement of equipment and training of manpower) rests with the individual military services, whereas the responsibility for *employing* these forces rests with a separate command structure. During peacetime, those with the direct responsibility for employing military forces—the unified and specified commanders—have little budget authority and little to do, except plan. The budgetary and procurement impetus of those responsible for commanding and employing military force vis-à-vis those responsible for maintaining the forces (military services), leads to a situation where operational requirements are, at best, interpreted, or guessed at, by those designing and providing C3I capabilities—the component military services. At worst such operational requirements are assigned relatively low priority in comparison with other factors. The problems associated with the procurement and acquisition of C3I systems are especially acute when the C3I functions cross organizational boundaries. Neither "maintaining" organization, on either side of the boundary, has much incentive for planning and procuring for *joint* employment of C3I capabilities: for example, systems that allow artillery companies to help armored companies target, systems that allow air forces to communicate with ground forces, and systems where the user of the service is not the provider of the service. For instance, the Defense Communication Agency provides many communication services to separate command structure facilities, and often such systems represent "orphans" without a sponsoring parent.

There have been many attempted bureaucratic and procedural "solutions" to what I perceive to be a structural problem in C3I procurement and employment. However, none of these "procedural solutions" seems to have worked very well.

To an organization theorist, deficiencies in C3I performance, stemming from structural properties of resource allocation processes, are not particularly surprising. The intent of this chapter is to offer a deeper understanding of those processes that produce the "undesired" C3I outcomes, and to use an "information-processing" (IP) approach to the study of organizations in order to provide such understanding. In other words, the "C3I problem" provides a context in which to explore the utility of information-processing approaches to organization theory. As will be seen below, the so-called garbage can theories of organizational choice represent a particularly appropriate approach in the general category of IP theories.

In the United States Defense Department, resource allocation, weapons acquisition and procurement processes, taken individually, are tightly coupled processes. The outcomes in question are the joint product of a confluence and convergence of these tightly coupled processes. The resulting complex of processes is, itself, loosely coupled, in the sense that these three individual processes are linked together in any given procurement issue in a somewhat ad hoc way.

The next sections of this chapter will briefly outline the theories of human organization utilized herein. Then the organizational substance of the C3I procurement process will be discussed, beginning with the relatively stable, underlying organizational processes, proceeding to many of the ways in which these underlying processes are linked to produce C3I procurement outcomes, and finally evaluating the utility of IP and garbage can theories in both their descriptive and prescriptive roles.

INFORMATION PROCESSING IN TIGHTLY COUPLED FORMAL SYSTEMS (ORGANIZATIONS)

Characteristics of Large Organizations

One can profitably view organizational decision making and information processing as a linked, coordinated set of individual decision processes (Inbar, 1979; Crecine, 1969, Chapter 6; Tuggle and Gerwin, 1980).

One of the reasons for creating an organization is to relax some of the constraints on individuals, as decision makers and information processors. For instance, humans generally approximate serial information processors—one thing at a time. The constraints on time, attention and expertise associated with individuals are relaxed somewhat when groups of individuals are organized. Although there is a real limit on what organizations can attend to and act on in an organized way, it is clear that a single organization can attend to more than a single human is able to. For example, one reason for organizing is the ability to support parallel processing and other kinds of divisions of labor and expertise. The limits on the short-term memory of an individual are similarly relaxed; the number of objects or problems that significant parts of an organization can be immediately aware of is much greater than that of individuals.

While the creation of an organization serves to relax some information processing constraints on individuals, the need for coordination introduces others. Both formal (plans and procedures) and informal (shared values, doctrines, scenarios) modes of coordination introduce additional constraints on attention, information flows and activity. The very need to coordinate individuals and to have communications that mean roughly the same things to sender and receiver tends to force the organization to create stylized representations of external conditions and realities and generally to reduce the variability and "richness" of the information environment that the organization operates in. Partly by restricting the range of communications circulating in an organization, the behavior of the subunits becomes more predictable and manageable and those (restricted) communications circulating internally are more likely to be understood—even if the link with "reality" is tenuous.

Over time, organizations develop structured, predictable and interpretable information environments. They also develop routines and standard operating procedures for processing the expected range of information in the context of shared images, scenarios, values and expectations. Once created, the shared images and processes are highly resistant to change. Organizational routines, sensors and decisions tend to homogenize a highly variable external environment and convert unfamiliar information and signals to the familiar. There are very strong tendencies for large organizations to convert situational definitions into problems and tasks that are consistent with the organization's capabilities (March and Simon, 1958, pp. 150–158; Cyert and March, 1963, pp. 101–113; Inbar, 1979, pp. 141–170). An extreme example is that of military organizations preparing to fight the *last* war, converting particular military threats into situations that the organization has dealt with before.

Other characteristics of large organizations are partly due to functional divisions of labor and to subsequent socialization of participants around subunit activities and well-defined technologies. Conflicting objectives, technologies and the like tend to develop among the various organizational subunits. As a result, the overall organization tends to resemble a coalition of partially conflicting interests and subunits rather than a coherent body with perfectly shared values. To ignore the special interests of the individual services that make up the U.S. Defense Department is not to understand U.S. national security policy and practice. Resulting organizational actions are likely to be less than internally consistent or coherent. This is because the inevitable conflict between coalitional subunits is imperfectly resolved and because there will be at least a partial failure to control organizational subunits in a consistent fashion. The larger and more complex the organization, the more divergent the subunit goals and values. The greater the degree of functional specialization, the more the organization must rely on formal procedures to coordinate its activities (March and Simon, 1958, pp. 144–146).

In general, organizations do not function in an *organized* way unless they have rehearsed their actions. Activities involving more than one operational subunit require rehearsal and development of coordination routines. As part of the rehearsal requirements for carrying on organized activities, there must be formal communication and control mechanisms and a stylized, predictable mode of communications.

In a large organization, internal cues and information generally dominate. Very simple links exist between information in the external environment and the information environment found internal to the organization. The information to coordinate generally dominates the information important for adapting to the external environment.

To understand information flows in an organization, one needs detailed information concerning goals and coalitions of subunits, the routines and procedures, divisions of labor, methods for adapting to changes in the outside world, the nature of the internal (organizationally created) information environment and the formal modes of coordination and communication.[1]

COORDINATION OF INDIVIDUAL INFORMATION-PROCESSING ACTIVITIES: ORGANIZED DECISION SYSTEMS

If humans possess relatively common information-processing capabilities, then any aggregation or organization of humans will also exhibit many of the same, elemental capabilities. Yet because organizations are composed of individuals with different roles and different beliefs, often clustered together in coalitions, the individual-to-organization analogy has limited validity. The following are some important differences in information-processing characteristics between individuals and organizations:

- Information, per se, assumes a more important role in organizational choice processes, is more formalized and less varied (Steinbruner, 1974, pp. 124–128).

- Alternatives are "pruned" from the choice set at an earlier stage in the decision process for organizations.
- Once an alternative emerges from an organization or an organizational subunit, it is not easily given up. This is primarily because support for an alternative requires assembling a coalition on some level. Once assembled, the coalition takes on a life of its own.
- Organizations use simple(r) coordination structures. Hierarchical structures are particularly prevalent partly because one of the properties of hierarchies is that they minimize the need for coordination and reduce the costs of communication.
- Preexisting processes and routines are more dominant in organizations, and inappropriate routines are seldom discarded. Even if situations arise that existing routines cannot deal with, "the construction of an entirely new program from detailed elements is rarely contemplated. In most cases, adaptation takes place through a recombination of lower-level programs already in existence." (March and Simon, 1958, p. 150).
- Decision and choice take longer in organizations (Steinbruner, 1974, pp. 128–129).
- There is a greater tendency in organizations to deal with partial definitions of problems, in particular those technical parts of a problem that can be dealt with routinely by subunits ("grooved thinking": Steinbruner, 1974, p. 125).
- Multiple justifications for a course of action or decision are more important in an organizational context. This is principally because each member of the organizational coalition must have some (often different) justification for supporting a decision (see Simon, 1964, for discussion of reasons for this).
- Simple strategies for dealing with uncertainty are generally found in organizations. This is partly because it is easier to communicate "certainty" or "point estimates" between members of an organization (Cyert and March, 1963, p. 26).
- In the short run, organizational capabilities (information processing or otherwise) are limited to those activities that have previously been rehearsed by the various subunits of an organization or that can be easily assembled from existing SOPs.

One unfortunate state of affairs is that there is far more empirical research on the information-processing characteristics of individuals than on institutions and organizations.

So far I have argued that human collectivities, viewed as complex information-processing systems, are analogous in a limited way to individuals as information-processing entities. The concepts that apply to individuals need to be augmented in significant ways in order to extend them to the organizational level. For example, "people (i.e., individuals) have goals; collectivities of people do not" (Cyert and March, 1963, p. 26). Information-processing (IP) views of organizations need to deal explicitly with the differences between the goals of individual participants. Most organization theorists view an organization as a coalition of subcoalitions, each having diverse but internally consistent sets of goals, procedures and capabilities, and memberships. To the extent that organizational structures determine who talks to whom about what, natural socialization processes would serve to account for the stability and internal homogeneity of organizationally based subcoalitions. From an IP point of view, the organizational-individual analogy holds quite well for *within*-subcoalition matters (allowing for parallel processing and some relaxation of attention span constraints) but not well at all for *between*-subcoalition phenomena. The IP concepts applying to individuals have to be modified to deal with the way in which conflicts between subcoalitions are resolved in an institutional setting.

The occasions for (selective) attention, interaction, conflict, problem solving and cooperation are largely defined by the structure of an institution or organization. As one might expect, information processing in a *tightly coupled* collectivity or organization (e.g., the U.S. Army, the Office of Management and Budget, the United Auto Workers or the National Institute of Education within the Department of Education) is different from that which occurs within a more *loosely coupled* system (e.g., the Department of Education, the U.S. Congress or the President's Economic Planning Advisory Group or any large university).

Partly on account of these differences, two IP-based theories will be discussed. Cyert and March's (1963) theory of choice in business firms has been widely applied in the political science literature to such seemingly diverse phenomena as the federal budgeting process (Wildavsky, 1964; Crecine, 1975a), the U.S. Congress (Kingdon, 1973), the Cuban Missile Crisis (Allison, 1972), municipal budgeting (Crecine, 1969; Larkey, 1979), municipal zoning decisions (Davis and Reuter, 1974) and public school finance (Gerwin, 1969). As organization theory, rather than as a theory of business firm behavior, the Cyert and March work has been especially useful to political scientists. This is primarily because it is a theory of politics—subcoalitional interaction—in the setting of a tightly coupled organization. A parallel theory of IP phenomena in loosely coupled organizations and institutions is the March, Cohen and Olsen (Cohen et al., 1972; Cohen and March, 1974; March and Olsen, 1976) theory of decision making in an "organized anarchy," somewhat misleadingly called the "garbage can" theory, which will be discussed later. To illustrate the distinction between tightly and loosely coupled collectivities, recall in Graham Allison's (1972) study of the Cuban Missile Crisis the "Model II," describing organizational processes where responsibilities are clearly delineated in an organization and are executed using well-rehearsed routines. Allison's Model II corresponds to a theory of "tightly coupled" organizations. His "Model III," used to depict the bureaucratic politics in the ExCom, set up by President Kennedy to deal with the Cuban Missile Crisis, is an example of decision making in a "loosely coupled" organization—where there are few rules or conventions guiding the interactions of individuals and bureaucracies. However, during the Cuban Missile Crisis, the participants identified by Allison were somewhat constrained by their organizational "hats," but exercised influence on issues not usually within their purview and were engaged in a much more fluid process than is usually found in a bureaucracy.

Tightly Coupled Systems

Perhaps the most widely known coherent theory of choice in tightly coupled organizations compatible with what is known of the characteristics of human information processing is Cyert and March's work, *A Behavioral Theory of the Firm* (1963). In this they argue that decision making in organizations can be analyzed in terms of variables that affect organizational goals, expectations and choice.[2]

1. Organizational goals. Organizational goals have "dimensions"—those things seen as important—and "levels" for each dimension. Variables affecting the set of things the organization views as important are "the composition of the organizational coalition, the organizational division of labor in decision making, and the definition of problems facing the organization. . . . Organizational goals change as new participants enter or old participants leave the coalition. . . . The operative goals for a particular decision are the goals of the subunit making the decision . . . [and] goals are evoked by problems" (Cyert and March, 1963, p. 115). The level of aspiration attached to any particular goal dimension is influenced by the organization's past goal and past performance on that dimension and by the observed performance of other, "comparable" organizations.

2. Organizational expectations. "Expectations are seen as the result of drawing inferences from available information. The way in which inferences are drawn might be characterized as an optimistic extrapolation from past experience. Information is made available to an organization both through monitoring the external environment and by actively searching. The amount of "slack" in the organization (influenced by past successes) affects both the intensity and probably the success of search. The direction of search is most strongly influenced by the "nature of the problem stimulating search and the location in the organization at which search is focused" (Cyert and March, 1963, p. 116).

3. Organizational choice. "Choice takes place in response to a problem, uses standard operating procedures, and involves identifying an alternative that is acceptable from the point of view of evoked goals" (Cyert and March, 1963, p. 116).

These three characteristics of organizational decision making are based on four major relational concepts, as follows:

1. Quasi resolution of conflict. An organization is a coalition of members having different goals, and most organizations most of the time exist and thrive with considerable latent conflict of goals.

- Goals are independent constraints applied to alternatives or choices.
- Local rationality—"an organization factors its decision problems into subproblems and assigns the subproblems to subunits in the organization. . . . [resulting] in the tendency for the individual subunits to deal with a limited set of problems and a limited set of goals" (Cyert and March, 1963, p. 117).
- Acceptable-level decision rules.
- Sequential attention to goals—"Organizations resolve conflict among goals, in part, by attending to different goals at different times" (Cyert and March, 1963, p. 117).

2. Uncertainty avoidance. Organizations do not deal directly with uncertainty. Mainly, they try to avoid it by
- Use of feedback-react decision procedures, solving problems serially as they arise and by ignoring as many interrelationships in decisions as possible.
- Creating a negotiated environment. By negotiating with aspects of the external environment likely to cause trouble (e.g., legislative bodies, interest groups, etc.) and through internal planning where subunits can avoid uncertainty about other units in making their decisions, through devices like budgets and legislative mandates (division of labor and responsibility).

3. Problemistic search. Problemistic search is stimulated by a specific problem and directed toward a solution to that problem. Characteristics of organizational search are

- Search is problem oriented. A problem is created when the organization fails to satisfy an acceptable-level goal and is solved either by finding an acceptable course of action or by revising the goal. "Solutions are also motivated to search for problems. Pet projects . . . look for crises" (Cyert and March, 1963, p. 121).
- Search is simple-minded and is conducted "in the neighborhood of the problem symptom" and "in the neighborhood of the current alternative." Unsuccessful search results in increasingly complex or "distant" search and search in more vulnerable areas of the organization, in weaker subunits (Cyert and March, 1963, pp. 121–122).
- Search is biased by (1) the special training or orientation of organizational subunits conducting search, (2) hopes and expectations, and (3) communications biases in various parts of the organization (pattern of information contacts and sources).

4. Organizational learning. Organizations adapt to change in the external environment in three different phases of decision making.
- Adaptation of goals to previous goals, previous experience and observed experience of comparable organizations.

- Adaptation in attention rules—organizations learn to attend to those aspects of the environment and those performance measures that produce generally satisfactory results.
- Adaptation in search rules—search is conducted in those areas and in those ways that have proven relatively successful in the past.

Tightly coupled decision systems—usually formal organizations—have the following characteristics:

- They are generally driven by well-defined choice opportunities or occasions where the organization is expected to make a recommendation or decision (e.g., budget request, draft legislation, ruling on an application, etc.).
- They generally deal with well-defined problems (or are able to convert ill-defined problems into well-defined problems) that some subunit "knows" how to cope with.
- They have a well-defined way of assigning problems to subunits and an explicit division of labor and attention among subunits.
- They have clear sets of procedures for dealing with conflict between subunits.
- They have clear (if minimal) information requirements associated with choices.
- They have sets of processes, routines or competencies distributed among subunits and/or subcoalitions that guide most behavior and condition expectations of other units.

Clearly an enormous percentage of the phenomena of interest to political scientists and other social scientists takes place in tightly coupled systems. The historical preference of students of choice and decision in political science for turning points, "critical" decisions and cases results in a serious undervaluation of the role of routine, systematic processes in generating outcomes of interest. Somehow, people and groups acting in systematic fashion do not fit the dynamic image of the pulling and hauling of "politics." Even if the cumulative effects of small, systematic changes add up to large changes, or even if the interaction of relatively simple processes results in very complex behavior (see Simon, 1969, pp. 23–26, and throughout, for elegant discussion of this point), most political scientists seem to equate politics with unsubtle "pulling and hauling" and observable, direct conflict. So far, the discussion of an information-processing approach to political and social phenomena has focused on systematic choice, decision and information-processing by individuals and relatively well-structured and "tightly coupled" organizations. The choice and decision behavior of what Karl Weick (1973) has termed *loosely coupled* and anarchistic systems, to be discussed in the next section, may conform more obviously to popular and professional conceptions of the processes of politics.

Cyert and March in their behavioral theory of the firm (1963) and others have created a conception of information processing and choice in public organizations that is based on the characteristics of human information processing in systems consisting of a coalition of groups, each having somewhat divergent capabilities and goals. In these systems, despite diversity, some basic division of activities and responsibilities among the coalition members is assumed, as are conventions governing the interactions and conflict between coalition members. In such systems, the links are predictable between *problems* of various types and the *participants*, or subcoalitions, in an organization who deal with them. This predictability is often based on some shared assumptions concerning the "technology" of producing goods or services—production engineers install new machines in the assembly line, the Office of Tax Legislation lawyers makes recommendations for changes in the tax code—goals and subgoals are usually operational (if not always shared by elements of the organizational coalition), at least some technologies for producing outputs (whether automobiles or welfare checks) are known, and the active participation of key decision makers and coalition members can be presumed. In tightly coupled systems, problems become associated with relevant solutions, and choices are made in order to solve problems. Less bureaucratic approaches are still consistent with bargaining and more political conceptions of choice, where coalitions are formed (from among organizational subunits) and political bargains struck. Choices are made by forming a group with sufficient power to enforce a joint solution to a problem.

Either under conditions where bargaining and politics are structured or where administrative and bureaucratic procedures exist within a relatively stable structure, one can expect relatively clear and shared criteria for determining "what alternatives or solutions are appropriately associated with what problems, and what problems are appropriately associated with what choices, what people appropriately participate in what choices, and what the particular distribution of power is" (March and Olsen, 1976, pp. 24–25). The linkages between problems, choices, solutions and people are structured and clear. Perhaps the most important implication of choice in a tightly coupled system is that once one knows the "problem" or external stimulus in such a system, one can make reasonable guesses about the sorts of solutions or alternatives the system is likely to generate, the people (or organizational subunits) who are likely to participate in any choice process and the choice(s) likely to emerge; "where you stand depends on where you sit" models will work.

Not all systems are tightly-coupled. James March and his colleagues have formulated an approach to information processing, choice and decision for "loosely coupled" systems, where goals and objectives are problematic, technologies are unclear and participation is fluid.

THEORY: INFORMATION PROCESSING IN LOOSELY COUPLED SYSTEMS

The following characteristics of choice are "particularly conspicuous in public, educational and illegitimate organizations. Although a college or public organization (or, political party, legislative committee, or interdepartmental liaison committee) operates within the metaphor of a political system or a hierarchical bureaucracy, the actual operation of either is considerably attenuated by the ambiguity of goals, by the lack of clarity in technology, and by the transient character of many participants" (March and Olsen, 1976, p. 25).

1. Preferences are often problematic. It is difficult to impute a set of preferences to the decision situation that satisfies the standard consistency requirements for a theory of choice. The organization operates on the basis of a variety of inconsistent and ill-defined preferences. It can be described better as a loose collection of ideas than as a coherent structure. Preferences are discovered through action as much as being the basis of action.

2. Technology is often unclear. Although the organization manages to survive and even produce, its own processes are not understood by its members. It operates on the basis of simple trial-and-error procedures, the residue of learning from the accidents of past experience and pragmatic inventions of necessity.

3. Participation is often fluid. Participants vary in the amount of time and effort they devote to different domains; involvement varies from one time to another. As a result, the boundaries of the organization are uncertain and changing; the audiences and decision makers for any particular kind of choice change capriciously. No single participant dominates the choice in all its phases (March and Olsen, 1976).

In the March, Cohen and Olsen theory, the key variables in the system are the following:

1. Problems. Problems arc the concerns of people inside and outside an organization or institution. Problems require attention, but are distinct from choices. Problems are seldom solved when a choice is made. "Unequal standards of medical care and unequal access to it" may be the problem. The choice may be a national health service or "socialized medicine." The connection between problem and choice may be plausible, but it is not necessarily functional.

2. Solutions. "A solution is somebody's product." A policy or a computer is not simply a solution to a problem. Rather it is an idea or device that belongs to, or is advocated by, a person or subunit that is actively looking for a problem to which it is the solution. "Open classrooms," "management by objectives," "manned bombers," and "investment tax credits" were and/or are "solutions looking for problems." For example, the U.S. Air Force's justification for a new, manned bomber to replace the B-52 began in the early 1950s. The justification (the "problem" to which the "manned bomber" was the solution) changed dramatically, first with the existence of missiles of both the defensive (surface to air) and offensive (ICBMs) varieties, and second with the evolution of radar and electronic warfare, fighters, and so forth. Over the past 30 years, the nature of the threat/problem has changed dramatically. Until the most recent proposal, the radar-invisible "Stealth" aircraft, the evolution of the design of the

"solution" has changed only very marginally through the RB-70 and various versions of the B-1—a classic case of the independence of solution and problem.

3. Participants. People and subunits often have considerable discretion over whether to become involved in choices and decisions. Participation in a particular choice situation is constrained by other demands on a participant's time and attention. A secretary of state actively participating in arms control negotiations is unlikely to participate simultaneously in the formulation of a new foreign trade bill or to press a European plea for lower U.S. interest rates within the Federal Reserve Board. The number of people who could plausibly become engaged on an issue is always far greater than the number who actually do become involved.

4. Choice opportunities. Choice opportunities are occasions when an organization or institution is expected to produce something that can be called a decision. Budgets must be passed, bills must be voted on, vacant positions must be filled and contracts must be let. Choice opportunities arise regularly. In addition, organizations can create choice opportunities. For example, appointing a task force charged with making recommendations about anything is one way of creating a choice opportunity (March and Olsen, 1976, p. 82).

The March, Cohen and Olsen theory argues that, while there may be more or less stable processes governing the generation, recognition and interpretation of problems, the production of solutions, the degrees of participation and the appearance of choice opportunities, these processes constitute *separate* streams of activity. The argument is that they are often loosely coupled processes and that the coupling or bringing together of these streams takes place in the context of, and is stimulated by, "choice opportunities." The metaphor is of a "choice opportunity" as a "garbage can" into which one can dump different mixtures of participants, problems and solutions, mix them up (couple them in a particular way), cart the "garbage can"/"choice" away by making a decision and bring in the next "can" to start another cycle.

The March, Cohen and Olsen theory is a model of choice in an "organized anarchy." It is organized in the sense that the processes or policy streams that generate problems, solutions, participation and choice opportunities (or combinations of the four) are each somewhat stable and systematic. It is an anarchy in the sense that there is no particular way in which processes become linked up or coupled to one another—there is no unique technology of choice.

In complex decision systems, an IP approach can be quite useful in understanding individual policy processes. An IP approach is also directly useful where the interactions among individual policy processes are systematic and regular—in analyzing tightly coupled systems. In loosely coupled systems—organized anarchies—an IP approach adequately deals with individual processes but cannot, by itself, deal with the system as a whole. Also required is a conception of organization—a "theory of coupling" of the individual processes. Any such theories capable of making very precise predictions, or of providing very rich explanations, will by definition be somewhat unique to each situation.

In spite of the context-specific nature of the theory of loosely coupled decision systems, it is possible to discuss some of the general characteristics of choice in such a system. March, Cohen and Olsen constructed a formal simulation model of decision making in an organized anarchy and used it to trace out the implications of a variety of different organizational structures. The model was then used to "assign problems and decision makers to choices, to determine the energy (and attention) required and effective energy applied to choices, to make such choices and resolve such problems as the assignments and energies indicate (were) feasible" (March and Olsen, 1976, p. 33).

In an organized anarchy, some of the major properties of the model of choice are the following (March and Olsen, 1976, pp. 33–37; Cohen et al., 1972):

- Resolution of problems through choice, or by making a decision, is *not* the most common decisional style. According to Cohen et al. (1972), decision making by flight (problems move from one choice opportunity to a more attractive one, then on to a more attractive one, etc.) and oversight (choice made with minimum of energy and with little regard for solving long-term problems) is a major feature of the process in general. Decision making is not, primarily, problem solving.

- The process of choice is extremely sensitive to changes in load—the balance between choice opportunities and problems, choice opportunities and solutions, and the energy and attention of decision makers. "An increase in the net energy load on the system generally increases problem activity, decision maker activity, decision difficulty, and the uses of flight and oversight. Problems are less likely to be solved, decision makers are likely to shift from one problem to another more frequently, choices are likely to take longer to make and to be less likely to solve problems" (March and Olsen, 1976, p. 34).

- Decision makers and problems tend to track each other through choices. Both decision makers and problems tend to move together from choice to choice (March and Olsen, 1976, p. 34).

- The interconnections among problem activity (unresolved problems actively attached to choices), problem latency (active problems, but unlinked to any choice) and decision time are somewhat perverse. "Some structures reduce the number of unresolved problems active in the organization but at the cost of increasing the latency period of problems and . . . time devoted to reaching decisions. Other structures decrease problem latency, but at the cost of increasing problem activity and decision time" (March and Olsen, 1976, p. 35).

- The nature of the decision processes are "frequently sharply interactive. . . . Many of the outcomes are produced by distinct consequences of the particular time phasing of choices, problems, and participant availability" (March and Olsen, 1976, p. 35.) (This is a characteristic of choice in political life of which authors of case studies are acutely aware).

- "Important *problems* are more likely to be solved than unimportant ones" (March and Olsen, 1976, p. 35). One of the implications of the model (not an assumption built into it directly) is that problems in a queue are dealt with in the order of their importance and arrival at the queue.
- "Important *choices* are much *less* likely to resolve problems than are unimportant choices" (March and Olsen, 1976, p. 35).
- Although most choice opportunities result in choices, failures that do occur "are concentrated among the most important and least important choices" (March and Olsen, 1976, pp. 35–36).

Decision making in a "garbage can process," in an organized anarchy as modeled by March, Cohen and Olsen, is described in the ways that problems, solutions and participants move from choice opportunity to choice opportunity and in the ways choice opportunities arrive over time. In such a system, choice is highly dependent on context. Context is defined at least partly by the time-dependent "arrival" (or coupling) of a set of participants, a set of problems and a set of solutions—by what is in a "garbage can" at a particular point in time. This concept of decision making in loosely coupled systems provides clear justification for a case study mode of political science research. It simultaneously argues for an understanding of those processes and streams of behavior that generate the "problems," "solutions," "participants," and "choice opportunities" that are so capriciously linked together in the context of a particular choice.

In loosely coupled systems the capriciousness of the way in which problems, solutions, participants and choices are structured may make it difficult to construct general theory. To a political actor, the situation presents an opportunity. To influence choices is to influence the ways in which choices are created and problems, solutions and participants linked to them.[3]

In reality, and in most of the complex decision systems of interest to political scientists, some combination of tightly coupled and loosely coupled systems is found. Few situations are as capriciously structured as the March, Cohen and Olsen system suggests. Most systems have some tightly structured elements linked with other tightly structured elements in an ad hoc fashion.

A more precise specification or "theory" of coupling or linkage is needed to operationalize the notion of loosely coupled systems. Linkages in loosely coupled systems are very context specific. This creates considerable problems for any theory claiming to deal with complex human information processing and institutional or political choice. Such research demands a good deal of empirical work. Without a "theory of coupling" of organization, other approaches that ignore interaction effects, or assume they obey some objective logic, seem dubious. The research problems inherent in a world populated by loose coupling cannot be assumed away.

Given the above problems, I will now focus on an attempt to study organizations by means of an information-processing approach in order to explain the causes of some major deficiencies in U.S. military C3I systems, and how these result from the nature of the processes governing the procurement of such systems. Because such processes are "loosely coupled" to military mission requirements, the C3I procurement process provides an excellent opportunity to explore the utility of "garbage can theories" of organizational choice.

THE CASE OF C3 PROCUREMENT

Historical Perspective and Organizational Division of Labor

The broad context within which the U.S. military command structure functions, and the way in which its supporting equipment and systems are procured and its military manpower recruited and trained, was established by the National Security Act of 1947, when the Department of Defense was created. It was in this act that the responsibilities for "providing and maintaining" military forces were separated from the responsibility for commanding or "employing" those forces (see Figure 5.1).

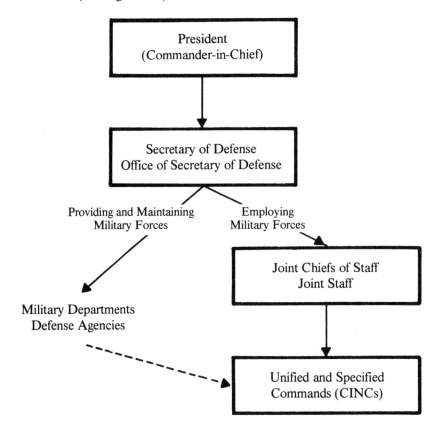

Figure 5.1 Macro-organization of U.S. military establishment (National Security Act of 1947, ammended).

MACROORGANIZATION OF THE U.S. MILITARY

The military departments or services (army, navy, air force) were granted the responsibility for *providing and maintaining* the U.S. military forces—for procuring weapons and equipment and for recruiting and training military manpower. A separate command structure was established for *employing* the service-provided forces, starting with the president as commander-in-chief and running down through the Secretary of Defense, through the Joint Chiefs of Staff, to a group of unified and specified commands headed by field military commanders (CINCs). In time of war (and during certain military exercises), military personnel and equipment, under the control of and trained by the services, are assigned for employment to CINCs.

During peacetime, the wartime command structure—those in the military responsible for actually fighting a war and commanding troops—has little to allocate in the way of resources and has little more than planning functions to perform. Although the CINCs have nominal inputs to the defense resource allocation process, through the Joint Chiefs of Staff, their input is in the nature of attempts to persuade the various services, upon whose forces they will ultimately rely, to provide personnel and equipment in adequate quantities and appropriate to the military task. In practice, persuading service subunits to divert scarce resources to perform functions that are often perceived by the service as "overhead" (e.g., communications and coordination) has proven exceedingly difficult. The CINCs have generally been even less successful in persuading one service to contribute to the capabilities (e.g., communications) of another service. It has been argued, rather forcefully in some quarters, that the solution to the problem of inadequate C3I is to directly provide the CINCs with greater budgetary authority for multiservice capabilities.

Currently, the macroorganization of the U.S. military establishment provides for a separation of authority and responsibility with respect to the provision and maintenance of forces and the employment of those forces. This fundamental division of labor means, among other things, that those responsible for securing, maintaining and training the elements of U.S. military force will not necessarily share in any detailed sense the priorities of those responsible for fighting wars. In particular, communications, coordination and control functions attached to force elements and weapons systems, while of primary importance to the command functions, may appear relatively less important to any individual service or their respective subunits.

DEFENSE DEPARTMENT ORGANIZATION FOR PROCUREMENT

There have been attempts to correct deficiencies resulting from the organizational and historical divisions between the "provision and maintenance of forces" function and the "command or employment" function. For instance, provision is made in the defense resource allocation process for soliciting the inputs of those responsible for force employment during the resource allocation and weapons procurement processes. This is done through a process whereby the unified and specified commanders (the CINCs) are asked to specify their "Requirements of Command" (ROCs) to the staff arm of the Joint Chiefs of Staff, the Joint Staff. These military requirements, once reviewed, modified and synthesized by the Joint Chiefs of Staff, then become inputs to the annual Department of Defense (DoD) resource allocation process. The DoD resource allocation process covers all DoD resources found in the military budget, including weapons and materiel procurement. Hence, C3I procurement issues are dealt with through the annual defense budgetary process, and operational C3I requirements are supposed to be fed into the process through the CINCs and the Joint Staff.

The overall organization for resource allocation, vis-à-vis weapons and materiel procurement, is outlined in Figure 5.2. The President's Defense bud-

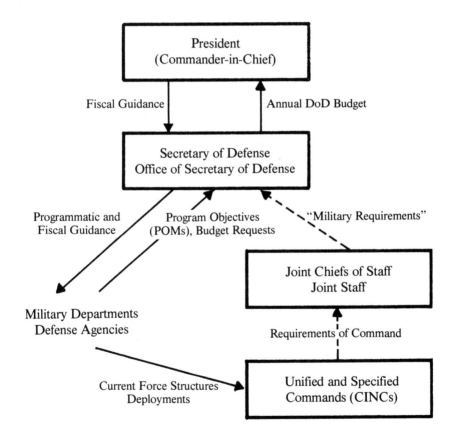

Figure 5.2 Defense organization for weapons and matériel procurement.

get, as presented to the Congress, consists of the results of internal DoD negotiations and analysis. In principle, the Joint Chiefs of Staff, representing the "employment" arm, have the responsibility for establishing military requirements. These requirements are often generally established without strict adherence to fiscal restraints. In practice, those "requirements" actually provided are usually determined in budgetary negotiations that take place between the Office of the Secretary of Defense (OSD) and the military services and defense agencies. Parties to the negotiation are those organizations whose budgets are the direct objects of resource allocation decisions, not those charged with prosecuting military plans. In a stylized way, the OSD issues programmatic and fiscal guidelines to the services, based on the "military requirements" specified by the Joint Chiefs of Staff and on fiscal guidance from the President and the Office of Management and Budget (OMB), on an assessment of the military threat faced in the country, and on an independent assessment of the adequacy of U.S. forces. Programmatic and fiscal guidance by the OSD is responded to by proposed program (Program Objective Memoranda, or POMs) and budget requests from the various services. The Office of the Secretary of Defense approves a set of program objectives, supported by formal budget requests.

Before any weapons, equipment or matériel are actually designed, developed or procured by the Department of Defense, the request must go through three major organizational decision processes. Taken individually, each of these decision processes is relatively tightly coupled. The coupling and sequence of the three processes is much more ambiguous and problematic.

Underlying, Tightly Coupled C3I Procurement Processes

The three underlying, tightly coupled, processes involved in C3I procurement are the following:

1. The process whereby the JCS determines "military requirements," based on the "Requirements of Commands" (ROCs) provided by the CINCs. This is an annual process.

2. The annual Planning Programming Budget process of the U.S. Department of Defense, which results in the annual President's Defense budget, also an annual process.

3. The normal matériel acquisition processes of a particular service subunit, based on approved and budgeted programs. This process almost always extends over several years and appears to be different for each military service. There is also a considerable degree of "customization" of the process for each development or procurement item.

Each of these three underlying decision streams or processes will now be examined.

Planning, Programming and Budgeting System: 1963–1984

In broad outline, the resource allocation and planning process, instituted by Robert McNamara in the early 1960s, remains unchanged. There is considerable evidence that McNamara's Planning, Programming, and Budgeting System (PPBS) only marginally changed the "old" line-item or appropriations-title approach to DoD resource allocation. Such change had no radical effect in terms of its impact on the macroallocational processes in DoD (Crecine, 1970; 1975b). Nevertheless, there is no doubt that PPBS has changed the rhetoric used in the annual allocation process, the kinds of justifications deemed appropriate and the analysis done to support allocational requests. Style considerations are very important despite the fact that allocation is still very much a "top-down" process. It is one driven significantly by the overall fiscal constraint and negotiated (with the White House and OMB) total for Defense (Fischer and Crecine, 1981; Fischer and Kamlet, 1982), rather than a strictly bottom-up, needs-driven process, as indicated by the PPBS, especially at the micro-level (including decisions on most weapons systems).

One can somewhat arbitrarily divide the annual PPB cycle into planning, programming and budgeting phases (see Figure 5.3). Decisions that help shape C3I hardware outcomes occur during all three phases. Throughout the planning and programming phases, the evolving set of "approved" plans and programs is expected to be loosely consistent with the administration's strategic doctrine, with approved Defense programs (as contained in the Five-Year Defense Plan, the FYDP) and with a plausible level of DoD spending.

PLANNING PHASE

The planning phase of the annual Defense budgeting process is shaped by formal Program Guidance from the Secretary of Defense. This Guidance consists of an elaboration of the administration's national security policy and defense force posture. The intent of the Guidance is to suggest the broad implications of administration policies for the upcoming Defense budget, to be submitted by the President to the Congress. In recent years, the secretary of defense has also provided overall fiscal guidance—information on what Defense budget totals should approximate (Puritano, 1983; Mr. Puritano was Assistant Secretary of Defense, comptroller when this paper was written). Additional planning inputs to the programming phase come from the Joint Chiefs of Staff, in their statement of the JCS view of "military requirements" that would enable the country to meet its security obligations, given the nature of the threat to U.S. security. The JCS statement of military requirements generally includes some sort of "risk assessment"—given the nature of the threat, the "risks" that the U.S. runs with various U.S. force levels.

An important input to the JCS military requirements and risk assessment is the input the JCS receives from the wartime command structure of the U.S. military establishment. The JCS solicits and receives a statement of the "Requirements of Command" (ROCs) from the commanders of U.S. forces (the CINCs or commanders-in-chief). For example, the commander-in-chief of the

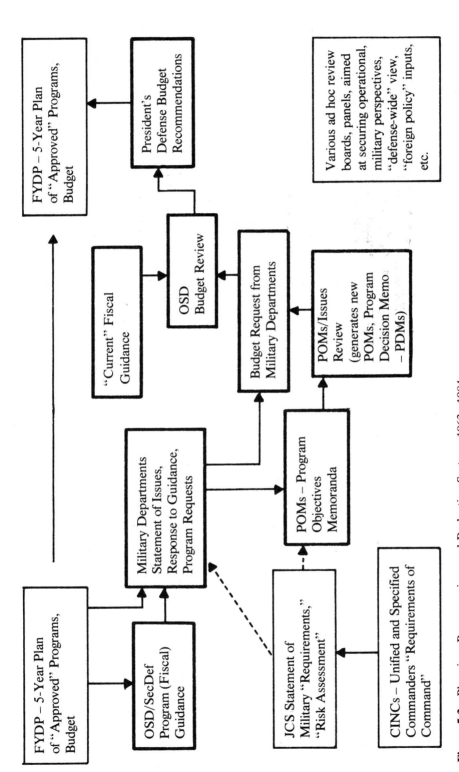

Figure 5.3 Planning, Programming, and Budgeting System: 1963–1984.

FYDP – 5-Year Plan of "Approved" Programs, Budget

President's Defense Budget Recommendations

Various ad hoc review boards, panels, aimed at securing operational, military perspectives, "defense-wide" view, "foreign policy" inputs, etc.

"Current" Fiscal Guidance

OSD Budget Review

Budget Request from Military Departments

POMs/Issues Review (generates new POMs, Program Decision Memo – PDMs)

Military Departments Statement of Issues, Response to Guidance, Program Requests

POMs – Program Objectives Memoranda

FYDP – 5-Year Plan of "Approved" Programs, Budget

OSD/SecDef Program (Fiscal) Guidance

JCS Statement of Military "Requirements," "Risk Assessment"

CINCs – Unified and Specified Commanders "Requirements of Command"

European Command (EUCOM) or Pacific Command (PACOM) will state the requirements for personnel, equipment or training he sees as necessary to carry out the responsibilities associated with his command. In peacetime, relative to the military services, the CINCs have very little in the way of budget or resources. The services have the responsibility and the budget to procure weapons and equipment and to recruit and train the military manpower. In wartime, weapons and manpower are transferred from the control of the services to one of the CINCs for employment against an enemy force. When forces are exercised (during exercises and maneuvers) or "on deployment" (for example, when submarines or P-3 squadrons are actively patrolling on ASW missions, or when a military unit is assigned to handle a crisis situation), military personnel and equipment are "loaned" to wartime commanders. The CINCs must accept whatever the services have available; they choose from a service-generated menu.

For C3 functions that cut across service lines, virtually the only actors in the system with a compelling interest in interservice command, control and communications are the operational commanders. For this reason, many current and former CINCs, who have noted serious C3 deficiencies while exercising command functions or planning for the employment of military force, argued for direct allocation of resources to the CINCs on the grounds that the military services cannot be depended on to anticipate and adequately provide for C3 functions.[4] Over the past four or five years, CINCs have been provided with small budgets, mostly for dealing with headquarters and communications items.

An important contributing factor for explaining C3I deficiencies stems from the nature of U.S. weapons system research and development (R&D) processes and the role of program officers located in the services who manage the passage of a weapons system from R&D into the procurement phase. Weapons systems, whether in the planning or procurement phase, "belong" to a military service. In the R&D phase, the prime evaluative criteria relate to the properties of the weapons system or platform itself, and generally not to how such systems interact with other elements of the force. The planning of weapons systems communications and coordination functions assume secondary importance. Evidence that the CINCs feel that C3 functions are undervalued in normal procurement processes can be found in the ROCs, submitted annually to the JCS. In this work the most frequently mentioned unmet "requirement" or deficiency is C3.

Because C3 equipment and capability is often seen by the services as an "add on" to weapons systems or units of force (Cushman, 1983), much of the CINC-Joint Staff "planning" activity with respect to C3 consists of lobbying with one or more services to include elements of a C3 system in service budgets. The problem is especially difficult for interservice communications; persuading both the Army and the Air Force to fund their piece of an improved air-ground communications package is difficult. In recent years, there has been increased recognition of these problems, with attempts to compensate for problems created by the separation of the force-providing (the military services) from the force-employment functions. For example, over a decade ago the Defense Resources Board (DRB) was established, consisting mostly of the heads of OSD organizations. Recently, the DRB was expanded to include service secretaries and the Chairman of the Joint Chiefs of Staff to provide stronger professional military input during the planning phase of the PPBS process. The DRB was "given the authority as the major governing body of the DoD resource allocation process" (Puritano, 1983, p. 23). Most relevant for this discussion was the DRB decision to invite the CINCs to participate twice a year during planning and programming deliberations.

PROGRAMMING PHASE

Once OSD (comptrollers) has analyzed the CINC-generated ROCs and the JCS statement of military requirements and assessment of the "risks" associated with current and proposed force postures, and the military departments/services respond to the Secretary of Defense's program and fiscal guidance, a series of Program Objective Memoranda (POMs) is drafted in OSD, outlining the major program issues for the year's PPB cycle. The POMs provide the framework for the budget requests from the military departments (see Figure 5.3). There are many who contend that the JCS, and by implication the CINCs, have little influence in the evolution of the Secretary of Defense's Program Guidance into the POMs, and finally into the budgeting and expenditure phase. The argument is that the services, in their roles as administrative, force-provisioning departments, and the OSD, as the representative of civilian and political objectives, simply overwhelm the JCS and the CINCs who represent military operations objectives (Crecine, 1975c; Fallows, 1982). Certainly if one compares the JCS/CINCs with the OSD/Services on the basis of annual budgets, the number of analytic or budget staff or any other measure of bureaucratic strength, such a conclusion would not seem surprising. And procedurally the role of the JCS is indirect.

"In the programming phase, the *services and defense agencies propose* programs that are designed to meet the mid-range (five year) objectives of the Defense Guidance and to fit within the fiscal contraints of the projected DoD budgets . . . these programs, in the form of Program Objective Memoranda (POMs) . . . are submitted to the Secretary for his review" (Puritano, 1983, p. 6; emphasis added). The program review is intended to check programs for compliance with overall guidance and to integrate and coordinate programs that cross service lines. The program review is conducted principally by the OSD, with participation by the JCS and service staffs. "That review results in the development of key issues covering a range of alternatives and arguments. These issues, about 40 to 45, are presented to the Defense Resources Board (DRB)" (Puritano, 1983, p. 6). The results of the POM issues review are documented in ammended POMs and a series of Program Decision Memoranda (PDMs) and now distributed through the Deputy Secretary of Defense, who chairs the DRB.

BUDGETING PHASE

On the basis of the "approved" POMs, the services and defense agencies (OSD units) submit their annual budget requests to the DoD Comptroller. Partly because the budget review is conducted in significantly greater detail than either the planning or program reviews, there are many important decisions made during the budgeting phase of PPBS. Many argue that most real decisions are made during the budgeting phase. The OMB participates in the budget review phase, although by most accounts it exerts little independent influence over outcomes. The OSD Comptroller's staff prepares a series of draft Program Budget Decisions (PBDs) for the Secretary of Defense. The secretary then has some final conferences and negotiations with OMB and the President. The result is the president's defense budget, which is then submitted to the Congress.

It is important to note that, from the standpoint of participation in the budgetary process and execution of policy following a Congressionally approved Defense budget, there is little influence by those most directly concerned with military operations or with the details of interunit communications and C3.

In response to very serious problems with C3 systems, a subunit of the Defense Review Board was created to review and provide policy guidance for resource allocation issues involving C3 systems. Called the C3ExCom (C3 Executive Committee), it consists of service, Joint Staff, and OSD C3 Directorate personnel organized into panels that deal with particular C3 systems.[5] The panels are forums for discussing joint C3 programs and have served to have OSD, and hence a defense-wide perspective, involved early in the planning and development of new systems. The panels make recommendations to the C3ExCom Review Council, which is the primary decision body for the C3ExCom. The Review Council decides which programs are to be continued, canceled or accelerated even though it does not formally participate in the budgetary process. The Review Council has nine members at the assistant secretary and Office directorate level, including three service representatives.[6]

Given the complexity of the R&D and procurement process and the length of time it takes for any given weapons or communication system to move from concept to design (research) to development to procurement to deployment, it remains to be seen if the 2-year-old C3ExCom proves to be the bureaucratic mechanism that "fixes" the deficiencies in C3 systems—especially those at the organizational "seams" in the U.S. military establishment.

At the operational level, one can profitably view the C3 systems procurement process as simply another instance of the matériel acquisition process found in each military service. The length of the matériel acquisition process for any particular C3 system may be from 5 to 15 years. Such processes have no sharp beginning and ending points and are punctuated with changes in doctrine, changes in political administration and OSD leadership and changes in systems design and technology, and must pass several PPBS and budgetary check points. Like the most expensive weapons system, for a C3 program or system to go from need to concept to deployment requires the assembling of an impressive bureaucratic coalition.[7]

It will come as no surprise that generalizations about material and weapons acquisition are difficult to come by. Some characteristics of the material acquisition processes are relevant to this discussion, however:

- Each service has its own, "generic" matériel acquisition process.
- Generally, C3 equipment and systems are embedded in other weapons systems. Communications is an "add on" to most weapons systems.
- Within each service there are special R&D procurement processes for C3 systems.
- The process is lengthy, with many changes in participants in the course of a complete process.

Fortunately, General John Cushman (1983) has documented the major C3I research and evaluation activities in the various services. The process found in the U.S. Army is used to illustrate general features of such processes.

C3 R&D, Procurement: U.S. Army Example

Figure 5.4 is an adaptation of a description of the army's C3 R&D and procurement process provided by Cushman (1983). Added to this are plausible lengths of time to perform various tasks (in days). The details behind the acronyms of the various army units' performing tasks are not important for this discussion. It is assumed that the "concept" for the C3 system was initiated January 1, 1984. Under the assumptions of task completion times indicated in Figure 5.4 and assuming no delays due to programming or budgeting cycles, this hypothetical army system would be through the evaluation stage in the middle of 1991, or 7½ years from the date of initiation. Production, training and final deployment would add at least another 3 years to the process.

One need not go more deeply into the C3 acquisition process to understand that the outcomes emerging from these basically ad hoc combinations of processes, procedures and decisions are not planned in any precise sense. In general, C3 systems that come to fruition and are finally deployed may or may not support military operations or enhance military capability. Systems that do come to fruition have by some means assembled a coalition of support. Consider how many different Army organizations formally must "sign off" on the hypothetical system in Figure 5.4 in order to get through the Service System Evaluation stage. Consider the external support necessary in moving from successful system evaluation to planning and programming, and finally the support necessary for budgeting and deployment.

Pulling together the underlying processes that account for C3I procurement outcomes is not a trivial task. This is especially true if those outcomes are also required to support military concepts and operations. Taken collectively, the set of doctrine formation, concept initiation, research, development, evaluation, resource allocation, programming, procurement, deployment, training

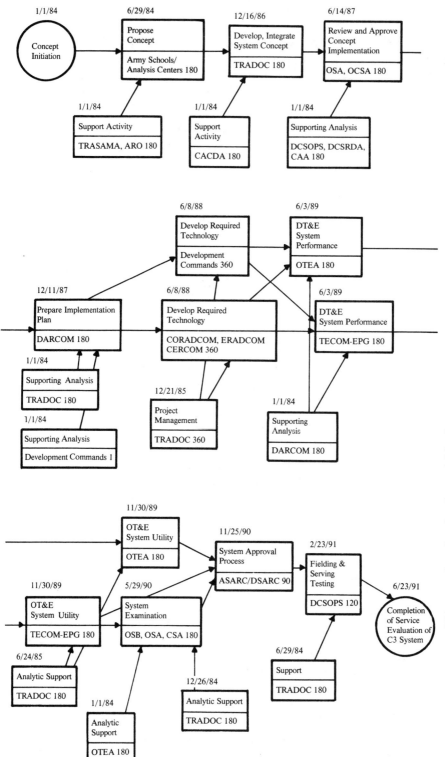

Figure 5.4 Flow of army C3I research and evaluation activities (courtesy J. H. Cushman, C2 of Theater Forces).

and utilization processes represents an "anarchy of processes." The particular ways in which the "anarchy of processes" is itself organized or combined will have important effects on outcomes.

"COUPLING" THE PARALLEL PROCESSES: ATTEMPTS TO SHAPE C3 PROCUREMENT OUTCOMES

In the classic "garbage can" model of organizational choice, the phenomena of interest deal with the ways in which problems, solutions and participants move from choice opportunity to choice opportunity (from "garbage can" to "garbage can"). It is clear from the discussion in the previous section that a set of more or less "tightly coupled" routine bureaucratic processes account for many of the choice opportunities and partially specify participants in those "choices." Examples of tight coupling are found in the annual defense resource allocation processes and in service-specific weapon system research, development and procurement processes (see Figures 5.3 and 5.4). "Solutions" or C3I systems move from "garbage can" to "garbage can" until some finally emerge as deployed systems. This "anarchy" of solutions, problems, participants and choice opportunities is partially organized by a set of underlying, "tightly coupled" processes. The way in which the underlying processes are put together completes the "organization of the anarchy" and the explanation of outcomes/"solutions."

There are many ways in which the complex of decision processes that collectively govern C3 outcomes can be organized or influenced in order to produce coherent and/or intended outcomes. It should be clear however, that without explicit attempts to organize the anarchy, it is extremely unlikely that outcomes will support military operations and concepts in the ways intended when a project is initially conceived. After a more than decade-long process, involving a cast of characters that is programmed to change (e.g., military personnel with limited tours of duty), compromises in design and concept, as new processes and participants are encountered, each with their own concerns and constraints, and changing technologies and military threats, it is a wonder that any system emerging would reflect any coherent conception at all.

Two case studies of weapons system development and procurement provide some insights into the leadership, entrepreneurship and processes involved in shepherding a concept from start to finish. One is a study of the Navy's Fleet Ballistic Missile System, Polaris, and the other is the development of the TFX or F111 (Sapolsky, 1969; Coulam, 1977).

- Both cases illustrate the extreme difficulty of developing a weapons system for more than one service—the missile for the Polaris system was originally intended to be a joint, Army-Navy project and the TFX a multi-service, multi-mission aircraft.
- Both show that design and performance specifications and requirements are closely linked to the bureaucratic coalition that must be assembled if the project is to move from one step to the next in the development process. For example, the set of design features embod-

ied in the first production version of the F-111 (originally, the TFX) makes far more sense when viewed as the accumulation of various military units which are members of a supporting coalition for the project, each of which introduces some independent design constraints as the price for coalition membership, than it does when viewed as a straightforward weapon system engineering and design process. The "fit" of a design-as-bureaucratic-coalition view is especially striking when one tracks design modifications over time. It is the classic "a camel is a horse designed by committee" syndrome. Once produced and "in the inventory," a different set of influences overtakes the TFX—influences more attuned to combat performance criteria—and the final deployed product (the F-111) makes far more military sense than do the initial production versions.

- Both illustrate the importance of individual entrepreneurship. In the case of Polaris, it is impossible to conceive of success without the organizing efforts and patronage of Admiral Raborn and without the project management efforts of Admiral Smith and, much later, Admiral Rickover. Raborn constructed a development team, created a high esprit de corps, secured more than adequate resources and secured insulation from external pressures with large, external research budgets and visible (but "unused") management techniques, such as PERT.[8] There were several key program managers in the TFX development project, but it is clear that without Secretary McNamara's direct interest, persistence, and determination to make the TFX a model for joint development and interservice cooperation, the F-111 would never have come into being. (Coulam, 1977)

The most difficult C3 problems are those involving coordination and communication at the "seams" of military organizations (Coulam et al., 1983; Crecine et al., 1981). The most difficult organizational "seams" are those involving different service units (e.g., TAC vs. SAC or submariners vs. Naval air) or different services (e.g., Army division and a Tactical Air Squadron) in joint operations. Creation of an effective command and communication system to support joint operations is functionally equivalent to jointly designing a weapon system that is to be integral to both units.

Creation of an effective command, control and communications system to support joint operations is more difficult than jointly designing a single weapons system. This is due to the fact that most C3 systems are, to some degree at least, embedded systems. Nonheadquarters communications and intelligence systems are embedded in another weapons system, sensor or platform. Especially in the design phase, C3I systems are often seen as ancillary to the principal function of the sensor or platform.[9] Consider, for example, air-ground coordination and communication. Ground forces attempting to perform targeting functions for close air support missions generally use either targeting or locating devices that are designed around weapons organic to a company or division. Information (coordinates, type of target, terrain, etc.)

tends to be customized for surface-to-surface weapons. Radio communications are part of the standard ground forces network. The airframe communications, navigational and targeting aids are fully embedded in the airframe design and Air Force communication systems. Close coordination of air and ground forces requires an additional level of coordination at the design stage, over and above that required to produce a single (albeit, joint) weapons system. The difficulties in bringing the Joint Tactical Information Distribution System (JTIDS) project for air-ground communications and targeting to fruition merely illustrates the general point (General Accounting Office, 1980a). (The history of the BETA system contains a similar lesson—General Accounting Office, 1980b). Coordinating two systems that are themselves embedded systems is more difficult than simply coordinating two systems.

There are, of course, alternatives to an explicit coordination of operations or explicit management of the C3 systems development and procurement process. If each of the involved individuals and organizations in a situation shares a conception of objectives and means, then that very shared conception serves to coordinate individual behavior. The principal objective of doctrine and training in a military organization is to create such shared understandings. Common belief systems are efficient substitutes for formal organization, and this is the underlying reason why (a) within-unit coordination is inherently easier than between-unit coordination, and (b) C3 systems organic to a single military service support that service's military operations and concepts far better than C3 systems spanning service boundaries. In the design and procurement of C3 systems, by separating the organizational structures that provide and train military force from those that use it, a need is created for modes of explicit coordination.

In examining Army C3I research, evaluation, development, procurement and deployment processes (see Figures 5-3 and 5-4), it may be useful to briefly explore some of the major mechanisms for coordinating or pulling together the various component processes in the context of a particular C3 system.

Individual Entrepreneurship

The story of the development of those weapons systems that make it from the laboratory or development phase into the force is a story of individual persistence. Often, the emphasis in the telling is on the persistence of a high-level patron, be they civilian or military. Often it is the story of a skilled and clever program manager. In most cases a patron and program manager are both required. The march from "needs assessment" and concept, first through development and evaluation (see Figure 5.4 for this process in the Army), second through the planning, programming and budgeting cycle (see Figure 5.3) and lastly through the deployment of a system into the force, is a lengthy process. It is one where the opportunities for going astray are many. Failure (or more accurately, "perceived failure") to pass any one of a large number of performance or budgetary check points is sufficient to keep a weapons system out of the force. Program managers are charged with shepherding a given program or weapons project through this lengthy process. They work both with people inside the military and with external contractors in order to keep this complex of processes "on track."

For purely C3I systems, the C3I program manager must manage the process. For C3I systems that are embedded in a larger weapons system (e.g., the C3I components of a new attack submarine), the program manager for the larger weapons system must also coordinate the C3I subsystem development process.

Again, a quick referral to the development process governing Army C3I systems (Figure 5.4) reveals that in order to get a proposed C3I system through the evaluation phase, it is necessary to orchestrate the inputs of at least 20 different organizations. Simply managing the logistics of such a process requires organization and entrepreneurship. The program manager is generally charged with this task.

When more than one service is involved, there will be a similarly complex process in each military service.

Actors-to-Be-Convinced: Building a Coalition of Parallel Processes

Wherever the C3I system crosses service boundaries or is embedded in a larger weapons system, there are two or more parallel weapons system development processes to be coordinated. Generally, there are different participants in each process, and each process has a different "manager." In practice, the successful shepherding of a C3I system from concept to an evaluated and a deployed system requires assembling a coalition representing each of the major development and evaluation processes required. In the context of the army C3I process used here as an example (Figure 5.4), each of the major tasks represents a sequence of more or less well-defined subtasks required of a different organization (e.g., TRASANA, TRADOC, CADDA, etc.). As the C3I system flows from stage to stage, the original concept is inevitably modified and becomes more concrete as it is dealt with by successive organizations. In some cases, each organization adds its own preferred features to the design. The process of accumulating support of the organizational unit involved at each stage can easily modify the original concept so that the cumulative effects of the modifications result in unrecognizable outcomes.

To orchestrate the assembling of a broad coalition successfully usually requires a "patron"—an Admiral Raborn or a Robert McNamara for multiservice systems of major importance—not only to facilitate the cooperation of the various units but also to generate compliance with an overall plan or concept. Difficulty in gaining compliance from two services is difficult for weapons like aircraft, whose utility is obvious (at least to the military services). It is doubly difficult in cases like C3, where the system is embedded in a larger, joint weapons system. Often C3I is treated as an afterthought: "Command and control is today treated by many strategies as incidental, uncontrolled and even uncontrollable. Communications is mentioned when it fails. Intelligence appears as a matter of sheer cloak-and-dagger luck instead of as an often deadly battle over information" (Rechtin, 1984, pp. 23−24). The "afterthoughts" of two or more groups are very difficult to coordinate.

C3 Executive Committee: Attempt at a Structural Solution

Partly due to the difficulties of coordinating C3 developments—especially between the services—and partly in response to the growing realization of the serious shortcomings of existing C3 systems in conventional forces,[10] a C3 Executive Committee was created recently in OSD. The purpose of the C3ECCOM is

> to facilitate information flows and coordinate joint programs; a role that previously was only partially filled by the JCS and the "somewhat inactive" WWMCCS (World Wide Military Command and Control System) Council. C3EXCOM has three levels: the Executive Council, the Review Council, and eight panels. The Executive Council has three members . . . (Secretary of Defense, Chrm. JCS, and Principal Deputy Undersecretary of Defense Research and Engineering). . . . The Review Council has nine members (chaired by Deputy Under-secretary of Defense [C3I] and including) . . . a representative from each of the services. The eight panels and their parental organizations are: Computer Information and Security (OSD), Defense Communications Systems (OSD), International C3 (OSD), Military Satellites (OSD), Strategic C3 (OSD), Theater and Tactical C3 or T2C3 (JCS), WWMCCS Information Systems or WIS(JCS), and High Frequency C3 (Navy). (Rice, 1984, p. 16).
> The panels average about seven members, often have subgroups and meet about once a month.

A longtime OSD/Joint Staff official involved in C3 policy matters feels that the C3ExCom is "the only real internal management tool" in the C3 systems development process (Rice, 1984, p. 17). Others lessen the significance of this body, emphasizing only its importance for coordinating projects and for disseminating information about ongoing C3 programs. Regardless, it is clear that the C3ExCom Review Council, which meets twice monthly, is the center of influence in the C3ExCom activities. In terms of pulling together the C3 systems development process and the PPBS process, the Review Council is important. Although the Review Council does not directly participate in the budgeting process, it "does the ground work for the budgeting process by checking for technical adequacy and funding" (Rice, 1984, p. 17).

In pulling together the pieces of the C3 procurement process, two broad functions are being performed. First, certain cost and performance requirements for systems are being articulated, formulated, designed, built and evaluated (see Figure 5.4, for instance)—the original systems concept is elaborated. Second, a political coalition is being formed which is both internal to the U.S.

military and necessary to the successful introduction of any new weapons system into the U.S. force. In operational terms, the conflict between these two functions often leads to weapons systems that satisfy the bureaucratic and political constraints but do not conform nearly as well to cost or minimum performance requirements.

In the aggregate, no weapons system enters the force without the necessary political coalition to support it. Coalitional support is a necessary condition for completion and introduction of any weapons system. In many cases, such support also appears to be a sufficient condition. Strict conformance to cost and performance objectives is neither a necessary nor a sufficient condition for the introduction of a new weapons system into the force.

For embedded systems, such as most C3I systems, first-order constraints have to do with the assembling of an adequate coalition of supporters. Second-order constraints involve the cost and performance objectives of the primary weapons system(s), and third-order constraints involve performance of C3I embedded systems. Under such circumstances, it is not surprising that C3I performance problems emerge from the process of systems research, design, development, evaluation and deployment.

HOW WELL DO GARBAGE CAN THEORIES FIT?

The "garbage can process" conceptualization of organizational decision making focuses on the ways that problems, solutions and participants move from choice opportunity to choice opportunity. A complete specification of a garbage can process also involves a discussion of the structure of "choice opportunities" and of the ways in which choice opportunities are sequenced over time. Choice in such a system—in an organized anarchy—is highly dependent on the context in which a particular choice is made or decision arrived at. This "context" involves the particular set of participants, problems and solutions brought together in a "choice opportunity," or "garbage can," at a particular point in time. Certainly, in a very broad sense, the complex of processes that produces C3I systems in the military conforms to the characteristics of a "garbage can" model of choice as outlined by Cohen et al. (1972). The preceding sections described in some detail the components of the C3 procurement process in the U.S. Army and then examined in a general way how these components are structured, how these loosely coupled decision processes interact to produce a given C3I system or outcome. At least in a superficial way, the garbage can theory fits C3I procurement.

The argument, broadly stated, is that in situations characterized by problematic preferences, uncertain (decision) technology and fluid participation of decision makers, a "garbage can" style of decision making will emerge (see section on Theory). I now turn to a brief examination of the degree to which these "preconditions" for a "garbage can" theory of choice exist for C3I procurement.

Problematic Preferences

"Preferences are often problematic. It is difficult to impute a set of preferences to the decision situation that satisfies the standard consistency requirements for a theory of choice. The organization operates on the basis of a variety of inconsistent and ill-defined preferences" (March and Olsen, 1976, p. 25). It is clear, both because of the length of the C3I procurement process and the numbers of different participants in the process, each with different perspectives, that one cannot impute a consistent set of preferences to any C3I procurement process.

One need only reflect briefly on the five- to ten-year duration of the procurement process in order to realize that in a world of rapid technological change, shifting military threats, changing political administrations and a normal flow of people through positions within the government and within the government contracting community consistency of preferences over time is as unrealizable as it is undesirable. Consider again Figures 5.3 and 5.4. Within Army C3I research and evaluation activities, even assuming the stability of the process that existed in the Army in 1983, the leadership in *each* of more than the 20 organizations involved in the C3I systems research and evaluation activities is *programmed* to change every two to three years. One might argue that organizations that have a more or less continuous role in the Army research and evaluation process such as TRADOC, tasked with providing analytical support and product management at key points throughout the process, would provide stability and consistency over time. Even in such organizations, it is clear that programmed change, implicit in the standard two- to three-year military tours of duty, means that even organizational continuity does not necessarily bring with it consistency with respect to preferences. Over the 7½-year course of the hypothetical research and evaluation process outlined in Figure 5.4, followed by an additional 3- to 6-year process for planning, budgeting and deployment of a weapons system, it is clear that participants and their preferences will change.

The observation that C3I systems are at least marginally sensitive to changes in technology—consider advances in computing and communications technology over the past three years only—and the shifting military capabilities of the Warsaw Pact in Central Europe is sufficient to make the point that preferences, vis-à-vis even the simplest weapon system, can and do change rather dramatically over the course of the systems development, evaluation and procurement cycles.

Simply given the complex of participants in the planning, programming and budgeting process, it is clear that no consistent single set of preferences exists (see Figure 4.3). There are widely differing views of the C3 requirements for operational military capability. The commanders-in-chief, the CINCs, have one set of views and attempt to convince the Joint Chiefs of Staff of the legitimacy of those views. The service subunits, through their service chiefs—those charged with procuring military forces—have another point of view concerning any given weapons system or C3I system. In general, those charged with employing military force have different views and preferences from those charged with procuring that same force. In many ways, it is the function of the OSD, through its various officials and through the annual PPBS process, to reconcile some of the major differences of opinion within the Department of Defense on major weapons systems. Indeed, the very existence of the PPBS process is predicated on the continuing existence of "problematic preferences" and is one of the key "preconditions" for garbage can models of choice.

Uncertain Technology

There are at least three senses in which C3 procurement "technology" is uncertain or unclear. First, C3 system architectures are extremely complicated. A division command post ties into various targeting and dedicated intelligence systems using radio, buried cable, microwave and so forth. There are links to companies and adjunct divisions, provisions for satellite communication to theatre, air force liaison officers with their own C3 system and so on and on. The overall architecture of such systems is itself very complicated. The underlying technologies—for example, satellite communication, high-frequency radio, telephone, high-band-width buried cable—are equally complicated. It is not clear, for example, whether some frequency-hopping, spread-spectrum technique for instant real-time communication is the "superior" communications technology or whether coordination is better achieved through detailed plans requiring little or no communications.

The C3 procurement technology is uncertain and unclear in the sense that there is no certain way to put the C3I procurement process together organizationally, politically and financially. Garnering the necessary support from individual organizations and from Congress is an art, not a science. While it may be clear what the organizational, political and financial preconditions must be for success in achieving a desired C3 procurement outcome, the technology for producing those preconditions is uncertain and unknown.

The very complexity of the PPBS, Defense Resources Board and C3 ExCom formal decision and control systems, especially when coupled with the services' own research and evaluation process, creates another degree of uncertainty in the technology of producing C3I outcomes. There are few individuals in the Pentagon who could provide a clear "roadmap" for a would-be C3I program manager to guide him through a service research and evaluation process, the PPBS and budgeting system, the Defense Resources Board, and the C3ExCom coordination process.

It is clear that the technology for producing C3I procurement outcomes is uncertain, unclear and unstable; this "uncertain technology" of choice is consistent with the second precondition for a "garbage can" theory of choice.

Fluid Participation: Partially Specified Participation Patterns

In the section on "Problematic Preferences," the case has already been made to support the conclusion that participation in C3I procurement processes is fluid. Perhaps the principal source of "fluid participation" in the decision process is the practice of rotating military personnel through positions every two to three years. Given the length of time—typically seven to fifteen years— for the process which takes a systems concept through to the deployment of a finished system, there is a virtual guarantee of fluid participation.

There is a second source of fluid participation in the process stemming from instabilities in the overall process. Any student of defense organization is aware of the fact that reorganization is a way of life in the Defense Department, especially in OSD and especially in areas where problems or deficiencies have been identified. For the past decade, C3I has been a "problem area." Coupled with changes in the political administration, this has led to more or less continuous changes in OSD for dealing with C3I affairs. A brief synopsis of the organizational changes in OSD made during Harold Brown's tenure as secretary of defense (1976–1980) and Caspar Weinberger's (1981–present) which affect C3 serves to illustrate this point.

During Brown's tenure, the title of Assistant Secretary of Defense for C3I was reinstated (1977), and its responsibilities were merged with that of the principal deputy undersecretary of defense for research and engineering (early 1979). It was widely believed that the merger of these two offices led to a bias in C3 affairs in OSD toward a more technical orientation. The post of director of C3 policy was created in 1979 but seems to have had relatively little influence. In 1980, four new deputy undersecretaries of OSD were assigned responsibilities for major aspects of C3. "Their titles are Deputy Undersecretaries for International Programs and Technology, for Research and Advanced Technology, for Strategic and Space Systems, and for Tactical Warfare Programs" (Rice, 1984, p. 10).

Secretary Weinberger also initiated changes in OSD affecting C3. A pair of offices was established to examine C3 architecture, and studies were conducted for NORAD, electronic warfare, theater nuclear forces, C3-CM and intelligence support for operational commanders. The post of assistant deputy undersecretary (systems integration) was created and given a subordinate Directorate for Long-Term Planning and Systems Evaluation. The Directorates for Systems Architecture and Analysis and C3I Resource Management were reassigned and placed under the Systems Integration Office. The C3I Resource Management Directorate was assigned the responsibility to serve as a bridge between OSD (comptroller) and the assistant secretary of defense for C3I. In addition, a Directorate for Defense Testing and Evaluation was established for dealing with C3I issues. This is in addition to the creation of the C3 ExCom discussed earlier (Rice, 1984, pp. 15–17). Although reorganization does not necessarily bring with it wholesale personnel changes, such moves do not contribute to stable participation in C3I procurement processes.

It is clear that the current complex of processes that collectively leads to C3I procurement decisions partially specifies the list of participants in any given C3I program and partially specifies the nature of that participation. It is also the case that program content partially determines who and which organizations participate in the decision process. For example, DoD Directive 4630.5

was issued in the early 1970s: "It specified that if a service identified a C3 standard or requirement it wanted on its equipment, it must circulate a notice saying so to the JCS and the other services. If any of them respond favorably to the notice, the subsequent program becomes a joint one" (Rice, 1984, p. 7). For example, the Position Location Reference System (PLRS) and JTIDS systems became a joint program under Army and Air Force control. Joint Army–Air Force programs generally require airborne platforms for surveillance and target acquisition coupled with ground-based analysis centers and maintains delivery (artillery and surface-to-surface missiles) systems. Again, the rules for participation in C3I procurement are only partially specified in advance.

Choice Opportunities

Choice opportunities, or proposed C3I systems, are generated in several ways. It is difficult to identify processes that automatically generate C3I choice opportunities routinely in the way for example, that the annual budgetary process routinely generates the opportunity for choice on military pay policies. With the emergence of C3I line items in the budget (e.g., "RDT&E: Intelligence and Communications"), which tend to change incrementally and smoothly, opportunities for C3I systems development decisions emerge when major C3I systems move from the development to the procurement stage, thereby creating an opening for the next concept to move into the R&D phase.

There are other processes that create choice opportunities, however, and these are worth characterizing.

SOLUTIONS IN SEARCH OF PROBLEMS (DEFENSE CONTRACTORS)

The underlying technology for C3I is changing very rapidly. The technological revolution underway in computing, information processing and communications spills over rather naturally into the C3I procurement processes. In a very broad sense, the shift from analog technologies to digital technologies in C3I areas is simply another way of saying that technological developments in the electronics and computing industries lead many manufacturers to propose new solutions to old problems and new components for existing systems. One need only read the advertisements in the *International Defense Review* or *Aviation Week* to observe technologically-driven "solutions in search of problems." Defense contractors continually press new products, techniques and inventions on the services for incorporation into the weapons inventory. Proposals are made to military personnel, RFPs are generated, small development contracts are let, and the system becomes pregnant with new choice opportunities.

VISIBLE PROBLEMS, SEARCHING FOR "SOLUTIONS"

There are many problems that become visible and therefore create the need for "solutions" and additional choice opportunities. Over the last decade, in the very broadest sense, C3I has become a visible problem for the U.S. military. In peacetime, the ways in which problems become known or visible can be very complex. For example, EMP (electromagnetic pulse) effects of nuclear air-bursts have been "known" since the first atmospheric test of atomic weapons. But EMP has only recently emerged as a "C3I problem" which demands a solution, such as hardening of facilities and shielding of equipment; EMP became a visible problem in part through a shift in U.S. doctrine and thought concerning the possibilities of protracted or limited nuclear exchanges.

The emergence of Soviet electronic warfare capabilities has created a "problem" and a need for antijamming solutions. Growing recognition of the physical vulnerability of NATO communication links and nodes, coupled with a growing realization that these facilities are seen as prime targets by the Soviets, leads to a class of "problems" or choice opportunities.

The results of armed conflict, real or simulated, also help identify and dramatize problems, creating the need for "solutions." The results of Israeli aircraft encounters with Syrian-operated Soviet air defense systems undoubt-edly identified some vulnerabilities thought to exist in the U.S. Air Force (in addition to identifying some previously underappreciated strengths). The Falk-lands battle between England and Argentina and the Yom Kippur War simi-larly identified problems in need of solutions.

"CREATED" OR EXISTING CHOICE OPPORTUNITIES

Military exercises and maneuvers, properly designed, help identify problems which demand solutions. Unfortunately, until recently the U.S. military (ex-cept for command post exercises) shied away from realistic tests of com-munications capabilities. In exercises, communications were always assumed to be "up"; whenever communications were severed by accident, or when backlogs occurred, interventions were made to correct communication out-ages[11] (Coulam et al., 1983). Military exercises, by dramatizing operational problems, can be an important source of choice opportunities in the C3I area.

DO GARBAGE CAN THEORIES HELP?

Garbage can theories of choice in an organized anarchy fit the surface charac-teristics of choice in the C3I procurement area; the underlying assumptions concerning situations where "garbage can processes" are likely to be found also fit C3I procurement. The question remaining is "so what?" There are two ways in which any theoretical framework can be useful. The first relates to the benefits from having a better understanding of the phenomena of interest— better descriptive theory leads to better diagnosis and, perhaps, better treat-ment. The second relates to useful prescriptions that are part of the theoretical framework itself. Both will be examined in the context of "garbage can theo-ries" and "C3I procurement."

Better Understanding of Phenomena and Origins of Difficulties?

Decision making and choice in an "organized anarchy," as outlined above, often appear capricious. "Garbage can" processes provide a framework that highlights the complex and often unpredictable ways in which problems, solutions and participants move from choice opportunity to choice opportunity and the ways in which choice opportunities "appear on the scene." In this setting, choice is partly dependent on the context of choice—which set of participants, problems and solutions is "coupled" with the time-dependent choice opportunity. As discussed in the fourth and fifth sections of this chapter, the C3I procurement process in the U.S. Defense Department is made up of a complex of tightly coupled processes, loosely coupled together. The PPBS (see Figure 5.3) and service-specific C3I research, development and evaluation processes (themselves subject to change over the life cycle of a C3I system; see Figure 5.4 for the Army's C3I research, development, test and evaluation process) are linked together in OSD through a variety of ad hoc and changing mechanisms (e.g., the C3 ExCom and shifting C3 directorates; see also Figure 5.2). This is all accomplished in the broader context of occasionally changing national security doctrines and a constant overall division of labor between subunits of the U.S. military establishment responsible for providing and maintaining military forces, and subunits responsible for employing the forces so provided (see Figure 5.1).

"Garbage can" concepts help draw attention to many of the structural features of the C3I systems procurement process—features that help explain some of the fundamental deficiencies in C3I systems in the U.S. military, discussed in the first section of this chapter.

PROBLEMS ARE STRUCTURAL/ORGANIZATIONAL IN NATURE

In basic terms, most military planners and commanders would prefer to see C3I systems evolve smoothly and cleanly, deriving logically from a precise specification of military needs and requirements—a design-to-requirements approach. In preference to the current political and organizational model, they would prefer an engineering model of design and procurement. Indeed, when one examines the shifting ad hoc ways in which OSD attempts to pull together the various elements of the process—doctrine, resource constraints, military requirements, service-generated C3I system proposals, and so on—it is clear that much of this OSD organizational effort has the objective of encouraging C3I system proposals to better support military operations, more closely approximating a requirements-driven C3I design process. For example, the C3ExCom discussed above attempts explicitly to reintroduce military requirements into the C3I system design and procurement decision processes and to coordinate the development of C3I systems for joint operations (Rice, 1984).

The primary purpose of the C3ExCom and most of the C3 directorates in OSD is to counter the negative effects of two basic structural features of the U.S. military establishment. The first is the separation of responsibility for providing and maintaining military forces (assigned to the military services) from the responsibility for commanding and employing those forces (assigned to the JCS, the Joint Staff and the CINCs), as specified in the National Security Act of 1947 (see Figure 5.1). The second involves the division of roles and missions among the separate military services, also specified in the National Security Act of 1947 (which established the U.S. Department of Defense) and subsequently modified through a series of administrative agreements and "treaties" between the services.

Although "garbage can" concepts are not essential for the identification of the broad, "structural" origins of C3I deficiencies, they provide a deeper understanding of the impacts of structure on choice and of the many and subtle ways in which structure influences the "context of choice"—which groups of participants, problems and solutions are brought together in a particular "garbage can" or choice opportunity, and what the string of garbage cans looks like that a particular C3 "solution" must pass through, jumping from can to can, in order to emerge as a deployed C3 system.

IMPACT OF SEPARATION OF FORCE EMPLOYMENT FROM FORCE PROVISION RESPONSIBILITIES

The reasons why C3I systems often do not support operational concepts and military operations is fairly obvious when one examines the inputs that personnel most directly concerned with the employment of military force provide in the complex of processes leading to a C3I system. First, when compared with the force provision bureaucracy—the military services—those responsible for employing force—the CINCs—have no resources. They cannot directly create C3I systems that support military operations. Even if they could, the development cycle is so long that it is not clear that a process begun nine or ten years earlier would generate outcomes appropriate for current requirements. Another option available to the CINCs might be simply to purchase, from the menu of available systems, those most appropriate for their operational requirements; a lack of resources also prevents this approach.

The separation of the force-employing from the force-provisioning responsibilities makes difficult the "coupling" of a needs/requirements input stream to design, development, evaluation and procurement decision streams, due to the considerable organizational separation involved. This is especially true when the force-employing (CINCs) stream involves commanders from a military service different from that of the service providing the resources and developing the C3I systems. "Coupling" the relevant decision streams becomes even more difficult if there are two military services involved in the provision of C3I systems—for example, systems to support air-ground communications.

"Coupling" force employment considerations with force provision decision streams is difficult given the structures and division of labor established by the National Security Act of 1947. To couple the relevant decision streams in such a way as to achieve desired outcomes is doubly difficult. The organizational separations, created when the U.S. Department of Defense was established, effectively remove military needs and requirements from playing the primary role in weapons development and procurement processes. Much of what passes for formal resource allocation (e.g., PPBS) and coordination activity (e.g., C3ExCom) in OSD represents an attempt at procedural fixes to an organic and structural problem in Defense Department organization.

Prescriptions: Structural and Strategic

Given the objective of deploying C3I systems that better support operational concepts and military operations, there are several structural changes that might be suggested so as to better couple "military requirements" with those processes that generate deployable weapons systems.

Perhaps the most radical proposal would be to redo the entire organization of the U.S. military, creating a truly unified military and eliminating the army, navy, air force, and marines as separate military services and administrative units. The purpose of such a proposal would be to make force employment considerations and military requirements an organic part of the force provisioning process and to eliminate parochial, service-specific approaches to force design and provisioning. Given the reactions to far more modest proposals, having far less effect on service autonomy than would the creation of a truly unified military, it is clear that a radical unification proposal, however sensible from a military capability point of view, is politically infeasible.

More modest proposals focus on the creation of an effective, central *military* planning and command structure, either a true general staff or a more effective Joint Chiefs of Staff. Although there is every reason to believe that an effective general staff form of military organization is more suited to the requirements of modern welfare, there is little evidence of necessary widespread political support for such a concept. Even the recent, more modest, very sensible proposals for strenghtening the Joint Staff and/or the office of the chairman of the Joint Chiefs of Staff have met with passive resistance—the appointment of study groups and commissions, the absence of presidential backing, and so forth.[12] Upon leaving office in 1983, the former chairman of the Joint Chiefs of Staff, General Jones, made a comprehensive series of proposals for strenthening the professional military advice available to the government and for more direct "military requirements" input into force-provisioning decisions. The obligatory Congressional hearings and study commissions followed, with no concrete results likely. There is widespread recognition of many of the structural problems contained in the current DoD organization but little interest in directly addressing these problems.

In lieu of more direct approaches to the major structural problems in U.S. military resource allocation and procurement, there have been a variety of attempts at modest "procedural fixes." Over the past decade, every secretary of defense, using a variety of bureaucratic mechanisms, has sought to bring "military requirements" and "support of operational concepts" more forcefully into the resource allocation and planning processes by "coupling" participants and problems with artificially created choice opportunities, using bureaucratic procedures. In part, this involves the creation of formal inputs from the CINCs (the ROCs) to the JCS in the PPBS resource allocation process (see Figure 5.3). This has had limited effect for the simple reason that the JCS itself has limited real influence in the PPBS and resource allocation processes (Crecine, 1975b). Similarly, there have been concerted attempts to involve the CINCs directly in OSD resource allocation and procurement processes where C3I is concerned (Rice, 1984). The C3ExCom and component panels are good examples of an attempt to bring a "military requirements" perspective to C3I systems decisions.

One additional modest structural change has been proposed that should be mentioned here. General John H. Cushman (1983), in a thorough examination of command and control issues surrounding theater-level conventional forces, has proposed providing commanders, the CINCs, with more influence in the JCS, OSD, and service decisions involving C3 systems and with budgets of their own to provide more effective control over the C3 assets necessary to support their commands. There has been some increase in the role of the CINCs in C3 procurement decisions, and they have been provided with very small budgets (in relation to the problems) for C3; mostly these resources have been used to invest in headquarters facilities and equipment.

For the near term at least, it is reasonably clear that any solutions to the considerable problems involving C3 procurement in the U.S. military will consist of a series of modest procedural fixes, similar to those outlined above. In other words, regardless of how deficient the current system is, it is unlikely to change in any significant way. Given that the existing C3I procurement system approximates the "organized anarchy" described in "garbage can" theories of choice, what kinds of organizational tactics are likely to be effective? Are there ways to influence C3I outcomes in positive ways, without changing the structure of the system in a major way? Can "garbage can" theories help in prescribing ways for achieving objectives in C3I procurement processes?

Prescriptions for Being Effective in Loosely Coupled Systems: Tactical and Operations

Recall the discussion in the fifth section of this chapter of "coupling parallel processes" which together make up the C3I procurement process. Influence in an "organized anarchy" or "garbage can" situation partly consists of arranging for an appropriate coupling of component processes, participants, problems, solutions and choice opportunities so as to achieve a desired outcome. It is in this broader context that March and Cohen (1976) offer some additional advice for being effective in an organized anarchy.[13] This "Machiavellian guide" for organizational tactics in an organized anarchy includes some of the following rules of thumb:

- Be persistent.
- Be flexible on priorities and goals and on the order in which they are pursued.

- Link preferred "solutions" to "problems" in an opportunistic way.
- Manipulate energies and activities of other participants.
- Trade symbols for substance.
- Create ad hoc "choice opportunities."

I will attempt to translate the March and Cohen advice into the C3I procurement process; readers familiar with the ways of the U.S. military establishment and the Department of Defense may judge for themselves the likely utility of "garbage can" concepts as a source of tactical advice.

For purposes of exposition, the March and Cohen "advice" will be directed toward a weapons program manager in one of the services, a senior official in one of the OSD or JCS/C3 directorates, or a key staffer to a high service or OSD official. The thread that runs through the "garbage can" theories of decision making in an organized anarchy is that decisions or choices are very "context specific." The outcome is highly dependent upon the "context" in which choice is made, where "context" depends very much on what is in the "garbage can" or choice opportunity when a decision is made. The particular mix of participants, problems and solutions is not preordained. Once the mix is specified, the choice or decision is anticlimactic and generally predictable. The path to effective influence is an ability to orchestrate the creation of choice opportunities or "garbage cans" and the particular mix of participants, problems and solutions in the "garbage can." The March-Cohen advice to would-be influentials in the C3I procurement process, regardless of their particular objectives, is aimed at creating the right "context" for choice, where right is defined as the mix of participants, problems, and solutions in an appropriate "garbage can" that will lead to the desired outcome.

Because there is no predetermined connection between problems, solutions, participants and choice opportunities, there are two fundamental ways in which linkages are established:(1) linkages created by chance; and (2) linkages consciously orchestrated or arranged. One reason chance linkages are of interest is because this is the source of many misinterpretations of the "cause" of choices or outcomes—individuals seldom, if ever, ascribe outcomes to "chance." Influence exercisers can discover linkages that are advantageous to long-run objectives and exploit them for personal advantage, or they can help create linkages that further their own objectives. The advice offered can be interpreted as strategies for discovering and creating those linkages of participants, problems, solutions and/or choice opportunities that further a particular set of objectives, in a setting where such linkages cannot be completely controlled.

In a world where participants come and go—via fixed tours of duty, for example—each "generation" of participants represents a new opportunity to persuade participants that situation X is a problem and solution Y is the solution. In this sense, there is never a permanent "no" to any proposal. Consider, for instance, the longevity of the soon-to-be-produced B-1 bomber. The initial design was done in the early 1960s. The proposed new manned bomber for the air force was rejected on numerous occasions by the OSD, by the President, and by the Congress. The rationale for the weapons system (the "problem" to which the B-1 was the solution) has shifted several times. "persistence" pays.

In a world where linkages between problems and solutions are somewhat arbitrary, such linkages, when established, are often the result of sociological processes as much as rational argument. Ideas or belief systems concerning problems or solutions have a gestation period and take time to evolve. Merely repeating arguments long enough and often enough is sometimes sufficient to connect preferred solutions to problems.

In the fluid world of "garbage can processes" and organized anarchy, it is very difficult to predict in advance what the context (mix of participants, problems and solutions) of choice will be in a given choice opportunity. If one is attempting to exercise influence in pursuit of a long-term goal, where achievement of the goal requires a series of particular choices/outcomes achieved in a particular order, achievement of the overall goal may take a very long time if there is only partial control over the mix of problems, solutions and participants at each stage. If the order in which things are done is flexible, then any one of the list of "intermediate solutions" not yet accomplished is a candidate to be "dumped" into the "garbage can" or choice opportunity of the moment, rather than just one. A long menu of "solutions" to be pursued, or a long list of problems to be addressed, rather than just one, means that it is more likely that any given choice opportunity that presents itself can serve as the appropriate context for introducing some problem or solution or participant. Under such circumstances, flexibility and a menu of objectives (problems and/or solutions) will well serve an individual attempting to exercise influence.

In the C3I area in the U.S. military, often involving more than one service, there are many opportunities for "trading symbols for substance." This is possible simply because the linkages between problems and solutions are problematic. Consider, for example, an Army CINC or C3 weapons development manager for the Army portion of JTIDS (Joint Tactical Information Distribution System). In order to coordinate close air support with ground forces, JTIDS represents the link between two systems. The Army system is one in which targets are located first for ground force artillery. The Army desires to pass this information on to Air Force squadrons providing close air support. The army does not have control over those air units supporting ground operations; air units are controlled (assigned to missions) at the theater level, and Army units at the division level (two levels below). This difference in command structure means that air units are assigned ground targets, some often a considerable time after the mission was requested by the Army, by which time the targets and their location generally have changed. So the Army is very interested in providing target information to supporting air squadrons on a real-time basis. The JTIDS is a set of computer terminals, linked by radio transmission between ground forces and supporting air forces. Naturally, there are two standards for radio communications and a different (different in terms of communication protocols and operating characteristics) "terminal." Volunteering to adopt air force standards for the ground link in a visible way (symbol) would enable the Army to achieve real-time ground target acquisition (substance) more quickly than if the Army insisted on pressing for the adoption of the Army standards.

Still another way to change the "context" (mix of participants, problems and solutions) of a choice opportunity is to attempt to manipulate the timing of a choice opportunity so that it occurs when enemies are busy and friends are able to participate fully. This can often be done simply by noting when enemies are likely to be preoccupied on other issues, away on business, and so forth. Consider, for example, a C3I procurement situation where a mild opponent of a particular "solution" does periodic field inspections, is required to prepare for and give Congressional testimony, or must occasionally be immersed in the budget process. It is obvious from this itinerary when to schedule key meetings.

Generally, it is not possible for a single individual to control either the nature and timing of choice opportunities or the associated mix of participants, problems and solutions. For example, there is a regular budgeting cycle—the PPBS—which defines a set of choice opportunities and, usually, the participants. Problems and solutions are often unspecified and change from budget cycle to budget cycle. Budgetary processes link choice opportunities and participants. Official military doctrine limits the range of what can be introduced as a "problem" to be dealt with in a choice opportunity.

There is, of course, the possibility of creating choice opportunities. On a fairly high level, the creation of a series of C3 directorates and the C3ExCom with its many panels, established a set of "choice opportunities" in the C3I procurement process. By defining responsibilities and representation and reporting relationships, the mix of participants, problems and solutions associated with choice opportunities is partially specified. A traditional, bureaucratic way of "creating" a problem and linking that problem to a set of possible solutions is through establishing commissions, task forces or study groups. Individuals in OSD and the services with resources for research contracts and studies generally use those resources as a way of creating linkages between particular problems and particular solutions, some of which are then "dumped into" garbage cans at an opportune moment.

Finally, in an ad hoc way, problems are "created" and dramatized in the hopes that this will lead to the establishment of a series of choice opportunities. For example, perhaps the most effective tactic for an Army field commander concerned about inadequate C3I capabilities would be to promote actively a field or command post exercise designed to practice and test C3I capabilities rather than tactics or ground maneuvers. Visible, demonstrable performance deficiencies or failure helps create "problems" that can then be equally visibly linked to preferred solutions.

SUMMARY

The purpose of this chapter is to suggest that "garbage can" concepts of organizational decision making could be profitably applied to choice and decision making in the U.S. military, and in the C3I procurement process in particular. "Garbage can" concepts were used to better understand both the details and macrostructure of portions of the defense resource allocation, weapons systems development and evaluation, and procurement processes. "Garbage can" concepts were used to diagnose several of the known deficiencies in the current system and to suggest a variety of structural and procedural "corrections." Finally, some very general tactical suggestions were explored for being effective in "garbage can" environments—organized anarchies.

By means of practical examples, this paper explored the utility of "garbage can" approaches to decision making in military organizations in two ways. As positive or descriptive theory, "garbage can" concepts were used to better understand C3I procurement processes. As normative or prescriptive theory, "garbage can" concepts were used both to suggest structural reforms in C3I procurement processes and to suggest tactical approaches operating within existing processes.

NOTES

1. The knowledge required by an IP approach is to be contrasted with the knowledge requirements of economists and management scientists; for them, all one needs to know is the task environment. Given the task, the organization is presumed to behave "optimally."

2. Cyert and March (1963) formulate their theory for business firms, but the application of their framework to nonmarket organizations is clearly just as appropriate, perhaps even more so.

3. See Cohen and March (1974, pp. 195–229, especially pp. 205–215) for some very insightful suggestions on how to exercise influence in a loosely coupled decision system—an "organized anarchy."

4. See Cushman (1983) for a persuasive and thorough argument for providing CINCs with more control over the composition of forces they command. Major General Cushman writes from the perspective of a former deputy-CINC.

5. Currently, there are eight C3ExCom panels: Computer Information and Security (OSD), Defense Communications System (OSD), International C3 (OSD), Military Satellites (OSD), Strategic C3 (OSD), Theater and Tactical C3 (JCS), World Wide Military Command and Communications System (JCS) and High Frequency C3 (Navy).

6. Information on the C3ExCom and its operation was gathered by Peter Rice.

7. There are many excellent case studies of weapons acquisition. See, for instance, Coulam (1977).

8. Research grants have an uncanny ability to deflect the interests of technical critics. Similarly, the Program Evaluation Review Technique (PERT) was of more use as a political symbol of good management than as a tool used to manage a complex program (Sapolsky, 1969).

9. For a similar argument, see Eberhardt Rechtin (1984, p. 12)—". . . command and control systems that in the past have been, or appeared to be, fragmented and unrelated developments."

10. Growing concern with C3I deficiencies is evidenced by growing references to C3I in the annual force posture statements and annual reports to Congress of the secretary of defense, in increased appropriations explicitly earmarked for C3, in the growing number of C3 directorates in the services, the JCS and the OSD, and more frequent DoD directives initiating joint C3 system development over the past six or seven years (Rice, 1984).

11. The cost of conducting exercises—assembling men and equipment—is cited as the reason for not allowing communication outages to go uncorrected. When the principal purpose of the exercise is to try out new tactics and new equipment, and to train soldiers, it is tempting not to let mere communication outages bring this expensive logistical arrangement to a halt. As a result, the C3I systems are seldom exercised realistically.

12. The secretary of defense has shown little interest in the proposals made by former chairman of the Joint Chiefs of Staff, General Jones.

13. The "organizational tactics" in this section are suggested in Cohen and March (1974). Implicit in the description in the fifth section of this chapter of various ways of "coupling parallel processes" are some guides for action for those who wish to influence C3I procurement outcomes.

REFERENCES

Allison, Graham T. *Essence of Decision: The Cuban Missile Crisis*. Boston: Little, Brown, 1972.

Cohen, M.D., and March, J. G. *Leadership and Ambiguity: The American College Presidency*. New York: Carnegie Corporation, 1974.

Cohen, M. D., March, J. G., and Olsen, J. P. "A Garbage Can Model of Organizational Choice." *Administrative Science Quarterly* 17 (1972): 1–25.

Coulam, Robert F. *Illusions of Choice: The F-111 and the Problem of Weapons Acquisition Reform*. Princeton, N.J.: Princeton University Press, 1977.

Coulam, R., Crecine, J. P., Fischer, G. W., and Salomone, M. D. (assisted by Hammond, P. Y.). "Problems of Command and Control in a Major European War." Marina del Rey, Calif.: Analytical Assessments Corporation Report. No. AAC-TR-21201/83, October 1983.

Crecine, J. P. *Governmental Problem Solving: A Computer Simulation of Municipal Budgeting*. Chicago: Rand McNally, 1969.

Crecine, J. P. "Defense Budgeting: Organizational Adaptation to Environmental Constraints." Santa Monica, Calif.: The Rand Corporation Report No. RM-6121-PR, 1970.

Crecine, J. P. "Making Defense Budgets." In *Appendices: Commission on the Organization of the Government for the Conduct of Foreign Policy*, vol. 4. Washington D.C.: Government Printing Office, 1975a.

Crecine, J. P. "Defense Resource Allocation." In *Appendices: Commission on the Organization of the Government for the Conduct of Foreign Policy*, vol. 4. Washington D.C.: Government Printing Office, 1975b.

Crecine, J. P. "The Shape of the Defense Budget." In *Appendices: Commission on the Organization of the Government for the Conduct of Foreign Policy*, vol. 4. Washington D.C.: Government Printing Office, 1975c.

Crecine, J. P., Fischer, G. W., and Salomone, M. D. "Data Analysis for Assessment of C3I Capabilities and Vulnerabilities." Marina del Rey, Calif.: Analytical Assessments Corporation Report No. AAC-TR-21201/82, December 1981.

Cushman, J. H. *Command and Control of Theatre Forces: Adequacy*. Cambridge, Mass.: Center for Information Policy Research, Harvard University Report No. P-83-1, 1983.

Cyert, R. M., and March, J. G. *A Behavioral Theory of the Firm*. Englewood Cliffs, N.J.: Prentice-Hall, 1963.

Davis, O. A., and Reuter, F. "A Simulation of Municipal Zoning Decisions." *Management Sciences* (1972): 39–77.

Fallows, James. *National Security*. 1982.

Fischer, G. W., and Crecine, J. P. "How Much Is Enough?: Explaining Presidential Defense Budget Requests." *Arms Control* (September 1981): 66–106.

Fischer, G. W., and Kamlet, M. S. "Explaining Presidential Priorities: The Competing Aspirations Model of Macrobudgetary Decision Making." *American Political Science Review* March (1984): 356–371.

General Accounting Office. "The Joint Tactical Information Distribution System: How Important Is It?" Unpublished Technical Report PSAD-80-22 (Comptroller General). June 30, 1980.

General Accounting Office. "Review of the Battlefield Exploitation and Targeting System." Unpublished Technical Report LCD-80-38. March 3, 1980b.

Gerwin, Donald. *Budgeting Public Funds*. Madison, Wis.: Wisconsin University Press, 1969.

Inbar, Michael, *Routine Decision Making*. Beverly Hills, Calif.: Sage Publications, 1979.

Kingdon, John. *Congressmen's Voting Decisions*. New York: Harper & Row, 1973.

Larkey, P. D. *Process Models and Program Evaluation: The Impact of General Revenue Sharing on Municipal Behavior*. Princeton, N.J.: Princeton University Press, 1979.

March, J. G., and Olsen, J. P. (eds.). *Ambiguity and Choice in Organizations*. Universitetsforlaget, Norway, 1976.

March, J. G., and Simon, H. A. *Organizations*. New York: Wiley, 1958.

Puritano, V. "The Budget Process in DoD." Paper presented at the Patterson School, December 1983.

Rechtin, Eberhardt, "The Technology of Command." *U.S. Naval War College Review* (March/April 1984): 5–25.

Rice, P. "Recent History of C3I Policy Evolution, Expenditures, and Organizational Prominence." Unpublished paper. Pittsburgh: Carnegie-Mellon University, 1984.

Sapolsky, Harvey. "Creating the Fleet Ballistic Missile System: The Interaction of Technology and Organization in the Development of a Major Weapon System." Cambridge, Mass.: M.I.T. Report No. IL-C-3386, 1969.

Simon, Herbert A. "On the Concept of Organizational Goal." *Administrative Science Quarterly* (1964): 1–22.

Simon, H. A. *The Architecture of Complexity*. Cambridge, Mass.: MIT Press, 1969.

Steinbruner, John. *The Cybernetic Theory of Decision: New Dimensions of Political Analysis*. Princeton, N.J.; Princeton University Press, 1974.

Tuggle, F., and Gerwin, D. "An Information Processing Model of Organizational Perception, Strategy, and Choice." *Management Science* (1980): 575–592.

Weick, Karl. "Educational Organizations as Loosely Coupled Systems." *Administrative Science Quarterly* 21 (1973): 1–19.

Wildavsky, Aaron. *The Politics of the Budgetary Process*. Boston: Little, Brown, 1964.

6

Planning Systems in Large Organizations: A Garbage Can Approach with Application to Defense PPBS

PHILIP BROMILEY

Point One: Organizations are blunt instruments.
Point Two: You don't sharpen an axe like a scalpel.

INTRODUCTION

Often we are concerned with the average behavior of large organizations—the normal performance of a planning system, the normal outcomes of budgetary decision making, the average performance of a management system. Let us use the Department of Defense's Planning, Programming, and Budgeting System (PPBS) as an example of such systems and ask, "How do we get a conceptual handle on how such systems will behave in aggregate?"

Several observations come to mind. First, we are dealing with organizations and suborganizations rather than simple individual decision making. Second, the theories we use to attack such problems often deal with far more

Philip Bromiley is on the faculty at the Naval Postgraduate School and is a Visiting Professor at the University of Minnesota.

Funding from the NPS Foundation research program is gratefully acknowledged. I also wish to thank Kenneth Euske, Esther Hamilton, Thomas Hayward, Roger Weissinger-Baylon and Alfred Whittle for their comments on earlier versions of this paper, and Tom Finnerty and Hank Rudge for helpful examples. I retain responsibility for any shortcomings of this paper.

microphenomena than we wish to handle. Third, the garbage can approach may provide some perspective on the problem.

In considering PPBS, we are asking how an organization of three million people is going to plan and budget two to three hundred billion dollars per year for the next five years, being aware that many of the decisions are thirty-year commitments. Research on individual decision making can be of limited assistance in this area. While we have an enormous set of literature that tells us many interesting things about how individuals in isolation, or in small groups, deal with problems and handle information, we have no evidence that such phenomena carry over in relatively neat fashion to aggregates. For example, behavioral decision theory, which attempts to explain how individuals handle risk and uncertainty, works for individuals even when they are playing with real money, but it is not clear that such phenomena hold for organizational forecasts, organizational risk taking, and so forth. Indeed, the three relevant studies of which I am aware (Larkey and Smith 1981; Shannon and Schwiering, 1983; Bromiley, 1985) appear to be inconsistent with the simple application of behavioral decision theory to organizational forecasts. Larkey and Smith (1981) found extremely stable biases in municipal budget forecasts, but the biases were readily explained by organizational phenomena rather than by cognitive biases. Shannon and Schwiering (1983) examined both Navy budget forecasts and corporate sales plans but found no simple biases at work—the forecasts did not reflect conservatism or anchoring and adjustment (adapting suboptimally from a previous figure when using new information). Likewise, Bromiley (1985), examining a variety of corporate and public data, found substantial biases, but the biases varied across organizations and items rather than being stable as one would expect from cognitive biases. While one would expect that some of the cognitive biases found with individuals would carry over into organizational forecasts, there is little evidence that this is the case. Overall, it may be best to assume that we just do not know.

In addition, the stability in a system lies in the organization, not in the individuals. In defense, top military and civilian decision makers rotate through jobs every three years (Collins, 1982). Since planning and budgeting operate on a one-year cycle, changing personnel triennially is a quick turnover.[1]

Theories that rest on individual-level phenomena, such as risk preferences or decision style, may be of limited relevance, unless we can show that such tendencies are homogeneous across the population of potential jobholders and that these tendencies are not overwhelmed by structural or organizational features. In addition, rules specify participation by organizational unit or position, not by actual individuals. If we wish to address normal performance, we need a framework that is not completely tied to individuals. In some sense, this is the opposite problem to the economists' problem of level of analysis. Whereas the economist usually assumes there is nothing interesting below the firm level, the organizational theorist has often assumed that anything of interest must be built up from individuals. As Simon (1981, p. 221) notes, in hierarchical systems such as organizations, the parameters from the next lower level are of interest, but the detailed working of the lower levels should not be needed to explain higher level phenomena. That is, to understand the operations of the macroplanning system, we should be able to build on the units that participate rather than the individuals within these units. Of course, we address average behavior while recognizing that idiosyncratic behavior does occur.[2]

So what can we do with organizational units? (1) We can make these units rational, unitary actors and invoke a power model—the defense budget is determined by the personal and organizational objectives and relative power of the secretary of defense, the president, the services and Congress. (2) We can make such units unitary, limited information processors and invoke behavioral decision theory or cognitive psychology—the defense budget is determined by judgmental heuristics, problem representations, and so forth. (3) We can make the units rational actors with "proper" preferences and invoke an economic model of the organization—the defense budget is an attempt to allocate resources optimally to maximize the defense capability of the United States. (4) We can make the units rule-bound and look at standard operating procedures—the defense budget is largely a simple update, by standard operating procedure, of a previous budget in light of changes in the relevant environment, particularly the funds available. All four of these approaches make strong assumptions about the internal behavior patterns of organizational units, and all have some validity. Here, let us try to make a more restricted set of assumptions about individual behavior and develop the analysis through the garbage can framework (see March and Olsen, 1976). In employing the garbage can approach, we are not asserting that it is inherently superior to the other approaches, nor that it is the "true" theory of the process, but rather, following Allison (1971), that it is an approach that may illuminate some interesting parts of a very complex reality.

The garbage can approach provides four basic entities with which one can describe a system: choice situations, participants, problems and solutions. Thus, a planning system can be described as a series of choice situations with the following characteristics:

1. Choice situations are ordered in a predefined pattern.

2. Participants are defined as organizational units.

3. Explicit rules define much of the task environment for the decisions—these may be thought of as eligibility criteria for problems and solutions (see Bromiley, 1981, on the task environment in budgetary decision making). Such rules specify total funds available, essential funding levels for prior commitments, deadlines, and so forth.

4. Certain participants specify part of the task environment for other (later) participants. This provision works both through formal procedures (e.g., formal planning guidance) and through managers acting outside the formal planning process. That is, certain participants can provide other participants in other choice situations with problems or solutions.

5. Choices relate to future, as contrasted with immediate, actions.

What we have is a chain of garbage cans with structure on the connections among the cans, problems, solutions and participants.

Given this conception, let us specify some questions that can guide us in analyzing the system.

1. What are the allowable garbage cans (choice situations)?

2. Who participates in each choice?

3. What structures are there on the transmission of problems, solutions and task environment structures from choice to choice?

4. What additional rules govern the allowability of problems, solutions and participants to given cans?

5. What problems, solutions and constraints will the various participants bring to the various cans?

6. How will these cans, problems, solutions and participants fit together in a dynamic system?

The garbage can framework here refers to a set of terms and concepts that can be used to parse the system, not to describe a particular decision. These questions can be sensibly answered in systems that are not considered organized anarchies. Thus, even in a very analytical organization, the researcher can pose these questions and discover useful information from that exercise. Most previous research using garbage can approaches has highlighted garbage can decisions per se. In contrast, this research uses the garbage can approach to study how choice situations are structured (by participants, problems and solutions) but does not address how specific choice situations become resolved.

GENERAL SCHEMA OF GARBAGE CAN PLANNING SYSTEM

Figure 6.1 presents a general schema that has the primary components of a garbage can analysis of a planning system. First, the system is specified in terms of a hierarchy or sequence of decision points or choice situations. Second, attached to each choice situation is a set of participants. Third, the participants bring a set of problems and solutions to each choice. Fourth, there are connections among choice situations and among participants at different points in the planning sequence.

Let us consider the two stereotypical planning systems—top-down and bottom-up.

A Top-Down Planning System

In a standard top-down planning system, top managers make "strategic decisions" in the first choice situation. As in textbook strategic planning, the top management makes the big decisions and passes these to the next tier of

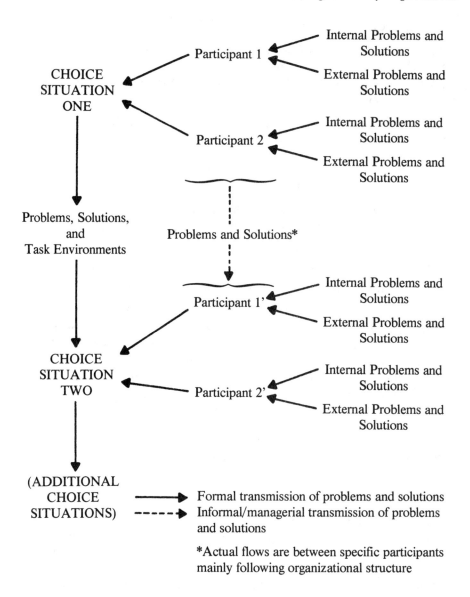

Figure 6.1 A garbage can perception of a planning process.

management, which plans to implement the strategic decisions. In a business, top-level managers bring solutions such as acquisitions, divestitures and major new strategic directions, and problems such as low-profit divisions, environmental changes that impact basic competitive positions and corporate financing as a whole, to the strategic choice situation. The output of the strategic choice situation is a set of problems and solutions that are transmitted, by a formal strategic guidance, to the lower level organizational units. Usually, many members of top management supervise subunits in the organization.

Consequently, these members may transmit problems and solutions directly, in addition to those that come through the plan. The next tier proceeds to develop a set of more detailed plans. They work with three separate inputs. First, they have the strategic problems and solutions developed by the top management and sent to them through the formal guidance. Their primary job is implementing these strategies. Second, they have the specific problems and solutions that top managers have handed down to them outside the strategic guidance. Third, they have their own repertoire of problems and solutions, including those that are produced by their subordinate units.

A Bottom-Up Planning System

A bottom-up planning system would work in the opposite direction. It begins with an extremely broad set of problems and solutions considered simultaneously by a number of suborganizations. As they move up the chain, the problems and solutions are selected, refined and abstracted. The choices at each level include the problems and solutions submitted by the lower level and those attached by the participants at the given level. Decisions are often judgments to exclude, drop or forget a given problem or solution in transmittal to higher levels. End runs—efforts to transmit problems and solutions over one hierarchical level—might be found in this system, depending on the rules of exclusion for such behaviors (see Anthony and Hertzlinger, 1975, on the rules in the Department of Defense). The debate at higher levels would be structured by the problems and solutions coming from the lower levels. Higher level managers would be addressing "smaller" problems and solutions than in top-down systems.

To make this analysis more concrete, it will be phrased in terms of the Planning, Programming, and Budgeting System (PPBS) used in the Department of Defense. While PPBS is used as an example, the analysis will attempt to develop some general patterns of interaction that would be expected in a garbage can characterization of a planning system. The defense examples outlined below are offered only as illustrations and hypotheses. While they are in accordance with both the personal observations of a number of military officers and some of the academic literature on defense, they may not be accurate descriptions of the behavior of the current system.

AN ACTUAL PLANNING SYSTEM

The Planning, Programming, and Budgeting System (PPBS) in the Department of Defense is a variant of a top-down planning system. Let us briefly examine the system[3] as shown in Figure 6.2.

The system starts with the "Joint Strategic Planning Document" of the Joint Chiefs of Staff (JCS)—a statement of the threats to U.S. security and recommended military strategy and force structure response. The Office of the Secretary of Defense (OSD) produces (after input on a draft version) a Defense Guidance that is the authoritative statement on fundamental strategy,

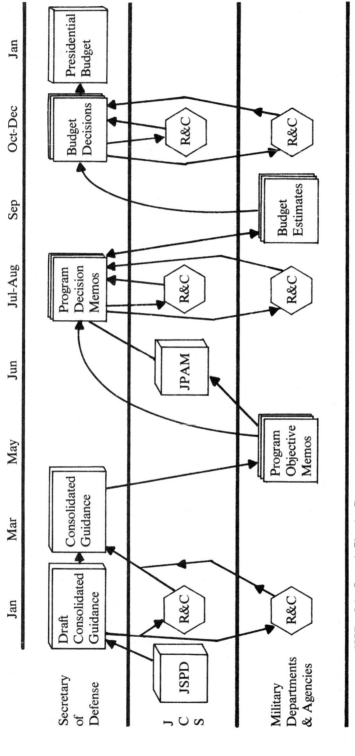

Figure 6.2 Planning, Programming, and Budgeting System Cycle.

JSPD – Joint Strategic Planning Document
JPAM – Joint Program Assessment Memorandum

R&C – Review and Comment

issues and fiscal guidance for program development. Given the Defense Guidance, the services develop their programs, which are presented in Program Objectives Memoranda (POMs). Following JCS input and decisions on the issues raised in the POMs, the secretary of defense issues Program Decision Memoranda (PDMs) on which the services build their budgets. Services submit their budgets to OSD and, after appropriate reviews and discussions, a final budget is approved.

A basic pattern is repeated throughout the planning and budgeting process. While the connection of the Defense Guidance (top policy statement) to the POM (mid-range plan) will be used as the primary example, the same pattern is repeated throughout the process, in the ties between the POM and the budget, and at all levels, as major claimants provide guidance to subclaimants and receive budgets in return. At all stages in the process, the subsequent stage involves more detailed decisions culminating in the final stage (budgeting). This stage is the formal output of the system that is presented to Congress.

In a top-down planning system, as described in PPBS, we have the repeated application of the delegated planning hierarchy presented in Figure 6.3.

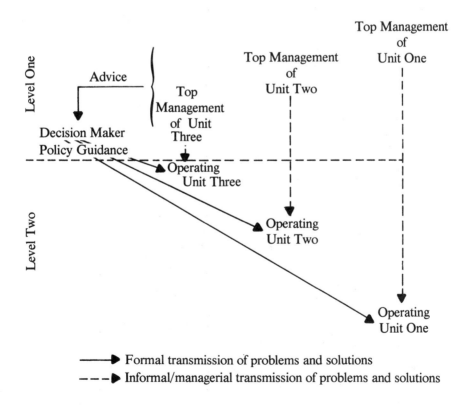

——▶ Formal transmission of problems and solutions
– – –▶ Informal/managerial transmission of problems and solutions

Figure 6.3 Policy guidance.

At level one, a person or committee makes decisions on the plan, and these decisions are passed on to level two for detailed planning. But, the members of the (level one) committee are connected to the subordinate organizations (level two) in the system. Let level one represent the Joint Chiefs of Staff and the OSD. The Joint Chiefs (top management of units) provide input to the secretary of defense (decision maker) on the Defense Guidance, which is then promulgated down through the service secretaries to the members of the Joint Chiefs (wearing their service chiefs hats) for program development. The service chiefs may also bring problems and solutions directly from the strategic discussion to their staffs (the informal managerial transmission of problems and solutions in Figure 6.3).

In Figure 6.4, we see the return of the POM. The Defense Guidance presents the services with a set of constraints, problems and solutions. Each service responds with a set of programs (the POM) which are submitted up through the senior management of the services (service chief and secretary) to the top decision maker (OSD and secretary of defense). In developing the POM, the services integrate both the problems and solutions provided by the Guidance and the problems and solutions they currently have active. The

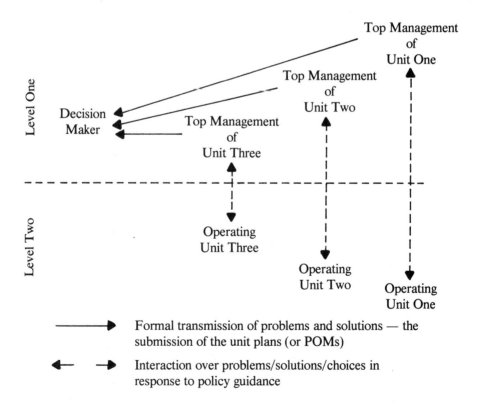

Figure 6.4 Return of the plans.

services attempt to push their current solutions and attempt to address their current problems within the context of the Guidance. The OSD will police, to some extent, the conformity of the proposed programs with the Guidance.

The system's performance critically depends on how efficiently the system eliminates problems and solutions and restricts the attention of various levels to appropriate problems and solutions. Consider a system that was not good at eliminating problems and solutions. Rather than a cycle where strategic decisions are made based on strategic concerns and passed down for programming, the cyclic property means that the problems that organizations find in Figure 6.4 are active and remembered in the next cycle for Figure 6.3. Rather than cycling, we create a community of problems and solutions—a community that is only marginally differentiated by hierarchy and that is relatively stable. What the planning process will be doing, if anything, is injecting some new problems and solutions into the existing stable community rather than redefining the community as a whole. While the implications of such a system will be discussed further below, these can easily be pointed out: top managers deal with lower level problems, lower level problems and solutions may be injected in strategic choices, and these advantages of specialization in planning are lost.

Under what conditions would a planning system avoid the to-be-described difficulties of problems and solutions not being eliminated and drifting across levels in the hierarchy?

As noted in the garbage can simulations (Cohen et al., 1972), organizations are most likely to solve problems and solutions efficiently when they have lots of resources and few problems and solutions. We might expect such conditions to exist if defense budgets expanded at such a rapid rate that aspirations could not keep pace. This hypothesis makes two assumptions. It assumes that resources can eliminate problems or solutions and that the population of active problems and solutions is not determined by the resources. But problems or solutions that are not resolvable by the kind of resources available in the system may be attached to choices in the system. Often the DoD has been seen as a mechanism for solving societal problems, which may be outside the realm of possibility for the organization—for example, disparity in racial opportunity, illiteracy, the decline of small business and the decline of the U.S. merchant marine. Perhaps some problems cannot be eliminated by any managerial decision, with the exception of a decision not to recognize the problem.

Also the definition of resource scarcity must always be a relative one, depending on the aspiration levels of the participants. While Cohen et al. (1972) discuss system load as an objective phenomenon, in most cases the load of problems and solutions to be associated with a choice is determined by the participants, not by an exogenous force. As aspiration levels rise, the participants will associate more problems (attempting to fix more problems) and more solutions (attempting to purchase more things or do more things) with the choice situations available in the planning system. For example, if a participant aspires to a given budget level, a set of problems and solutions will be introduced that justify that budget level.

We must differentiate between two models of aspirations. First, in traditional Cyert and March (1963) style, organizations look at current performance and adjust aspirations. Here, aspirations are totally relative with respect to the current level of performance. Second, organizations may have well-defined latent aspiration levels but only operate on a lower level of aspiration that is contingent on what is perceived to be realistic. In defense, senior military decision makers argue that a serious analysis of the need yields requirements that are well beyond any politically conceivable budget level. Similar structures probably exist in many public organizations where an analytical definition of the problem to be solved yields budgetary implications far from current or conceivable levels (e.g., highway maintenance, urban infrastructure, and so forth, have analyses that indicate massive increases in budgets in order to avert serious problems). In these cases, the load of problems and solutions provided by the agency will be contingent on what is allowed rather than on a traditional aspiration function. Given high latent aspiration levels, agencies would push for increased budgets, regardless of how well they happen to be doing in historical perspective. I have observed Navy presentations where speakers complained bitterly of how low their budget was while displaying slides showing a 36% real growth in their budget over a three year period. Given high latent aspirations, observed aspirations can rise quickly. Rising aspirations may act to extend the range of problems and solutions associated with a given choice, and consequently to overload a system's ability to eliminate problems and solutions.

Even in a system with long-lived problems and solutions, strong, clear relevance criteria for such problems and solutions might stop them from spreading across levels. For example, dollar-level cutoffs in capital budgeting may keep small project problems and solutions off the agenda for senior management. Yet, in many cases, such criteria are hard to define, and perhaps harder still to enforce. Policy analysts often complain that managers want to make low-level operational decisions rather than plan (see, for instance, House, 1982; Collins, 1982). Managers often want to be involved in the minute details that appear to be below their appropriate level of attention. Micromanagement (as the term is used in DoD) is a common problem.

Alternatively, organizations may exist in environments where problems and solutions evaporate. Just as Steinbeck's Doc found that if left unopened for a couple of weeks most letters resolved themselves, there may exist environments where problems and solutions that are not quickly resolved simply become unavailable. Consider, for example, job candidates. If a choice is heavily affected by the presence of a given job candidate (a solution perhaps) then it might simply resolve itself when the candidate gets tired of waiting. Some unemployment "problems" simply resolve themselves as discouraged workers quit looking for work.

Finally, if all units share common perceptions about which problems and solutions are appropriate for which choices, then the undesirable drifting of problems and solutions may be avoided. If all units perceived that a given class of problems should be handled at a given level, higher and lower levels would send such problems to that level, eliminating inappropriate problems and solutions from the other levels. Formal accord on appropriate levels does not suffice—if managers want to handle problems and solutions at other levels, they will soon circumvent formal accords. Many formal planning systems assume that participants agree on appropriate levels for problems and solutions—PPBS, for example, assumes that threat and counter measures can be defined "objectively," without undue concern for the lower level problems and solutions implied by such definitions. All participants are assumed to have the same view of the appropriate problems and solutions to be handled at the strategic level and are not injecting (even informally or surreptitiously) other problems and solutions. The history of interservice and interorganizational battles within the Department of Defense make such coherence a faint hope. If an organization has pluralistic values or information, relevance rules are hard to define and enforce.

An operational example of this problem can be seen in the observation that the constraints of the Defense Guidance are not self-enforcing. The generality of the Guidance lets the different parts of OSD and the different services make substantially different interpretations. If the senior decision maker does not have the capability to check the consistency of the POMs with the Guidance, the chances are low that they will be highly consistent. The POMs carefully point out all the ways they do adhere to the Guidance, and some reasons for noncompliance where they don't adhere, thereby increasing the complexity of judging compliance. The problems and solutions that demand greatest attention within a service are probably either those that are independently transmitted by the senior management of the service (i.e., problems and solutions which the senior management of the service either cares about or has had impressed upon it as essential) or those which are clearly going to be enforced in subsequent review at the higher levels. Many commentators have emphasized the difficulty of getting "compliance" with intended policy guidance.

IMPLICATIONS

To the extent that the above characterization is correct, one basic difficulty emerges. As the problems of all stages become integrated into a "community" of problems and solutions, the division of attention intended by planning-programming-budgeting may be subverted. As top management becomes more involved in lower level problems in the budgeting phase, they will be less able to think strategically in the planning phase. Both phases occur at approximately the same time. Whereas PPBS was designed to have planning driving budgeting, it may, in fact, have evolved into budgeting driving planning. The budget is the most tangible output of the PPBS process. The PPBS plans resource allocation, not war. To the extent that the strategic thinking in the Joint Strategic Planning Document influences operational plans and decisions, these may be degraded by this integration of budgeting into planning.

If the system works to create a community of problems and solutions, we would expect that problems and solutions from the final budget stage would attach to choices in earlier stages. If organizations in the planning process see the resource implications of the plans, they will bring their budgeting concerns to the plan. In analyzing the "response to the threat," a major issue would be what the war scenario implies for the activities of the various participants. Planning would address big wars rather than small wars—it's easier for everyone to get a piece of the action. Scenarios that allowed both air force and navy aviation roles would be more likely than ones which only used one service's aviation. Major sea conflicts may be included to provide a piece of the action for the navy and major land wars to provide the army with something other than the marine's jurisdiction. It would not be surprising if the major scenarios of the Joint Chiefs of Staff were not coherent if they are driven by budgetary needs rather than strategic analysis.

As POMs and budgets come back up the hierarchy, we should see that the papers transmitting the formal responses do not represent problems and solutions—participants do. Where problems and solutions are not directly represented by participants at the decision level, it is likely that they will be resolved by oversight—not chosen, but placed into the pile of "fine ideas, but we can't do it this year." If we have a personnel system such that managers of a given level represent only portions of the organizations bringing issues up from below them, problems and solutions from unrepresented units are unlikely to be aggressively brought to the choice situation and are more likely to be handled by oversight or flight than by resolution. This is a significant problem in several services where the promotion chain for certain areas cuts off at low levels, while that for other areas goes all the way to the top. Thus, in the Marine Corps, where traditionally the flag ranks fall on infantry and air divisions officers (with a smattering of artillery and a token of supply), we would expect issues related to support to be forgotten—raised perennially by the support staffs perhaps, but resolved by oversight at the decision level. The same might hold for aircraft maintenance and spare parts in the navy, and the other unglamorous jobs of the other services.

The superior-subordinate patterns in Figures 6.3 and 6.4 repeat throughout the organization and, along with the pattern, will go the development of problem-solution communities. Just as problems and solutions spread in the top planning community, the multitude of lower level communities will have populations of problems and solutions that characterize their community. Due to differing organizational systems, the bounds of the communities need not be constant for differing problems and solutions. It might not be surprising to find problems and solutions which were originally defined in a given community spreading across communities (problem drift). One such kind of spread has been extensively studied—technological innovation—but other kinds of innovation, such as managerial innovations or definitions of appropriate treatment, probably spread in a similar manner. We would expect to find the plans of a given group addressing a specific problem in one year and then subsequently see other organizations addressing the same problem by a pattern of transmission.

In the traditional procedure, we would expect research and development to proceed from an analysis of the needs of the system—you have a problem and you develop research to meet the needs. But in the garbage can framework, one of the primary variables of interest is the variance in the problems coming down the chain. The services compete for resources in a world in which a small number of important problems appear in a random manner. Some organizational component will succeed in attaching its solution to that problem, increasing the chances of having the solution approved and implemented and potentially increasing its resources or jurisdiction. The obvious strategy is to develop an extremely broad set of research projects in order to be in a better position to claim any interesting new problems as your own. For example, after the Iran rescue mission would have been a good time to sell a new helicopter or desert warfare equipment. Major plane accidents are good problems for all kinds of organizations, from psychologists interested in vigilance or human factors to aircraft designers, from aircraft support equipment designers to drug abuse and training experts—all of these could claim the problem required additional applications of their solutions. Given long lead times for development, solutions must be ready when the problem arrives.

Thus, we would expect to see research and development dollars spread very widely in order to stake claims in as many problems as possible. We would also expect to see current research projects translated into relevant "data" for newly arising problems. We would hypothesize that research and development projects greatly overwhelm available or anticipated production dollars and that projects that do make it through the process would be finally justified by problems that were not mentioned in the original justifications (see, for example, Allison, 1977, on the changing justifications for multiple independently targeted reentry vehicles—MIRVs).

POSSIBLE PRESCRIPTIONS

If this is the kind of world you live in, what could you do to make it work more effectively, to be responsive to top management direction, and to manage efficiently within such direction?

The most advanced proposal for dealing with this kind of planning process is the Program Planning Model (PPM) developed by Delbecq and Van de Ven (1971). The model has five phases (Van de Ven, 1980a, 1980b). *Phase one*, a planning policy board representing various interest groups, is created along with a planning staff. The planning staff and board lay out a procedural plan to guide the planning process along the course described in phases two to four. *Phase two*, the planning staff investigates the needs of the community. A number of techniques help identify the problems: the most effective technique used was direct meetings with interested groups. *Phase three*, the planning staff summarizes problems and presents them to the board. The board selects some of the identified needs for further examination. Experts assist in exploring what kinds of programs could address the problem, and the board subsequently approves a report that identifies the problem-program question of highest priority. *Phase four*, using the program design recommendations of the experts, representatives from related service organizations and interest groups interactively design a program to meet the highest priority need. The program design is presented to the board and other "resource providers" who modify it to satisfy the interests of the various constituencies. *Phase five*, the program is implemented and evaluated. In research on new program development for child-related services in Texas, programs developed using the PPM appeared to be more effective than ones based on more conventional, planner-based plans (Van de Ven, 1980a).

The PPM has a number of extremely interesting features. First, it explicitly differentiates planning stages and at each stage identifies different kinds of input needed. For example, broad community input is sought for problem identification, but experts are used for problem exploration. Second, rather than trying to hide from divergent views, the system forces satisfying of the alternative interest groups. Third, operational and planning personnel are integrated to facilitate learning. Planners cannot learn if they do not see the outcomes of their plans.

Van de Ven was dealing with a community development problem. What would an application of this approach look like in the area of defense? Consider major weapons systems acquisitions. Following the PPM approach in developing a weapons system, several stages would be used. The need or desire for the system must be defined. This definition involves massive input from the affected communities. From among the alternative needs, those which can and should be pursued are selected and explicit system development begun. The selection is a political process that involves an "oversight board" representing the participants needed to make the program work. Experts assist in developing the implications of the needs and proposing solutions to the problems posed in the need statements. The final program development involves all interested and needed parties, including resource providers. Evaluation and implementation are explicitly provided for, and with no evasion.

Within the DoD context, the development of needs must come primarily from either the services or the Office of the Secretary of Defense. But the role of a "board of directors," which is supposed to keep the development of projects within the appropriate bounds, would have to be filled by a somewhat new relation among the current participants. Rather than excluding many important participants until the last possible moment, the PPM would include them as early as possible. Thus, the needs statements would have to be developed with participation by various constituencies within a given service (for an aircraft, aviation, logistics, maintenance, supply and strategic planning) and the constituencies outside of the service (OSD, the other services, contractors, OMB and Congress). Given a needs statement, service and contractor expertise would be needed to develop potential remedies. Such expertise would likely take the form of alternative weapons systems proposals or maybe prototypes. The details of the final purchase decisions would, again, be worked out among the various interested groups, including relevant service functions, OSD, OMB, and Congress.

What this approach does is to bring many people into the process at an early stage rather than a very late stage. It opens up the process. The question is, could it be useful in defense? The garbage can analysis outlined above raises concerns that PPM's success in the community development area might not be replicated in defense.

First, the system does not appear to have been used in an ongoing system over time. The basic problem with the planning system characterized in Figures 6.3 and 6.4 is not that it cannot produce good results the first time but that it becomes homogenized over time, thereby producing undesirable results. The implications of the "threat" definition for budgets may not be totally evident the first time through the process, but they will be by the fourth time. Problems and solutions will drift from budgets to threat and plan.

Second, there is a question of the structure of the game. If the world is such that competition is forced into the system (e.g., there is a budget constraint and no new money is available), then participants will game the system. The Van de Ven implementation involved a net gain for all participants—new money was added to the local pot. If the participants are competing for funds, then additional stages of widespread approvals, rather than limited approvals, may increase the potential for deadlock and serious failure of the system.

Third, the system and the problems may be so big that all the interest groups with vetos cannot be involved. A big navy program could require support from many navy communities and would impact many communities. Any major policy that impacts many groups will certainly impact groups not properly represented in the prior discussions.

Fourth, following Kanter's (1975) arguments, outside involvement in defense matters has often been viewed by the services as an illegitimate intrusion. Systems that would require additional involvement might be viewed with great concern by the military.

Fifth, the sticking points in the current system may not be adequately supported by the new system. Congressional involvement, in particular, may be both extremely difficult to structure and obtain at the initial and intermediary stages, and may not be able to keep commitment at the final approvals stages. A big advantage for the PPM is that it allows commitments to be made early and then held through the system. But Congress is not likely to be able to commit to a proposal in the early stages and then follow through at the end. The need for a given weapon system may be debated, agreed to and rejected several times during the development of the system.

Sixth, many decision makers work best in concrete outcomes (Lindblom, 1959). If the real choice is between concrete alternative outcomes, the debates over needs and so forth may take on the character of some debates over objective—interesting, but largely futile.

While the preceding points may count against the PPM approach, the system nevertheless has several good aspects. It might promise to involve Congress early. It might force the debate over specified capabilities and approaches into public view. It might result in less foot dragging and fewer "we" versus "they" confrontations between the executive and Congress on defense procurement issues. Given political realities, these benefits seem possible, but very unlikely.

The garbage can perspective requires an underlying change in the perception of what is going on in planning and budgeting. The idea that the evaluation of the military threat to U.S. security does not drive the generation of all problems and solutions is foreign to the theory of PPBS. The system was designed to work from the threat down, and we pretend that the system is, in fact, driven that way. Yet if problems and solutions can survive over time, then the top-down conception is, at best, only partially correct. Strategic planning is just another source of problems and solutions, and not necessarily the source of the problems and solutions which come to dominate the decision process.

Suppose planners and top management attempted a more limited approach to defense planning. Recognize that planning is but one source of problems and solutions. Recognize that participants have limited time and energy to push a given set of problems and solutions. Recognize that budget constraints are permanent and essential structures. In such a context, the top management (of the department, of the unit, of the subunit) might focus its attention on two levels: first, on the total funds provided to the lower levels, second, on a a subset of problems and solutions that it wishes to see addressed in the plans developed by the lower levels. That is, in dealing with the services, the OSD is allocating funds among the four and defining a small set of problems and solutions it wants handled. The services are left to develop whatever other problems, solutions and budget allocations they wish within the guidelines of the OSD.

Such a system conserves OSD resources. All the services know that on budget development they have OSD outstaffed and that OSD lacks time to really evaluate the proposed budgets. The same can be said for the DoD versus OMB. The strategy allows strong efforts to check compliance with the (limited) guidance: OSD asks for less but can check that it gets what it has asked for. And it allows the services to exercise creativity within their own jurisdictions.[4]

What this sort of approach would do would be to reduce the required flow of problems and solutions and to allow greater emphasis on controlling and forcing those flows that management really wants to control. If attention is scarce, you do not set up systems that require attending to everything.

What underlies this approach is the potential to uncouple planning and budgeting. Planning is simply another source of problems and solutions, which are not contextually different from the other problems and solutions recognized by the participants. Observers and participants in the process have recognized that this is what has happened de facto in the process over the past decade, but have viewed it as extremely undesirable. In a system that is attempting to couple planning and budgeting, and attempting to drive all budgeting through planning, lack of plan-to-budget control is a serious problem. A more limited view of planning offers the potential for an effective top management, on a limited set of issues, coupled with an effective middle management dealing with another set of issues. To some extent, this is similar to Quinn's (1980) proposals for "logical incrementalism"—attempting to move the system not by total definition of where to go and how to get there, but rather by defining parts of where to go and letting the organization be creative and positive in adapting to such definitions.

CONCLUSIONS

This paper has outlined a way to look at planning systems from the garbage can perspective. Some of the implications of such a view have been developed, and some defense examples have been noted. Two modifications to the current PPBS system were also considered.

While this paper is largely hypothetical, however, the outlines in Figures 6.1, 6.3, and 6.4 open the possibility of empirical investigation of policy processes in a manner very different from previous research. What we are really dealing with is the ecology of a system of problems, solutions, participants and choice situations. Think about taking snapshots of such a community and tying the snapshots together over time.[5] The snapshots could come from any combination of three sources. First, one could do a content analysis of budgetary or policy documents over time. Second, repeated interviews could be used much as Kingdon (forthcoming) does. Third, structured surveys could be used to get a broad picture of problems, solutions, participants, choice situations and their interconnections at any given time.

You might begin to develop a set of data that directly address the dynamics of the policy process. Essentially, the data are a series of schema such as Figure 6.1 with real participants, choice situations, problems and solutions substituted in the appropriate place. The research could expect to find different patterns of flow for different types of problems and solutions. A new conception or categorization of policy types might be the first empirical output of such an approach, followed by ways of talking about the behavior of such problems and solutions. Are some kinds of problems always dropped by the wayside or solved by oversight? Do some always reach the top? How long do different types of problems and solutions survive? The first analysis would be qualitative, to begin to develop an understanding of the process and the kinds of structures being observed. Such analysis would, of necessity, be interactive with the collection of the data—as analysis indicated holes in the data being collected, the collection procedure would change. Given this initial investigation, at least two more formal analyses would be possible. One approach to the data might look much like manpower models (vacancy chain, Markov, etc.) except that the underlying data have very different meaning. The models would attempt to explain how problems and solutions of different kinds move from one spot to another spot in the planning system.

Alternatively, a classic garbage can simulation approach might be feasible. The potential richness of the data base might open several new ways of analyzing policy and planning processes.

This paper has speculated on planning systems from a garbage can perspective. The speculation has lead to the possibility that a garbage can approach could be usefully and rigorously applied to develop a dynamic conception of the issues and substance of planning and budgeting processes.

NOTES

1. This is not simply a government problem. Equally rapid job change has also been reported for the "comers" industry (Bower, 1970).

2. For example, practitioners report exceptional, perhaps charismatic, individuals who substantially change system performance during their tenure. We want to discuss normal system behavior, not these rare exceptions.

3. For simplicity, the Defense Resources Board and many other facets of the process are omitted from this discussion. As noted above, the discussion of defense systems is for illustration only and does not match the complexity of the actual systems. In addition, some standard deviations from the formal systems, such as end runs and other political tactics, are ignored despite their importance.

4. An experienced participant reports that this has been tried to a degree, but, if the guidance does not agree with service culture, it still creates problems of noncompliance.

5. Based on an oral presentation and phone conversation, I believe that Kingdon (forthcoming) reports similar research, based on interviewing many executive and legislative policy professionals in a domestic policy area. Kingdon interviewed a broad sample of professionals and then repeated the interviewing at approximately one-year intervals. There are strong similarities between his research and the approach proposed here, but they differ in that the policy community he dealt with did not have the strong organizational structure that characterizes the system described here. The structural features may allow the posing of questions and the use of the analytical techniques that were not feasible in a less structured situation.

REFERENCES

Allison, Graham T. *Essence of Decision.* Boston: Little, Brown, 1971.

Allision, Graham T. "Questions about the Arms Race: Who's Racing Whom? A Bureaucratic Perspective." In *American Defense Policy*, 4th ed., edited by John E. Endicott and Roy W. Stafford, Jr., pp. 424–441. Baltimore: Johns Hopkins University Press, 1977.

Anthony, Robert N., and Hertzlinger, R. E. *Management Control in Nonprofit Organizations.* Homewood, Ill.: Richard D. Irwin, 1975.

Bower, Joseph L. *Managing the Resource Allocation Process.* Boston: Graduate School of Business. Harvard University, 1970.

Bromiley, Philip. "Task Environments and Budgetary Decision-Making." *Academy of Management Review* 6 (1981): 277–288.

Bromiley, Philip. "Testing Forecasts for Anchoring and Adjustment: An Organizational Level Test of a Behavioral Decision Theory Phenomenon." Mimeographed. Naval Postgraduate School, 1985.

Cohen, Michael D., March, James G., and Olsen, Johan P. "A Garbage Can Model of Organizational Choice." *Administrative Science Quarterly* 17 (1972): 1–25.

Collins, John M. *U.S. Defense Planning.* Boulder, Colo.: Westview Press, 1982.

Cyert, Richard M., and March, James G. *A Behavioral Theory of the Firm.* Englewood Cliffs, N.J.: Prentice-Hall, 1963.

Delbecq, A. L., and Van de Ven, A. H. "A Group Process Model for Problem Identification and Program Planning." *Journal of Applied Behavioral Science* 7 (1971): 466–492.

House, Peter W. *The Art of Public Policy Analysis*. Beverly Hills, Calif.: Sage Publications, 1982.

Kanter, Arnold. *Defense Politics: A Budgetary Perspective*. Chicago: University of Chicago Press, 1975.

Kingdon, John W. *Agendas, Alternatives, and Public Policies*. Boston: Little, Brown, forthcoming.

Larkey, Patrick D., and Smith, Richard A. "Strategic Misrepresentation and Justification of Budget Problems." Mimeographed. Carnegie-Mellon University, 1981.

Lindblom, Charles E. "The Science of 'Muddling Through.'" *Public Administration Review* 19 (1959): 79–88.

March, James G., and Olsen, Johan P. (eds). *Ambiguity and Choice in Organizations*. Bergen, Norway: Universitetsforlaget, 1976.

Quinn, James Brian. *Strategies for Change: Logical Incrementalism*. Homewood, Ill.: Richard D. Irwin, 1980.

Shannon, John T., and Schwiering, David. "An Empirical Examination of Heuristics and Biases in Forecasting." Masters thesis, Naval Postgraduate School, 1983.

Simon, Herbert A. *The Sciences of the Artificial*. 2nd ed. Cambridge, Mass.: The MIT Press, 1981.

Van de Ven, Andrew H. "Problem Solving, Planning, and Innovation, Part I. Test of the Program Planning Model." *Human Relations* 33 (1980a): 771–790.

Van de Ven, Andrew H. "Problem Solving, Planning, and Innovation, Part II. Speculations for Theory and Practice." *Human Relations* 33 (1980b): 575–779.

7

A Monte Carlo Model of a
Garbage Can Decision Process

PAUL A. ANDERSON

and

GREGORY W. FISCHER

INTRODUCTION

Although organizations are typically characterized in terms of a rational model of action which holds that action is directed at solving organizational problems, a number of organizational theorists have suggested that the rational model of organizations is not an adequate description of how organizations make choices (Cohen et al., 1972; March and Olsen, 1976; Simon, 1976; Weick, 1979; March, 1981). One of the most influential alternative models of organizational action is the "garbage can" model of choice in organized anarchies developed by Cohen, March and Olsen (1972). In conventional models, organizational action is stimulated by the recognition of a problem situation, and this recognition starts a problem-solving process directed at discovering a course of action that will solve the problem. This view is simply the standard model of intentional individual problem solving transferred to a collective setting. This intentional model is plausible as a model of collective action only when there is clear agreement on collective goals (which identifies collective problems) and

Paul A. Anderson and Gregory W. Fischer are, respectively, Assistant Professor and Associate Professor in the Department of Social Sciences at Carnegie-Mellon University.

The authors would like to thank Jay Kadane for his comments on an earlier draft.

when there is clear agreement on the effects of adopting a particular course of action (which produces agreement on a solution to a problem). The garbage can metaphor suggests an alternative interpretation of organizational action, an interpretation that does not assume either agreement on collective goals or agreement on the effects of organizational actions.

While the key metaphor of rational organizational action is collective problems guiding the search for collective solutions, the key metaphor of action in a garbage can process is one of decision makers attempting to get the organization to solve their parochial problems. Garbage can processes involve choice situations looking for solutions, solutions looking for problems and decision makers looking for something to do. In a very real sense, it is a system where goals are strong properties of individuals and only weak properties of the collective and where the collective agenda is the sum of the private agendas of the organizational players.

What makes the garbage can model attractive as a theory of organizational choice is the degree to which it seems to capture so much of the day-to-day activity of most organizations. The personal experience of participants in organizations suggests that solutions are powerful forces. Examples include weapons (the MX) in search of missions and doctrines, military concepts (counterinsurgency) in search of applications, and technology (personal computers) in search of uses. Unlike the rational organization, where problems drive the system, garbage can decision processes are driven by individuals with solutions in search of problems.

Although the notion of *solutions in search of problems* captures much of what seems to happen in many organizations, one consequence of recognizing that solutions can be as powerful as collective objectives in determining organizational action is that it is far harder to understand the implications of organizational structure and design. Models of organizations which assume coherent collective goals and beliefs are analytically far more tractable than garbage can processes. Action in a rational model is driven by collective goals and organizational problems. As a result, it is relatively easy to predict behavior and evaluate alternative designs once goals and problems have been identified. No such powerful levers exist for understanding the behavior of garbage can decision processes. The garbage can metaphor is devoid of the simplifying assumptions central to the rational model of organizational action.

One consequence of the lack of simplifying assumptions in the garbage can model is that it is extraordinarily difficult to determine the empirical adequacy of the basic model or to anticipate the consequences of adopting different organizational structures. Although the metaphor is provocative and suggestive, it remains a metaphor with no clear rules of inference to deduce unambiguous consequences. In the absence of any clear implications, the evidence concerning the empirical adequacy of the metaphor comes from a very small set of case studies (Cohen and March, 1974; March and Olsen, 1976; Sproull et al., 1978) only loosely coupled to the theory.

The work reported here is an effort to provide a strong set of deductions from the model structure which could, in principle, be tested against experience. We have adopted a Monte Carlo computer model to represent a broad class of garbage can decision situations. By performing a set of controlled experiments on the model, we can determine just what it means to say that an organization is characterized by garbage can decision processes.

MODEL DESCRIPTION

However suggestive the garbage can metaphor may be, it remains a metaphor with few immediate predictions about how organizations will behave. The first task, then, is to generate a specific interpretation of the garbage can metaphor that can provide a basis for constructing a computer model.

While the exact characteristics of garbage can decision processes are somewhat ambiguous, the basic propositions of the garbage can metaphor suggest that something like the following occurs:

1. Every person in the organization has a personal agenda of goals. Some of the goals may be exclusively personal, such as "do what is good for my career," or they may be shared with others in the organization and refer to a subunit of the organization or the organization as a whole. From the perspective of a garbage can, there are no collective goals per se, only widely shared individual goals.

2. From time to time, a choice opportunity arises. It may be a product of organizational routines like the budgetary or personnel system; it may be the result of an external event such as a crisis; or it may be produced by a superior instructing his subordinates to do something about some nagging organizational problem. As a first approximation, the source of the choice opportunity is immaterial. What is significant is that an occasion has arisen where an officially sanctioned decision can be made.

3. From the point of view of an organizational actor a choice opportunity represents a chance to solve one of the problems on his personal agenda. Individuals flock to choice opportunities and attempt to have solutions adopted that solve problems on their personal agendas.

Two forces keep this process from degenerating into an anarchic free-for-all. First, organizational recruitment and training procedures ensure that organizational participants share some common goals. Second, because choice opportunities are officially sanctioned occasions for organizational choice, proposed courses of action must be justified in terms of larger organizational objectives. Personal goals that do not require organizational resources in order to be satisfied thus fall out of the garbage can model.

Model Entities

Using this basic scenario of action in a garbage can as a basis, there are four basic entities in our interpretation of a garbage can:

1. *Individuals.*

   - *Goals.* Each individual has a set of goals he cares about. These goals may be shared by others or they may be unique to the individual. Each individual has an aspired level of performance for each goal. A problem results when the aspired level of performance falls below the current performance for a goal. We assume that experience influences the aspired level of performance. If the actual performance exceeds the aspired performance, the aspiration level rises. Similarly, if actual performance falls below the aspiration level, the aspired level of performance falls.
   - *Beliefs.* Each individual has beliefs about the relationship between solutions and problems. Solutions may make the problem worse, have no effect on the problem or make the problem better.
   - *Allocation of attention.* Each individual examines the available choice opportunities and selects the most attractive choice opportunity. The attractiveness of an opportunity to an individual is positively related to the importance of the problems that can be solved and inversely related to the number of competing solutions and the attractiveness of the opportunity to other participants.

2. *Problems.* Problems arise for individuals when specific goals are not met. An individual's problem becomes a problem for the organization only when an individual attaches it to a choice opportunity. In this view, the problem is an organizational problem only in the sense that it is the reason an individual attaches its solution to a choice opportunity.

3. *Solutions.* A solution affects a problem and can be thought of as an organizational standard operating procedure (SOP). Individuals link solutions to problems with their assessments of the likely effects of solutions on problems.

4. *Choice Opportunities.*

   - *Who may participate?* Each choice opportunity has a list of eligible participants.
   - *What solutions are appropriate?* Each choice opportunity has a set of solutions that may be attached to it. In this view, only certain solutions are appropriate for a particular choice.

Model Processes

Choice opportunities enter the organization over time. At any point in time, there are a set of current choice opportunities awaiting resolution, and each individual has a set of possible choice opportunities to which he can attend. Each individual attends the most attractive choice opportunity meeting each time period. Under most circumstances, each individual will propose that a particular solution be adopted as the solution to the choice opportunity. Each individual evaluates each proposed solution with respect to his beliefs about the relationship between solutions and his personal problems. If the solution has a net positive benefit, the individual votes for the solution. If the solution has a net negative benefit, the individual votes against the solution. If the net effect of the solution is zero, the individual abstains from voting. If the number of positive votes is greater than the number of negative votes, the solution is adopted. A choice opportunity is resolved—and the solutions implemented— only if all the solutions attached to the opportunity are approved.

Under certain circumstances an individual with no solution to support may attend a choice opportunity. This occurs under the special condition that the individual has no positive suggestions for his most attractive choice opportunity, that is, many of the individual's problems can be made worse by the solutions which may be proposed at a choice opportunity meeting. The individual attends the meeting for the sole purpose of voting against all solutions.

A choice opportunity is decided when the solutions attached to it are approved by the individuals attending to the choice. (Although the model allows for a variety of approval mechanisms, including unanimity, plurality and two-thirds majority rule, the results reported here were generated using a plurality decision procedure.) Three different *modes of resolution* are possible. *Decision by resolution* occurs when there is agreement among the participants. A choice opportunity is resolved by *flight* when, after having a variety of solutions and individuals attached to it with no agreement, all but one individual flees to more attractive choice opportunities. The lone decision maker has no opposition to his suggested solution and resolves the choice. A choice opportunity is resolved by *oversight* when a single individual makes the decision during the first time period the choice is active.

When a choice opportunity is resolved, the feedback effects of the adopted solutions are generated. The current state of each problem that an individual cares about is influenced by all the solutions adopted. The resolution of a choice opportunity generates effects to all individuals in the organization according to each individual's beliefs about the relationship between solutions and problems.

Is This a Garbage Can?

A central question for the present enterprise is whether the framework described above defines a garbage can decision setting. Certainly, the description is consistent with the propositions described in the original presentation of the garbage can by Cohen et al. (1972). In that paper, a garbage can decision setting was characterized by problematic collective preferences, ambiguous technology and fluid participation. But while the starting point is consistent with the original presentation, our interpretation of those propositions does differ from the original presentation.

In the original model described by Cohen et al. (1972), problems, solutions, individuals and choice opportunities were represented as independent streams entering the organization. Problems, which entered the system over time, were attached to those choice opportunities nearest to a decision. Similarly, individuals allocated their attention to the choice opportunity closest to a resolution. Individuals differed in the amount of energy they had to contribute toward the solution to a problem. The amount of energy required to make a decision was proportional to the number of problems attached to the choice opportunity, and the amount of energy available to make a decision was the sum of the energies of the individuals attached to it. Solutions were represented as coefficients that deflated the energy attached to an opportunity. When the search for solutions was "expensive," less of the available energy was available to make a decision.

This representation of a garbage can decision system is an energy allocation model: problems consume it and decision makers provide it. When participants contribute enough energy to solve the problems, a decision is made. Decisions are produced in three distinctive ways: by resolution, by oversight and by flight. Decision by resolution occurs when the total energy available for a choice is greater than the requirements of the problems. Decision by oversight occurs when problems are attached to other opportunities and there is sufficient energy available to make a choice without resolving any problems. Decision by flight occurs when problems detach themselves from the choice and flee to a more attractive choice opportunity. Since all the problems have left, the choice can be made with a minimum of energy.

Our detailed representation differs from the original (Cohen et al., 1972) model in three respects. The first variation is in the representation of individuals. In the original model, individuals enter the process as an independent stream, separate from solutions or problems, while in our model individuals are the vehicles which carry solutions and parochial problems to choice opportunities.

A second major variation from the original model is in the representation of solutions. In that model, solutions played a role only insofar as the search for solutions consumed energy which could have been applied to making decisions. Solutions themselves were not directly represented. In our model, solutions are directly represented as organizational courses of action that influence the current state of problems.

The third major deviation from the original framework is in the representation of problems. In the original model, problems were organizational problems. In our model, individuals have problems that may or may not be shared by others in the organization. What distinguishes these private problems from strictly personal problems is the fact that organizational resources are required to solve them. Our model assumes that organizational participants justify their private problems in terms of larger organizational objectives. This justification of private concerns in terms of larger organizational objectives is closely tied to the garbage can concept of solutions in search of problems. Thus, where solutions are in the background in the original model, collective organizational problems are in the background in our model. As a result, where the original model has rules for attaching problems to choice opportunities, our model has rules for attaching solutions to choice opportunities.

Although the basic structure of our model differs from the original (Cohen et al., 1972) model, because it is derived from the verbal theory of choice in garbage can decision systems, it is a member of the garbage can family.

Model Implementation

The basic model structure was implemented as a Monte Carlo computer model with stochastic choice arrival times, individual beliefs about the effects of solutions on problems, goal structures and aspired levels of performance. Five parameters control each simulation run: individual access structure; solution access structure; goal structure; choice arrival density; and benevolence of the technology. Each will be described in detail below.

INDIVIDUAL ACCESS STRUCTURE

The original model of Cohen, March and Olsen considered three different rules governing the access of an individual's choice opportunities: universal, linear hierarchy, and specialized. Under a *universal access structure* no constraints are placed on participation and any individual may attend any choice opportunity. The second access structure, termed a hierarchy in their model, does not define a hierarchy in the usual sense of organizational charts (e.g., the system of military ranks) but forms a *linear hierarchy* in which each person can attend all the choice opportunities available to his subordinates as well as one opportunity that his subordinates cannot attend. Figure 7.1 illustrates this linear hierarchy. The third access structure borrowed from the original model is the *specialized access structure*. Under a specialized structure each person has access to a small set of opportunities, some of which may be available to the individuals who are immediate supervisors or subordinates of the individual.

Because the linear hierarchy does not define a traditional tree structure, we have added a fourth access structure, termed a *tree hierarchy*. The structure of a tree hierarchy is the familiar pattern of organizational charts and is displayed in Figure 7.2.

SOLUTION ACCESS STRUCTURE

While the Cohen, March and Olsen model required rules for the allocation of problems to choice opportunities, individuals determine the allocation of problems in our model. However, it would be unreasonable to assume that solutions have free access to any choice opportunity: certain courses of action are reserved for particular choice opportunities, and certain choice opportunities cannot invoke particular courses of action. Thus, we require a rule for allocating solutions to choice opportunities. Four rules for allocating solutions to choice opportunities are available: universal, linear hierarchy, specialized, and tree hierarchy. The structure of these four rules is the same as for the allocation of participants to choice opportunities.

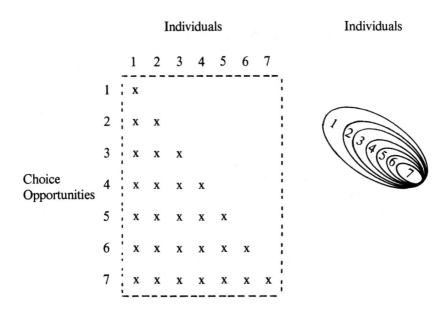

Figure 7.1 Representation of a linear hierarchy.

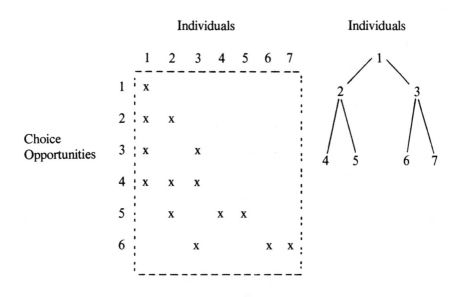

Figure 7.2 Representation of a tree hierarchy.

GOAL STRUCTURES

Each individual has a set of goals that motivate the search for choice opportunities. These goals are expressed in aspiration-level form. Each individual has three goals with an aspired level of performance drawn from a normal distribution with a mean and standard deviation of 10.0. The current performance for each goal is initialized at 0.0. As a result, individuals have a very high probability of having their aspirations exceed their current performance.

The total number of goals in the system was set at 21. With 10 individuals, 3 goals per individual, and 21 unique goals, some of the goals must be shared by individuals. Two different structures were used to allocate goals to individuals: a random goal structure and a hierarchical goal structure. Under a *random goal structure*, each individual was given three goals drawn from a uniform distribution between 1 and 21. In the *hierarchical goal structure* condition, goals were assigned along superior-subordinate lines such that individuals shared goals only with those directly above and below in a hierarchical authority structure.

Each goal is given an initial performance of 0.0. As solutions are adopted by the organization, the feedback of solutions to goals effects the current state of the goal. A simple additive rule is used in calculating effects where the effect of the adopted solution on the goal is simply added to the current state.

Whether a goal represents a *problem* for an individual depends on whether the current level of performance is below the aspired performance level. The assumption of aspiration-level goal representations is that aspirations change as a function of experience (Cyert and March, 1963). If actual performance exceeds the aspired performance, the aspiration level rises. Similarly, if actual performance falls below the aspired performance, the aspiration level falls. In the computer model, aspiration levels were set according to the following:

If $Actual_t \geq Aspired_t$, then $Aspired_{t+1} = Actual_t$

If $Actual_t < Aspired_t$, then $Aspired_{t+1} =$
$\quad 0.2 * Actual_t + 0.8 * Aspired_t$

Thus, if an individual exceeds his aspired level of performance, he changes his aspiration to meet the new performance. If, on the other hand, an individual fails to meet his aspired level of performance, the new aspiration is the weighted average of the actual and current aspiration.

GOAL-SOLUTION BELIEFS

Each individual has a set of *beliefs* linking goals and solutions. Beliefs are from the set $\{-10, -5, 0, 5, 10\}$ and reflect the ability of a solution to improve the goal. A -10 is interpreted as a solution that has a major negative impact on a goal, a 0 is a solution that does not influence the goal and a 10 represents a solution that has a major positive impact on a goal. Individual beliefs about the relationship between solutions and goals are generated using a stochastic procedure with parameters determining the relative proportion of positive, negative and neutral beliefs. Under this procedure, the degree to which pairs of individuals have the same belief about the relationship between a goal and a solution is a function of the relative proportion of beliefs in the system.

Three different *technologies* for decision making can be defined: low, medium and high benevolence. Under a low-benevolence technology, 50% of the goal-solution belief pairs have a negative sign, 30% are neutral, and 20% are positive. Under a medium-benevolence technology, 30% are negative, 30% are neutral, and 40% are positive. Finally, in a high-benevolence world, 20% of the beliefs are negative, 30% are neutral, and 50% are positive. For each level of benevolence, 60% of the positive beliefs have a value of 10 and 40% have a value of 5. Similarly, 60% of the negative beliefs are -10 and 40% are -5. Thus, under low benevolence, 30% of the beliefs have a value of -10, 20% have a value of -5, 30% have a value of 0, 8% have a value of 5, and 12% have a value of 10. This procedure for generating differing levels of technology benevolence has the effect of also manipulating the probability that any two individuals will have similar beliefs about a course of action. Under high benevolence, most solutions will have a positive impact on goals, and most individuals will agree on the advisability of initiating a course of action. Under low benevolence, most solutions will have a negative impact on goals, and most individuals will disagree on the advisability of initiating a course of action.

Although this procedure for assigning beliefs is highly artificial, as a first cut, it does have attractive properties (in addition to being simple to implement). First, the three rules produce three distinct levels of agreement on the advisability of adopting a course of action. Under a low-benevolence technology, it is very difficult to get individuals to agree on a course of action. Second, the larger the group of people, the less likely they are to agree on a solution. Third, the procedure produces a decision-making setting where the amount of consensus among decision makers is a function of the availability of positive solutions. If we lived in a world where most courses of action would make our individual problems worse, it would be difficult to get agreement on a particular course of action. The obvious shortcoming of this procedure for assigning beliefs to individuals is that it is impossible to represent the property that people with similar positions in the organization tend to have similar beliefs about the effect of solutions on problems. In this simulated world, each pair of individuals—regardless of their position in the organization—has the same probability of having similar beliefs about the link between a solution and a problem.

CHOICE ENTRY TIMES

In the original Cohen, March and Olsen computer model, the total number of choice opportunities was fixed at 10—one choice opportunity for each type of access structure. In that model one choice opportunity arrived every time period, and once ten opportunities had arisen no more could be created. In our model we relax the fixed arrival structure. Instead of having one choice opportunity of each type, we assume choice opportunities are continually created. What we vary is the rate at which they are created. The time between the arrival of choice opportunities is generated by a Poisson process under three different conditions: high, medium and low *choice densities*. Under the low-density condition, the average number of arrivals per time period is 0.5, resulting in one choice opportunity arriving every other time period. The medium-choice arrival condition has a mean arrival rate of 1.0, so that one choice arrives every time period. The high-density condition has a mean arrival rate of 1.5, or three new choice opportunities every two time periods. Once the number of arrivals is set, the type of each arriving choice opportunity is determined by assigning an equal probability to each opportunity type. Thus, it is possible for more than one choice opportunity of a given access type to be present in the system at a point in time.

ORGANIZATION TYPE

Drawing on the presentation in the original Cohen, March and Olsen (1972) article, we identified five different combinations of access structures that seem to exhibit the sorts of structures we might expect to find in real organizations. The combinations of individual and solution access structure define five different types of organizations:

	Individual access	Solution access	
1.	Universal	Universal	(U-U)
2.	Universal	Specialized	(U-S)
3.	Linear Hierarchy	Linear Hierarchy	(L-L)
4.	Specialized	Specialized	(S-S)
5.	Tree Hierarchy	Tree Hierarchy	(T-T)

Universal—universal organizations (U-U), with universal access by individuals and solutions to every choice opportunity, are organizations with pure participatory management where anyone can participate in any decision. Universal—specialized organizations (U-S) allow any individual to participate in any choice opportunity, but choice opportunities differ with respect to the solutions that may be enacted. In a linear hierarchy—linear hierarchy (L-L) model, lower level participants have fewer choice opportunities open to them and the choice opportunities they may attend can consider fewer solutions. Specialized—specialized organizations (S-S) represent organizations with extreme specialization and division of labor. Each individual has a small set of choice opportunities that are limited to a small set of solutions. Tree hierarchy—tree hierarchy organizations (T-T), like the S-S models, have specialization and division of labor. However, unlike the pure specialized model structure, the specialization flows along the standard tree hierarchy.

THE MONTE CARLO EXPERIMENT

The experiments with the computer model were designed to answer two questions about organizational choice in a garbage can setting. (1) What is the relative performance of different organizational structures in a garbage can decision setting? (2) How do different organizational structures perform under variations in the benevolence of the technology?

One of the costs of a more realistic representation of decision making is that it becomes much more difficult to determine exactly what the more realistic assumptions imply. Although the original presentation of the garbage can model (Cohen et al., 1972) included a computer model that helped to identify the behavioral properties of garbage can decision processes, the issue is far from resolved. First, our representation of a garbage can differs in a number of respects from their original computer model. Changing the assumptions upon which the model is built will change the results of the model. Thus, at a minimum, we need to determine the behavioral properties of our interpretation of a garbage can. Second, their paper did not systematically explore the range of parameters. For example, out of a possible universe of over 3,000,000 choice arrival sequences, two different choice arrival sequences were examined. Because the parameter space was not systematically explored, a basic uncertainty remains: were the results an artifact of the particular choice of parameters or were they truly representative of the model structure? Third, the results of their computer model were frequently averaged across organizational types. While some questions require averaging across organizational types, the answers to other questions are obscured by averaging across organizational types.

Garbage can processes are not undifferentiated, unorganized anarchies—there are different ways of organizing a garbage can. Choice opportunities differ with respect to the eligible participants and allowable solutions, and by establishing access rules, superiors can determine the types of choice opportunities open to their subordinates. Thus, management in a garbage can setting involves influencing the processes by influencing the access of individuals and solutions to choice opportunities. Therefore, in assessing the implications of different ways of organizing garbage can processes, it is important not to average across structures.

The experiments reported below attempt to determine the relative performance of these five different ways of organizing a garbage can. In addition to the relative performance of these five organizational types, we are interested in how they cope with adversity. In particular, we are interested in what happens when the benevolence of the technology varies. Low-benevolence technology has two correlated attributes: few of the available solutions will make problems better, and there is a low probability that any two individuals will agree to adopt a particular solution. Under conditions of high benevolence in technology, many solutions make problems better and there is high probability that two individuals will agree to adopt a particular solution. By varying the benevolence of the technology, we can determine how the five different organizational types respond to conflict and disagreement among the participants.

Design of the Experiment

The experiment was a full factorial design with five different organizational structures, two different goal structures, three levels of choice density, and three levels of technology, as shown in Table 7.1.

Table 7.1: Design of the Simulation Experiment	
FACTOR	*FACTOR LEVELS*
type of organization	1 = universal individual access, universal solution access 2 = universal individual access, specialized solution access 3 = specialized individual access, specialized solution access 4 = linear hierarchy individual access, linear hierarchy solution access 5 = tree hierarchy individual access, tree hierarchy solution access
goal structure	1 = tree hierarchy 2 = random
choice density	1 = high (1.5 per period) 2 = medium (1 per period) 3 = low (0.5 per period)
technology	1 = benign 2 = neutral 3 = hostile

For each of the 90 (5*2*3*3) cells in the design matrix, the model was run 30 times, for a total sample of 2700 runs of the model. For each observation, the model was run for 20 time periods with 10 individuals, 10 solutions, 21 goals and 10 choice opportunity types for all but T-T type organizations and 9 choice opportunity types for T-T organizations.[1]

Each run of the model produced 19 performance measures:

1. Total number of choice opportunities generated
2. Number of choice opportunities resolved
3. Average latency of resolved choice opportunities
4. Average queue length
5. Count of number of times current performance for some goal is improved by an adopted solution
6. Count of number of times current performance for some goal is decreased by an adopted solution
7. Number of decision makers active
8. Number of decision makers inactive for lack of interest
9. Number of decision makers inactive for lack of access
10. Running average aspiration level
11. Running average current performance
12. Running average of gap between aspiration and performance
13. Running average of proportion of goals with current performance below aspiration
14. Number of choices by resolution

15. Number of choices by flight
16. Number of choices by oversight
17. Proportion of choices by resolution
18. Proportion of choices by flight
19. Proportion of choices by oversight

Results of the Simulation Experiment

A modeling exercise as large as the one reported here produces a great volume of results. In this initial report, we focus on two aspects of these results. First, we analyze the relative performance of different organizational structures under a variety of conditions described below. For reasons illuminated by the simulation, an organizational structure involving unlimited access by individuals to a decision-making process, in which any alternative could be considered at any meeting, generally produced the best decisions. Second, we compare the results of our simulation with those reported by Cohen, March and Olsen (1972), focusing on key properties of a garbage can process as defined by Cohen, March and Olsen. As we argue below, though our representation of organizational decision processes differs considerably from theirs, the two models produce qualitatively similar results in those respects that define a garbage can process.

PERFORMANCE AND PROCESS MEASURES

The simulation model recorded or calculated a number of statistics that are useful both for evaluating the quality of the decisions made in a particular model run and for understanding how and why these decisions were made. Here, we briefly discuss those measures that are emphasized in the discussion below.

Performance Measures   Three measures are particularly useful for evaluating the quality of the decisions made in a model run. The first is AVGPERF, the average goal attainment score across goals, decision makers and time periods for a given model run. Since each goal was initialized with a score of 0 at the beginning of each model run, positive values of AVGPERF represent improvements over this initial performance level, and negative scores declines in performance. Thus, AVGPERF provides the most direct measure of the extent to which decision makers succeeded in maximizing performance with respect to their basic goals.

A second, and closely related, measure is AVGSAT, a measure of decision makers' experienced satisfaction with the outcomes they achieve. The AVGSAT measure is defined as the difference between actual performance and the aspiration level for each goal, averaged across goals, decision makers and time periods for a given model run. When performance exceeds aspirations, decision makers are satisfied, and AVGSAT is positive. When aspirations exceed performance, decision makers are dissatisfied, and AVGSAT is negative.

The final performance measure is AVGPROB, a measure of the average number of "problems" experienced by decision makers in each time period. As defined here, a decision maker experiences a problem whenever performance, with respect to a particular goal, falls below the aspiration level for that goal. The AVGPROB measure is calculated by tallying the number of problems experienced by each decision maker during a given time period, then averaging across decision makers and time periods to obtain an overall average score for a given model run.

Process Measures In addition to these quality-of-performance measures, we consider six process measures that are useful for understanding how and why different types of organizations differ in their decision-making styles and performance. The first four reflect how choice opportunities are resolved. They are PRES, the proportion of decisions by resolution, PFLT, the proportion of decisions by flight, POVER, the proportion of decisions by oversight; and PNONE, the proportion of choice opportunities that result in no decision.

The fifth and sixth process measures are POSIMP and NEGIMP, which reflect the extent to which decisions have positive or negative impacts on the goals of decision makers in the system. The POSIMP measure is calculated by first tallying for each time period the number of decisions having a positive impact on a given goal of a given decision maker, then summing across goals, decision makers and time periods. The NEGIMP measure is calculated in a similar fashion.

QUALITY OF PERFORMANCE BY DIFFERENT TYPES OF
ORGANIZATIONS

Recall that our simulation considered five different types of organizations, where each type was defined by a combination of a personal access structure and a solution access structure (see Table 7.1). The five types of organizations considered were universal–universal (U-U), universal-specialized (U-S), specialized–specialized (S-S), linear hierarchy–linear hierarchy (L-L) and tree hierarchy–tree hierarchy (T-T). In this section we compare the quality of performance achieved by these five types of organizations under different experimental conditions.

Average Performance To obtain an indication of the relative importance of different determinants of AVGPERF, we performed a Type of Organization × Goal Structure × Choice Density × Technology analysis of variance. One surprising result of this analysis was that none of the effects involving the Goal Structure factor approached conventional levels of statistical significance, despite the fact that the analysis involved 2700 observations. The Goal Structure effects were also statistically insignificant for the other measures of quality of performance. So in our discussions of results hereafter, we simply ignore the Goal Structure factor. Among the effects that were statistically significant at the 0.99 level of confidence, three accounted for most of the nonrandom variance in AVGPERF. In order of variance accounted for, these were the Technology main effect, the Type of Organization by Technology interaction and the Type of Organization main effect. Together, these three effects accounted for about 16% of the variance in AVGPERF. The Choice Density main effect was also significant, but accounted for less than 1% of the variance in AVGPERF.[2]

Means for the Type of Organization and Technology effects are presented in Table 7.2. The effect of Technology is large and readily apparent. The "hostile" and "neutral" levels of this factor gave rise to poor performance by all five types of organizations, with little difference in performance under the hostile and neutral technologies. No type of organization achieved a significant average improvement over the initial conditions under either the hostile or neutral technology. The "benign" technology, by contrast, gave rise to substantial and statistically significant performance improvements by all five types of organizations. Turning to the Type of Organization effects, there was effectively no difference in how well the different types performed under either the hostile or neutral technologies. But, under the benign technology, the universal–universal organizations substantially outperformed the other organizational structures. To our surprise, the tree hierarchy (T-T) organizations produced the worst average performance.

Average Number of Problems and Satisfaction Level In contrast to AVGPERF, which measures performance in absolute terms, the AVGPROB and AVGSAT measures evaluate performance relative to a decision maker's aspiration levels. Nonetheless, the results for these measures were qualita-

Table 7.2: Average Performance, Number of Problems and Satisfaction As a Function of Organization and Technology[a]

PERFORMANCE MEASURE	TYPE OF ORGANIZATION	TECHNOLOGY			ROW MEAN
		BENIGN	NEUTRAL	HOSTILE	
AVGPERF	U-U	12.2 (±3.1)	.3 (±.8)	−.4 (±.8)	4.0 (±1.2)
	U-S	5.8 (±1.6)	−.1 (±.8)	−.6 (±.8)	1.7 (±.7)
	S-S	4.5 (±1.2)	.4 (±.8)	−1.1 (±.8)	1.2 (±.6)
	L-L	7.4 (±1.7)	1.0 (±.8)	−.8 (±.8)	2.6 (±.7)
	T-T	3.8 (±1.1)	−.4 (±.8)	−.3 (±.8)	1.0 (±.5)
	mean	6.7 (±.9)	.2 (±.4)	−.6 (±.4)	—
AVGPROB	U-U	.60 (±.01)	.67 (±.01)	.68 (±.01)	.65 (±.006)
	U-S	.65 (±.01)	.70 (±.01)	.71 (±.01)	.69 (±.006)
	S-S	.65 (±.01)	.70 (±.01)	.71 (±.01)	.69 (±.006)
	L-L	.64 (±.01)	.69 (±.01)	.71 (±.01)	.68 (±.006)
	T-T	.66 (±.01)	.70 (±.01)	.70 (±.01)	.69 (±.006)
	mean	.64 (±.006)	.69 (±.004)	.70 (±.004)	—
AVGSAT	U-U	−4.4 (±.15)	−5.3 (±.13)	−5.5 (±.13)	−5.1 (±.09)
	U-S	−4.8 (±.12)	−5.6 (±.14)	−5.6 (±.13)	−5.3 (±.08)
	S-S	−4.9 (±.13)	−5.4 (±.14)	−5.7 (±.13)	−5.4 (±.08)
	L-L	−4.7 (±.13)	−5.4 (±.13)	−5.5 (±.15)	−5.2 (±.08)
	T-T	−5.0 (±.12)	−5.6 (±.13)	−5.4 (±.14)	−5.3 (±.08)
	mean	−4.8 (±.06)	−5.4 (±.06)	−5.5 (±.06)	—

[a]Means plus or minus two standard errors.

tively very similar to those for the AVGPERF measure. An analysis of variance for both dependent variables indicated that the Technology effect was the largest but that the Type of Organization and Type of Organization by Technology effects also accounted for a significant proportion of variance in each case. Means for both performance measures are presented in Table 7.2. For the AVGPROBS measure, there was little difference in performance under the hostile and neutral technologies, but all five types of organizations experienced significantly fewer problems under the benign technology. Comparing the five types of organizations, the only substantial differences arose under the benign technology, where the U-U structure was significantly better than the other four, which were all roughly equal.

A similar pattern arose for the AVGSAT measure (see Table 7.2). It is noteworthy here that, on the average, decision makers experienced negative satisfaction levels under all types of organizations and all types of technology. No matter how well an organization performed in absolute terms, our aspiration level model assumptions had the effect of keeping decision makers permanently striving for more than they attained. A second noteworthy feature is that there was relatively little variation in the AVGPROB or AVGSAT measures. The reason is that because aspirations were adjusted in light of performance, discrepancies between aspirations and performance tended to remain small and roughly constant. Thus, the number of problems and average satisfaction levels also tended to be relatively constant.

DECISION STYLES

As Table 7.3 reveals, different types of organizations tended to resolve decisions in different ways, and these differences varied under different types of technology.[3] The most striking difference in decision style was between the U-U organizations and the other four types. In general, the U-U organizations had a high rate of "no decisions." Averaging across all other factors, the U-U organizations failed to make decisions in almost 80% of the choice opportunities that arose. Further, because the U-U organizations involved collective meetings which all members were free to attend, when U-U organizations did make decisions they were decisions by resolution. In contrast, in a majority of instances, all of the other types of organizations made decisions when a choice opportunity arose. When they made decisions, most were decisions by resolution, but some were by flight and oversight.

Shifting attention to the effects of Technology on decision style, we see that the rate of decisions by resolution was highest for all types of organizations under the benign technology. The neutral and hostile technologies produced substantially higher levels of nondecisions and slightly higher levels of decisions by flight or resolution than did the benign technology. It is particularly noteworthy that, in contrast to the other organizational forms, the U-U organizations almost never made a decision under the neutral technology and never made any decisions under the hostile technology.

The effects of technology on mode of decision making appear to be due largely to the degree of conflict produced by the different levels of technology.

		MODE OF DECISION				
TECHNOLOGY	*MODEL*	*RESOLUTION*	*FLIGHT*	*OVERSIGHT*	*NONE*	*ROW N*
benign	U-U	60.3[a]	0	0	39.7	3557
	U-S	85.9	3.8	5.6	4.8	3645
	S-S	66.6	9.3	12.5	11.6	3619
	L-L	62.1	12.2	14.7	11.0	3679
	T-T	58.9	10.2	14.4	16.6	3639
	total	66.8	7.1	9.5	16.6	18139
neutral	U-U	1.2	0	0	98.8	3659
	U-S	46.1	18.5	9.2	26.3	3568
	S-S	35.5	19.2	12.3	33.0	3648
	L-L	26.7	26.0	15.0	32.4	3647
	T-T	36.3	14.6	12.5	36.5	3514
	total	29.0	15.6	9.8	45.6	18036
hostile	U-U	0	0	0	100.0	3518
	U-S	13.8	18.9	6.7	60.6	3556
	S-S	12.6	18.6	8.0	60.0	3478
	L-L	10.1	27.1	10.5	52.3	3512
	T-T	16.4	13.7	8.1	61.9	3523
	total	10.6	15.7	6.7	67.1	17587
Totals	U-U	20.4	0.0	0.0	79.6	10734
	U-S	48.9	13.6	7.2	30.3	10769
	S-S	38.6	15.6	11.0	34.8	10745
	L-L	33.3	21.7	13.4	31.6	10838
	T-T	37.4	12.8	11.7	38.1	10676
grand total		35.7	12.8	8.7	42.9	53792

Table 7.3: Model Structure, Technology and Mode of Decision

[a]Entries are row percentages.

As defined here, a benign technology is one in which actions that have positive impact on the goals of one decision maker will tend to have either a positive or neutral impact on the goals of other decision makers. A hostile technology is one in which actions that have positive impacts on one decision maker's goals tend to have negative effects on the goals of other decision makers. Thus, the neutral and especially the hostile technologies produced high levels of conflict between decision makers. Modes of organization like U-U, in which all decision makers can participate in every decision, tend to be immobilized by high levels of conflict. Modes of organization involving specialized access to meetings are more likely to produce meetings in which those present agree on courses of action, despite disagreement by nonattendees. That is what happened in our simulation.

EXPLAINING QUALITY OF PERFORMANCE

As Table 7.2 reveals, none of the five types of organizations performed well under either the neutral or hostile technologies, and there was little difference in the quality of the performance of the different types, under these technologies. Only under the benign technology were there substantial performance differences. There, the U-U organizations outperformed the rest. Here, we use the output of our simulation to make inferences concerning why the different organizational forms performed as they did.

Relative Performance Under Neutral and Hostile Technologies   Given the inability of U-U organizations to make decisions when confronted with a hostile or even a neutral technology (both of which generate high levels of disagreement), why did the U-U organizations do as well as the other types of organizations under these technologies? In brief, while the other types of organizations managed to make a substantial number of decisions under the hostile and neutral technologies, these decisions generally did not produce positive effects from the perspective of the organization as a whole. This can be seen from the values of AVGPERF in Table 7.2. A more direct demonstration is provided by a simple count of the number of decision-maker goals that were positively affected and negatively affected by the decisions taken (see Table 7.4). Under the neutral technology, the number of goals positively impacted (POSIMP) only slightly exceeded the number of goals negatively impacted (NEGIMP). Under the hostile technology, the number of negative impacts actually exceeded the number of positive impacts by roughly 2:1 for all types of organizations (except U-U, which made no decisions). While the decisions that were made were positively valued by those who made them, their negative effects on the goals of nonparticipants matched or outweighed their benefits to those who made them. Thus, the paralysis of the U-U organizations in the face of neutral and hostile technologies did not prove to be a disadvantage. Doing nothing was as good a response as any to the conflict created by the neutral and hostile technologies.

Relative Performance Under Benign Technology   The superiority of the U-U mode of organization arose entirely from its superior performance in a benign environment. Why did U-U organizations perform better here? The data in

Table 7.4: Positive and Negative Impacts of Adopted Alternatives as a Function of Model and Technology[a]

MEASURE	TYPE OF ORGANIZATION	TECHNOLOGY		
		BENIGN	NEUTRAL	HOSTILE
number of positive impacts	U-U	357 (±34)	5 (±6)	0 (±0)
	U-S	300 (±19)	133 (±10)	53 (±5)
	S-S	257 (±17)	123 (±9)	51 (±5)
	L-L	307 (±19)	132 (±10)	60 (±5)
	T-T	207 (±13)	97 (±7)	43 (±4)
number of negative impacts	U-U	49 (±6)	3 (±6)	0 (±0)
	U-S	79 (±5)	110 (±8)	105 (±10)
	S-S	70 (±5)	105 (±8)	106 (±10)
	L-L	64 (±5)	104 (±8)	128 (±11)
	T-T	60 (±4)	80 (±6)	84 (±8)

[a]Means plus or minus two standard errors (n = 180 model runs per cell).

Table 7.4 indicate that under benign technology the U-U organizations made decisions with about 20–30% fewer negative impacts and 20–30% more positive impacts than the other types of organizations. Given the greater number of positive impacts for all types of organizations, the difference in POSIMP is the larger source of the U-U organizations' superiority. The greater number of positive impacts is apparently due to the advantages associated with universal solution access. With universal solution access, any organizational meeting can consider any organizational alternative (solution). Under a benign technology, this is an advantage because it raises the possibility of adopting a large package of actions, each of whose components has positive impacts on most organization members' goals.

Given the assumptions of our simulation experiment, we can calculate the *expected* number of solutions available to each meeting for each type of solution access structure. With the universal solution access structure, the expected number of available solutions per meeting is 10; for the linear hierarchy solution access structure, 5.5; for the specialized solution access structure, 2.5; and for the tree hierarchy, 2.5. These expected values are ordinally consistent with the ranking of types of organizations in terms of AVGPERF under a benign technology (see Table 7.2). Thus, we infer that the richness of the solution sets adopted probably accounts for the greater number of positive impacts produced by the U-U organizations. In addition, it is clear that universal personal access improved the quality of decisions in a benign environment. The U-S and S-S organizations differed only in terms of their personal access structures, and the U-S organizations made decisions that resulted in more positive impacts and fewer negative impacts (see Table 7.4).

COMPARISON WITH THE COHEN-MARCH-OLSEN SIMULATION

Although the design of our computer model was drawn from the same key set of ideas about choice in an organized anarchy, it differs in a number of respects from the structure of the original Cohen, March and Olsen model. It is, therefore, appropriate to ask whether our model shares the important operating characteristics of their garbage can model.

Perhaps the three most striking general results from the original model (Cohen et al., 1972) were the following: (1) that decision by resolution was not the most frequent decision style; (2) that as load increased, the frequency of decision by resolution fell sharply; and (3) that there were marked nonlinearities in the behavior of the different organizational forms with respect to decision by resolution under increasing load. In the original model, variations in load reflected the amount of excess energy within the system available for making decisions. In our simulation, two factors may be interpreted as increasing the "load" on the system's decision makers. The first is the Choice Density factor, which involves differing rates of arrival for new choice opportunities. Higher arrival rates mean greater load, because decision makers have more decision meetings to choose among. The effects of Choice Density on mode of decision making are summarized in Table 7.5. These data closely

CHOICE DENSITY	MODEL	MODE OF DECISION				ROW N
		RESOLUTION	FLIGHT	OVERSIGHT	NONE	
low	U-U	28.3[a]	0.0	0.0	71.7	1793[b]
	U-S	54.3	9.7	3.4	32.7	1787
	S-S	44.1	13.5	7.4	34.9	1733
	L-L	38.6	17.1	10.6	33.8	1769
	T-T	42.2	8.5	8.4	40.9	1773
	total	41.5	9.7	5.9	42.9	8885
medium	U-U	22.8	0.0	0.0	77.2	3590
	U-S	51.7	12.8	6.6	28.9	3570
	S-S	37.3	16.0	9.9	36.9	3615
	L-L	36.1	20.0	13.5	30.5	3606
	T-T	37.3	13.5	12.3	36.9	3581
	total	37.0	12.5	8.5	42.1	17962
high	U-U	16.1	0.0	0.0	83.9	5351
	U-S	45.2	15.5	8.8	30.5	5412
	S-S	37.7	16.1	12.9	33.4	5397
	L-L	29.8	24.3	14.3	31.6	5463
	T-T	35.9	13.8	12.4	37.9	5322
	total	33.0	14.0	9.7	43.4	26945
grand total		35.7	12.8	8.7	42.9	53792

Table 7.5: Effects of Choice Density on Mode of Decision

[a]Entries are row percentages.
[b]Note that the expected number of choices per simulation run is a linearly increasing function of choice density.

resemble those of the Cohen, March and Olsen simulation in two important respects. First, decisions by resolution occurred less than half the time. Nondecision was, in fact, the most common response to choice opportunities. Second, the rate of decision by resolution declined as load (choice density) increased. The greater the load, the more likely a decision by flight or oversight. With more choice opportunities to attend to, there was a greater chance that only one decision maker would attend to a new opportunity or that all but one would abandon an old choice opportunity. In contrast to the Cohen, March and Olsen results, however, our simulation indicated that the effect of load (defined as choice density) was roughly linear.

The Technology factor provides a second operationalization of the load concept. Under the neutral and hostile technologies, decision makers experienced more problems (i.e., failure to achieve aspiration levels) and greater conflict with other decision makers. Thus, we can interpret the hostile technology as creating a high load on the system and the benign technology as creating a low load. As the results in Table 7.3 reveal, the rate of decision by resolution declined dramatically and nonlinearly as a function of load defined in these terms.[4] Under benign technology, 66.8% of all choice opportunities resulted in decisions by resolution; under the neutral technology, 29% of the choice opportunities did; and under the hostile technology, only 10.6% did.

Together, these results regarding decision style and load clearly support the assertion that our simulation possesses the defining behavioral properties of a garbage can decision process.

CONCLUSIONS

We draw four broad conclusions from our Monte Carlo experiments on decision making in a garbage can.

The first is that moving to a Monte Carlo model structure improves the quality and confidence of the results generated by the computer model. Monte Carlo methods allow a comprehensive and systematic sampling of the parameter space. Consequently, we have high confidence that the results of the model accurately represent the deductive implications of the assumptions of the model.

The second conclusion is that the computer model (for all of its shortcomings) does provide insight into how organizations behave under conditions of unclear goals, ambiguous technology and fluid participation. Computer models do not require the simplifying assumptions so common in attempts to solve analytically for the implications of a set of assumptions. While there is no question that the model represents a simplification of the complexities of the world, the simplification we have made have not been dictated by the requirements of analytic tractability.

The third conclusion is that this sort of computer modeling effort has real payoff for evaluating alternative organizational designs. One of the persistent problems in organizational design is the relatively weak methods we have to anticipate the consequences of particular organizational configurations under different circumstances. Much of what we believe about how organizations ought to be constructed is based on loose derivations from ambiguous verbal theories. Computer models of organizations provide a mechanism for generating true deductions from a set of assumptions without as many domain-restricting simplifying assumptions so prevalent in more orthodox deductive theorizing. A computer model is just as rigorous a deductive system as is an abstract mathematical theory. While any model must simplify the world, computer models do not place a premium on simplifying assumptions for the sake of analytic tractability.

The final conclusion has to do with a distinction between computer simulations and computer models. One of the most striking, but frequently overlooked, characteristics of the original Cohen, March and Olsen (1972) paper was the creative way the results of the garbage can model were connected to the world of decision making in academic organizations. The object in most computer simulation efforts is to represent a particular empirical system in as much detail as is feasible. Unfortunately, the monumental effort in capturing fine-grained details frequently drives out efforts devoted to considering alternative representations. Simulators make reference to sensitivity testing; but their real concern is with the model results. Our preference is for what is best termed a computer model rather than a computer simulation. Of course, we are concerned with the linkage between the model and the world of experience. The issue is how that link is to be established. There are two sorts of parameters in a computer model of an organization: those aspects of a real system that can be accurately measured and observed, and those for which accurate and reliable measurements are very expensive or impossible. Consider, for example, the problem of measuring the access structure of individuals to choice opportunities as opposed to the problem of determining the goals and beliefs of organizational participants. It is our view that measures of structure are far more practical than measures of goals or beliefs. A computer simulation approach would either make a set of arbitrary assumptions about goals and beliefs or produce some very problematic measures of the goals and beliefs of a few individuals. A computer model approach would recognize from the beginning that accurate measures of goals and beliefs was problematic. The solution would be to use the best available measurement techniques to constrain the set of plausible goals and beliefs and then, in producing conclusions, to exploit Monte Carlo techniques. Computer modeling techniques attempt to exploit what certainty there is and let the uncertainty vary in precise and systematic ways. Where simulations attempt to reproduce the details of the world, computer models attempt to place probability distributions over the possible outcomes. The distributional approach of computer models produces "weaker" conclusions; but, for all their weakness, they are far more certain conclusions.

But what do the results of our model have to say about decision making under ambiguity in military organizations? Universal−universal organization types had the best average performance under a variety of conditions. Should the navy be restructured so that any individual can involve himself in any decision? Clearly not. And the reasons why they should not reveal something of the utility of this sort of modeling exercise.

The most fundamental point is that the conclusions are true only of the model. If the world and the model are inconsistent, then the results are of no interest either to the military or to organization theorists: both groups are interested in the world of experience, not in imaginary computer worlds. One of the immediate tasks, therefore, is to connect the model more directly with the world of experience. Although none of the assumptions was chosen because it falsely depicted organization life, systematic efforts to validate the model empirically are needed. Connecting the model with empirical evidence requires observation—observations of real organizations making real decisions. The garbage can metaphor has produced several case studies describing decision making in organized anarchies (March and Olsen, 1976; Sproull et al., 1978). That list needs to be expanded to include decision making in more organizations, including the military. But case studies by themselves cannot provide the bridge between computer model and experience. The computer model makes predictions about organizational behavior under a variety of conditions, including organizational type, goal structures, choice density and technology; the case studies describe the behavior of a variety of organizations. The next step is to link the descriptions provided by the case studies with the parameters of the computer model. If they can be matched, then the computer model will predict the behavior of that case and the results can be compared.

The assumptions of the garbage can model were developed in the context of educational organizations. Military organizations are not universities, and if garbage cans and organized anarchies are to have any application in the defense establishment, careful efforts to describe how military organizations work is a high priority. The papers in this volume represent but a first step in extending the model to military organizations.

One of the fundamental elements of leadership is to make organizations do things they ordinarily would not do. This is as true of universities as it is of the navy. The computer model described here is an organization without leadership, processing information and making decisions according to a fixed set of rules. As a result, it does not describe the world as it must be but the world as it would be if no one tried to make it turn out differently. But understanding how to make the world turn out differently requires understanding how the world works. The sort of computer model described here provides a mechanism for describing how different worlds work, and while it does not provide a set of rules that would allow leaders to switch from one trajectory to another, it does attempt to explore the different trajectories that are available to the leaders of an organization. The model cannot tell leaders how to lead, but it can provide them with a set of results that will help them in getting organizations to do things they ordinarily would not do.

NOTES

1. Because the tree hierarchy naturally produced only 9 choice opportunity types, all measures sensitive to the number of choice opportunities were converted to proportions of the maximum possible number of opportunities.

2. Since our simulation involved important stochastic components, a substantial proportion of the variance in this (and other) measures was attributable to random factors in the organization's external environment. This was particularly true for the three quality of performance measures that were particularly sensitive to the random occurrence of positive and negative events in the external environment.

3. The chi square statistic for this three-way pattern of association was significant at the $p < 0.001$ level.

4. Because the different levels of technology were evenly spaced in terms of the degree of goal conflict they created, it is meaningful to say that the decline in decisions by resolution was nonlinear.

REFERENCES

Cohen, M. D., and March, J. G. *Leadership and Ambiguity*. New York: McGraw-Hill, 1974.

Cohen, M. D., March, J. G., and Olsen, J. P. "A Garbage Model of Organizational Choice." *Administrative Science Quarterly* 17 (1972): 1–26.

Cyert, R.M., and March, J. G. *A Behavioral Theory of the Firm*. Englewood-Cliffs, N.J.: Prentice-Hall, 1963.

March, J. G. "Decisions in Organizations and Theories of Choice." In *Perspectives on Organization Design and Behavior*, edited by A. H. Van de Ven and W. F. Joyce. New York: Wiley, 1981.

March, J. G., and Olsen, J. P. *Ambiguity and Choice in Organizations*. Bergen, Norway: Universitetsforlaget, 1976.

Simon, H. A. *Administrative Behavior*. New York: Free Press, 1976.

Sproull, L. S., Weiner, S., and Wolf, D. *Organizing an Anarchy: Belief, Bureaucracy, and Politics in the National Institute of Education*. Chicago: University of Chicago Press, 1978.

Weick, K. E. *The Social Psychology of Organizing*. Reading, Mass.: Addison-Wesley, 1979.

8

Measuring Efficiency
in a Garbage Can Hierarchy

KATHLEEN CARLEY

INTRODUCTION

Some organizations seem to be more efficient than others, either overall or
with respect to a single type of efficiency. Even within a single organization
there may exist a spectrum of inefficiencies, dependent on the way in which
efficiency is measured. For example, we can think of an organization as being
efficient politically—having staff members working only on those issues that
the chief executive officer (CEO) considers to be salient—or we can think of
the organization as being efficient structurally—where those in charge have
access to all the work done under their ostensible direction, with no blocks in
security clearance. Given that there is this spectrum, knowing potential causes
of inefficiency may aid the manager in making decisions. Further, when there is
a chance to set up an organization, for example, a joint task force or a
congressional committee, knowledge of those factors that lead to inefficiency
allows the construction of potentially more efficient organizations. Structural
features such as size and differentiation, the form of incoming data flows and
the criteria used for managerial decisions all vie for the dubious honor of being
the "cause" of inefficiency.

Kathleen Carley is Assistant Professor in the Department of Social Sciences at Carnegie-
Mellon University.

With ambiguous information flows, as the content and amount of information available on any given issue shifts and is less than complete, preferences over alternatives become problematic, the technology of deciding between alternatives, of making a decision, becomes unclear. As decision making takes on a more tactical flavor, and becomes less routine, those in charge may seek structural means of easing the difficulty of decision making. For example, they might choose a less hierarchical and more fluid notion of participation. This shift, while perhaps easing the burden of decision making, may make the organization less efficient.

Garbage can theory, or the theory of organized anarchies, tries to explain decision making in terms of information, people, problems and other aggregate flows.[1] Handling problematic data flows becomes the key to decision making and, by implication, to organizational success. As Perrow (1977) notes, the processes described in this literature seem curiously divorced from the more familiar hierarchical organizational structures, the phenomena of organizational differentiation and so on. Padgett (1980) argues that this divorce of the aggregate flows from the social structure inhibits the development of managerial implications; for example, this divorce precludes the determination of when to switch from a hierarchical to a more fluid participation structure. I would add to this that the divorce from structure also makes it difficult to construct measures of organizational efficiency, and so to talk about organization success in terms of that efficiency and to analyze managerial approaches vis-à-vis their impact on the organization's efficiency level.

Padgett (1980) showed that it was possible to combine the organized anarchy paradigm with a more classical social structure, a Weberian-type bureaucracy, with the result that it became possible to derive a number of managerial implications. By placing the organized anarchy into a hierarchical structure (although he did not proceed to do so) Padgett made it possible to talk about efficiency both in political and in structural terms. Based on the structure set up by Padgett, several measures of efficiency are developed in this paper. Further, placing the organized anarchy into the hierarchical structure was the key to studying the impact of managerial solutions on the overall efficiency of the organization.

In this paper, an analytic framework for looking at questions of efficiency is presented. This presentation takes the form of describing the underlying parameters and models used in a simulation program, GARCORG, for analyzing the impact of structural, political and managerial changes on the efficiency of the garbage can hierarchy. The following section contains a brief description of organizations as garbage can hierarchies and analytically defines the various flows of concern. Following this, in the third section, there is an analytic discussion of efficiency centering around the development and analysis of various measures of efficiency. Then long-run organizational behavior is analyzed by looking at the limiting behavior of the analytic functions that describe the organizational processes of interest. This paper is not intended as a description of how to use GARCORG, or even of the results that are obtained when using it; rather, it is a description of the underlying models and their analytic long-run behavior.

The symbols used in the analyses are the same as those used in a computer simulation program, GARCORG. Again, this program is based on the analytical measures of efficiency that are developed herein. The symbols are represented by names in bold face type; for example, the number of program chiefs per division is referred to as **PCVs** in the calculations and in the simulation program. Note that the GARCORG program is described in detail in a later chapter, where it is used to look at short-run organizational efficiency.

GARBAGE CAN HIERARCHIES—THE GENERAL MODEL

Some organizations can be thought of as *garbage can hierarchies*—garbage cans because they are organized anarchies with problematic flows, and hierarchies due to the fact that the people who work in the organization are structured in a hierarchical fashion. We can think of an organization as having more of or less of a garbage can nature, depending on the degree to which the following three criteria are met: (1) ambiguous information flows (e.g., amount and content of information varies) (2) ambiguous personnel flows; and (3) unclear decision technology (e.g., changing goals, changing values, changing equipment).

One claim about garbage can hierarchies is that their efficiency has been impaired by having to cope with problematic flows and that, therefore, new strategic styles of decision making may have to emerge. Simulation analysis would allow us to test this and similar claims by, for example, comparing the efficiency level of an organization with more problematic flows to one with less problematic flows. In the following description, I am presenting a set of parameters that allow these criteria to be met to varying extents and a set of models based on these parameters that can be used for measuring an organization's efficiency. A simulation program (GARCORG) based on these parameters has been built. This program can be used, in effect, to see what happens to an organization's efficiency as various flows become increasingly problematic.

Hierarchical Form

The hierarchical form used, like that suggested by Padgett (1980), is set to four tiers. These tiers, in order of descending control, are the following:

1. CEO—chief executive officer

2. AEO—assistant executive officer

3. PC—program chief

4. STAFF—staff members

The chief executive officer (CEO) is ostensibly in charge of an organization which is composed of several divisions. The CEO can be thought of as the president of a company, an admiral, the head of a task force, the commander-in-chief or a different type of executive officer. Note, there is only one CEO.

The assistant executive officer, AEO, is in charge of a division in the organization and oversees numerous programs. The set of assistant executive officers is denoted by **AEOS**. The AEOs can be thought of as the vice presidents of a company, captains, assorted commanders within the task force, or middle-level managers.

Each program is run by its own program chief, PC. The program chiefs can be thought of as middle-level managers, lieutenants, the senate and so on. The set of program chiefs is denoted as **PCV**. Each program chief is in charge of a particular program. A program might be a particular research group, the accounting division, a committee, the selection of an assault team, reconnaissance operations and so on.

Under each program chief are a number of staff members who analyze the information that comes in on a particular issue. Staff members can be thought of as engineers, ensigns and so forth. An issue can be thought of as the state of the hostages in Iran, or the movement of a particular fleet. The point here is that there are four levels in the hierarchy and that we are looking at a company or subset of a company that is under the control, management or command of a single individual.

Note that all the organizations simulated, regardless of the degree they resemble a "garbage can" have a basically hierarchical form in which information comes in at the bottom, is summarized into some form (e.g., a decision) which is then sent up to the next level, where it is again summarized, and so on. In Figure 8.1 the chain of command and flow of decisions in the generic organization is shown graphically.

Issues, Spots in an Organization

The chain of command flows down from the CEO to the staff, whereas decisions flow up from staff members to the CEO. These decisions are based on information that comes in on each of the issues. Associated with each division is a particular set of potential issues **[ISSUE]**. For now, we will assume that this set of issues is time invariant; it does not seem unreasonable to assume that at least in the medium run—e.g., several years—this is in fact the case. Further, this set of issues represents items that are potentially relevant to that division, not necessarily things with which they are currently concerned; therefore, in theory, there could be an infinite number of such issues; in which case the number of potential issues would certainly be fixed.

In each division there are a number of programs being worked on. The number of programs is set equal to the number of program chiefs. Each of the potential issues for the division are potentially relevant to any of the programs. For each program, for each potential issue, there is a particular position, or spot, for a staff member whose job would be to analyze all the information that comes in on that issue. Note, this means that each program has a potential number of staff positions—spots—equal to the potential number of issues per division. In each program some of these issues will be worked on, each by a different staff member. Each staff member analyzes information on only one

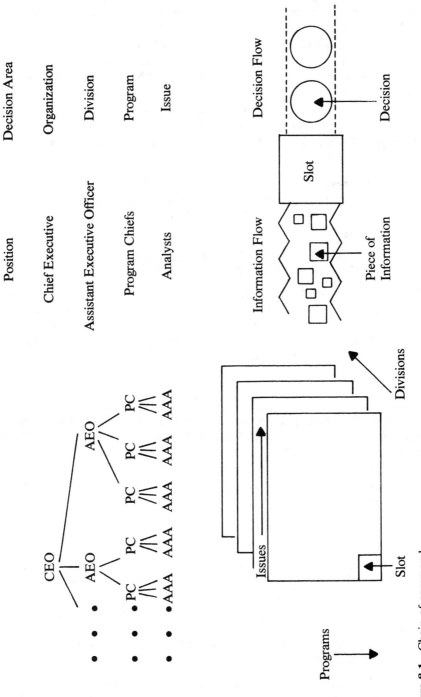

Figure 8.1 Chain of command.

issue at any one time. The same issue may be worked on by different staff members for different programs. Similarly, there may be some issues that are not being worked on at all.

The matrix **ANM** is a representation of whether or not there is a staff member in a particular spot, for a particular program. It describes which issues are being worked on by which staff member. Let **ANM** be a three-dimensional matrix whose dimensions are the number of AEOs in the organization, by the maximum number of program chiefs under any one AEO, by the number of potential issues available per division. Now, each element of **ANM**—(ANM$_{spi}$)—is assigned a value as follows (where the index for **AEOS** is s, for program chiefs is **p**, and for issues is **i**):

[1]   **ANM$_{spi}$** = 1

if there is a staff member working on issue (i) under program chief (p) who is working under AEO (s);

[2]   **ANM$_{spi}$** = 0

if there is no staff member working on issue (i) under program chief (p) who is working under AEO (s).

Note, each cell in the **ANM** matrix, in effect, represents a *spot* in the organization, an issue that may need to be analyzed. Into each of these spots, for each issue, information comes in, whether or not there is a staff member there to deal with it. When there is an analyst in the spot, the information that comes in is analyzed and decisions are based upon it (see Figure 8.1).

Models of Alternative Information Flows

The information that comes into each spot is characterized by the amount of information that comes in, **AMOUNTINFO$_{spi}$**, and the content (or quality) of that information, **CONTENT$_{spi}$**. There are many ways in which these parameters can be modeled, some deterministic and others stochastic. Herein, those models implemented in GARCORG are presented. These models allow the user to choose either a stochastic or a deterministic process.

MODELING AMOUNT OF INFORMATION

To create a range of mechanisms, the amount of information coming into a spot, **AMOUNTINFO$_{spi}$** is allowed to be constant, increasing or random. The first two of these are deterministic models, and the third is stochastic. In all cases, in GARCORG the option chosen first sets the initial amount of incoming information **AINIT$_{spi}$** per spot and then uses an algorithm for updating the amount of information available to that spot each time period **AMOUNTINFO$_{spi}$(t)**.

In GARCORG when the option chosen is *constant*, at time **t** = 0, the initial amount of information coming into each spot in the organization, **AINIT$_{spi}$** is chosen at random from a uniform distribution over the integers 0 to 100. During each of the following time periods the amount of information remains constant:

$$\textbf{AMOUNTINFO}_{\textbf{spi}}(t) = \textbf{AINIT}_{\textbf{spi}}.$$

In GARCORG when the option chosen is *increasing*, at time $\textbf{t} = 0$, the initial amount of information coming into each spot in the organization, $\textbf{AINIT}_{\textbf{spi}}$, is chosen at random from a uniform distribution over the integers 0 to 100. During each of the following time periods the amount of information increases. The user can choose a linear increase, with $\textbf{B}$ as the rate of increase,[2] in which case

$$\textbf{AMOUNTINFO}_{\textbf{spi}}(0) = \textbf{AINIT}_{\textbf{spi}}$$

and

$$\textbf{AMOUNTINFO}_{\textbf{spi}}(t + 1) = \textbf{AMOUNTINFO}_{\textbf{spi}}(t) + \textbf{B}.$$

Therefore,

$$\textbf{AMOUNTINFO}_{\textbf{spi}}(t) = \textbf{AINIT}_{\textbf{spi}} + \textbf{Bt}.$$

Or the user can choose an exponential increase, with a modulation of $\textbf{B}$, in which case

$$\textbf{AMOUNTINFO}_{\textbf{spi}}(0) = \textbf{AINIT}_{\textbf{spi}}$$

and

$$\textbf{AMOUNTINFO}_{\textbf{spi}}(t+1) = \textbf{AMOUNTINFO}_{\textbf{spi}}(t)e^{(t/\textbf{B})}.$$

In GARCORG when the option chosen is *random*, at time $\textbf{t} = 0$, the initial amount of information coming into each spot in the organization, $\textbf{AINIT}_{\textbf{spi}}$, is chosen at random from a uniform distribution over the integers 0 to 100. Each time period thereafter the amount of information per spot is again chosen at random from a uniform distribution over the integers 0 to 100.

MODELING CONTENT OF INFORMATION

To create a range of mechanisms, the content of information coming into a spot, $\textbf{CONTENT}_{\textbf{spi}}$, is allowed to be constant, or to have an increasing or decreasing average. Note, content is always modeled as a stochastic process; however, sometimes the mean is constant over time, and sometimes it is moving. In all cases, in GARCORG the option chosen first sets the initial average content of incoming information $\textbf{CINIT}_{\textbf{spi}}$ per spot, and then uses an algorithm for updating the average content of information available to that spot each time period $\textbf{AMOUNTINFO}_{\textbf{spi}}(t)$, and for determining the actual content per piece of information coming into the spot.

One difference between content and amount of information is that content is defined as a percentage with a 0/1 range, whereas amount is defined as a positive integer. Note, each piece of information that comes into the organization has a unique content. Further, each spot in the organization has an average content for all information that comes in to it. The value of a particular piece of information is chosen at random from a uniform distribution centered about the mean and scaled to lie between 0 and 1. The width of this distribution is chosen at random from a uniform distribution 0 to 100 and scaled to lie within the range -0.25 to $+0.25$. As will be seen later, when discussing the probability of having a staff member in a spot, only the mean content of information affects this likelihood.

In GARCORG when the option chosen is *constant average*, then at time $t = 0$, the initial average content of information coming into each spot in the organization, CINIT_{spi}, is chosen at random from a uniform distribution over the integers 0 to 100 and then scaled to lie in the interval 0 to 1.

In GARCORG when the option chosen is *moving average*, then at time $t = 0$, the initial average content of information coming into each spot in the organization, CINIT_{spi}, is chosen at random from a uniform distribution over the integers 0 to 100 and then scaled to lie in the interval 0 to 1. During each time period after this the average content moves.

The user can choose an increasing, a decreasing or a mixed increasing and decreasing average content of information. The moving average is linear, with a rate of change of Bt^3. In order to insure that the content level does not exceed 1 or decrease below 0 at time (t) such that the average content has reached 1/0, the rate of change becomes 0. This provides a ceiling/floor effect.[4] This whole process occurs once each time period.

Following is a brief description denoting, not the algorithm used in making a decision, but the kinds of organizational components that are important in the making of that decision, and that might impair the efficiency with which decisions are made. No decision algorithm is given as such. This is not a discussion of *how* managers decide; rather, it is a discussion of the kinds of organizational features, both structural and political, that impair the manager's ability to make decisions by constraining the flow of information.

I would like to suggest that efficiency, at any level, may be affected by the size of the subordinate staff; for example a commander who directs four lieutenants may be more efficient than a commander who directs two lieutenants, or one who directs 30. The overall size of the organization [SIZE], and its level of differentiation [DIF], correspond to the size of the subordinate staff. Note, in the four-tier structure, size is the sum of 1 (for the CEO) plus the number of AEOs [AEOS], plus the number of program chiefs per AEO, plus the number of staff members per program chief per AEO. Mathematically,

$$[3] \qquad \text{SIZE} = 1 + \text{AEOS} + \sum_{s=1}^{\text{AEOS}} \text{PCV}_s + \sum_{s=1}^{\text{AEOS}} \sum_{p=1}^{\text{PCV}_s} \sum_{i=1}^{\text{ISSUES}} \text{ANM}_{spi} .$$

Differentiation, the spread of the organization, at any level is the ratio of personnel at that level to personnel at the next lower level.[5] For now, we will measure differentiation [DIF] as the ratio of program chief managers to staff personnel:

[4]
$$DIF = \frac{\sum\limits_{s=1} PCV_s}{\sum\limits_{s=1}^{AEOS} \sum\limits_{p=1}^{PCV_s} \sum\limits_{i=1}^{ISSUES} ANM_{spi}}.$$

THE PROGRAM CHIEF'S DECISION

Each program chief makes a recommendation to the AEO on his program based on the analyses, of all the staff members under him, for only those issues to which he has access. Thus, there are as many recommendations to the AEO as there are programs. Structurally, the program chief's decision (i.e., his recommendation) is dependent on the number of analysts he has working under him and, therefore, the number of issues he has to consider. There are at least three structural aspects of the organization that might impair the program chief's efficiency: (1) the size of the organization; (2) the level of differentiation; and (3) the program chief's access to work done ostensibly under his control.

Mathematically, program chief access **[PCACCESS]**, is defined as a three-dimensional matrix with the same dimensions as **ANM**. **PCACCESS** describes which issues are accessible by which program chiefs. Let **PCACCESS** be of the same dimensions as **ANM**. Here, each element of **PCACCESS**—**(PCACCESS$_{spi}$)**—is assigned as follows:

[5] **PCACCESS$_{spi}$ = 1**
if program chief **(p)** working under AEO **(s)** has access to issue **(i)**;

[6] **PCACCESS$_{spi}$ = 0**
if program chief **(p)** working under AEO **(s)** does not have access to issue **(i)**.

There are many reasons why a manager might not have access to work done by one of his subordinates. For example, he may not have the right security clearance, he may not have enough technical expertise to evaluate a subordinate's work or the subordinate may not finish the analyses by the time the manager needs to make his report. It would seem that lack of access would lead to inefficiency; whether or not this is true, at the organizational level, is something that the proposed simulation program, GARCORG, could be used to study.

THE AEO'S DECISION

The AEO basically makes one recommendation to the CEO for each of the programs under his jurisdiction, based on all the analyses of all the staff members in all the programs under him for those issues to which he has access.

The AEO is thought to have access to all information that any of his immediate subordinates, the program chiefs, have access to. As long as one program chief under his direction has access to information on issue **i**, the AEO has access to issue **i**. AEO access is thus, logically, the *anding* of the access of the subordinate program chiefs. A result of this process is that access for a particular AEO is identical for all program chiefs under him.

The matrix **SACCESS** describes which **AEOS** have access to which issues. **SACCESS** has the same dimensions as **ANM**, and each element (**SACCESS$_{s*i}$**) is assigned as follows:[6]

[7]   **SACCESS$_{s*i}$** = 1
      if AEO (s) has access to issue **(i)**;

[8]   **SACCESS$_{s*i}$** = 0
      if AEO (s) does not have access to issue **(i)**.

Like the program chief's decision, we expect that the AEO's decision is affected by the size and differentiation of the organization, as well as by his access structure. To distinguish the AEO from the program chief, and to denote the increased authority of the AEO and the increasing strategic and unstructured nature of the decisions made at this level, the AEO decision process is seen as being affected by the AEO's saliency structure. Saliency for the AEO can be thought of as the degree to which the AEO thinks that the issue is important, relevant or central to the decision.

Like access, AEO saliency **[ASALIENCE]** is defined mathematically in terms of a matrix. **ASALIENCE** describes whether or not AEO **(s)** thinks that issue **(i)** is salient for program **(p)**. **ASALIENCE** has the same dimensions as **ANM**. The elements (**ASALIENCE$_{spi}$**) are defined as follows:

[9]   **ASALIENCE$_{spi}$** = 1
      if AEO **(s)** considers issue **(i)** to be salient to program **(p)**;

[10] **ASALIENCE$_{spi}$** = 0
      if AEO **(s)** does not consider issue **(i)** to be salient to program **(p)**.

The saliency variable can be used to represent the degree of belief in that issue. The point of distinction being made is that program chiefs are viewed as making primarily programmed decisions, as having to make reports on x, whereas, the AEOs are viewed as making less structured decisions in which they can trade off various aspects, various pieces of information. Another interpretation of the saliency vector for the AEO might be the relevance of the issue to the perceived political objective.

THE CEO'S DECISION

The CEO makes a final decision regarding each of the programs, based on the analyses of all the staff members in the entire population. The CEO is presumed to have complete access to information on all issues. Like the program

chiefs and the AEOs, the CEO is presumed to have his decision-making behavior affected by the size and differentiation of the organization. Complete
access means that lack of access cannot make his behavior less efficient.
Like the AEO, however, the CEO makes decisions in which the information he
receives is weighted by a particular level of salience. CEO saliency [PSALI-
ENCE], like AEO saliency, can be thought of as the CEO's belief in the issue,
the perceived relevance of that issue and so on. As with AEO saliency, the
purpose of CEO saliency is to distinguish the subjective availability of that
information. One might think of CEO saliency as the relevance of the information to the actual political objective.

Mathematically, CEO salience **PSALIENCE** is a matrix of the same
dimensions as **ANM**, and it describes which issues the CEO considers to be
salient to which programs. Which issues the CEO considers to be salient to
which programs vary over time. At a specific time, the elements of **PSALI-
ENCE ($PSALIENCE_{spi}$)** are defined as follows:

[11] $PSALIENCE_{spi} = 1$

if the CEO considers issue **(i)** to be salient to program **(p)**;

[12] $PSALIENCE_{spi} = 0$

if the CEO does not consider issue **(i)** to be salient to program
(p).

Personnel Transfers—Moving Staff Members through Spots

The main difference between this proposed model and that suggested by
Padgett (1980) is that in my model organizational membership is not fixed.
Staff members can be transferred into and out of any particular spot. Such
transfers can be thought of as hiring or firing personnel or simply as moving
them from one job to the next. Recall that a staff member's presence in a
particular spot means that there is a staff member analyzing a particular issue,
under a particular program chief, in a particular division.

There are many reasons for transferring staff members about. For example, the staff member may be incompetent, he may be needed elsewhere, there
may be nothing to do in the job and so on. If the efficiency of an organization is
affected by what kind of jobs are being done, as well as by who is doing which
job and how well that job is performed, then criteria that affect the jobs
being done may affect organizational efficiency. Further, whether or not
someone is doing a particular job, and whether or not there is a staff member
in a particular spot, affects whether or not the analysis of the corresponding issue is
available for upper level management when they are making decisions.

In this paper, the effect of three different personnel transfer criteria on
organizational efficiency are examined. These criteria are amount of information, content of information and saliency of information:

- *Amount:* Staff transfers are made on the basis of whether or not there is
  anything for staff members to do, that is, whether or not there is any or
  enough information coming in on the issue of concern. In the hostage

situation in Iran, for example, as more information on the hostage situation came in, a possible solution arose, which was to use the MH-53 helicopter which then necessitated the need to find assault pilots.

- *Content:* Staff transfers are made on the basis of whether or not the job is worth doing, that is, whether or not the information coming in on the issue of concern has a particular level of quality. In the Grenada crisis, for example, the lack of current up-to-date maps of the area created the need for staff members to do reconnaissance and develop or find maps of the area.

- *Saliency:* Staff transfers are made on the basis of whether or not the job a staff member is or will be doing is considered important to the CEO. For example, various commanders, or even entire units, may be moved about on the basis of whether or not their position is considered politically viable by the commander-in-chief.

These criteria are discussed in the following chapter, as they are the ones which are implemented in the simulation model, GARCORG. Finally, there are two other parameters that characterize the transference process— threshold and delay period. The threshold is simply the level of "x" that is needed before a staff member is transferred in/out of a spot. There is no threshold for the criteria saliency, as saliency is modeled as a binomial variable—*yes* salient, or *no* not salient. There are, however, thresholds for content and amount of information, as these are modeled as discrete flows. For the criterion amount, this threshold is denoted by **THA**, and for the criterion content it is denoted by **THC**. The delay period is the number of time periods that the criterion is met before a staff member is transferred in/out of a particular spot, **R**.

So whether or not there is a staff member in a particular spot is dependent on the personnel transfer mechanism. When the personnel transfer criterion is set to amount or content, the personnel transfer decision involves a comparison with a threshold. For simplicity, at this point we will assume not only that the same type of criterion is used for in transfers as out but also that the threshold level for transferring someone into a spot is equal to that for transferring someone out of a spot[7]. Setting these thresholds equal to each other produces a general threshold—**THA** for amount and **THC** for content.

Thus, if the personnel transfer criterion is amount, then if for **R** consecutive time periods,

[13] $[\textbf{AMOUNTINFO}_{spi} > \textbf{THA}] \rightarrow \textbf{ANM}_{spi} = 1,$

or else, if for those **R** consecutive time periods,

[14] $[\textbf{AMOUNTINFO}_{spi} \leq \textbf{THA}] \rightarrow \textbf{ANM}_{spi} = 0.$

Similarly, if the criteria is content, then if for **R** consecutive time periods,

[15] $[\textbf{CONTENT}_{spi} > \textbf{THC}] \rightarrow \textbf{ANM}_{spi} = 1,$

or else, if for those **R** consecutive time periods,

[16] $[\textbf{CONTENT}_{\textbf{spi}} \leqslant \textbf{THC}] \rightarrow \textbf{ANM}_{\textbf{spi}} = 0.$

Whereas, when the criterion is saliency, there is no threshold per se; rather if for **R** consecutive time periods,

[17] $[\textbf{SALIENCE}_{\textbf{spi}} = 1] \rightarrow \textbf{ANM}_{\textbf{spi}} = \textbf{1},$

or else, if for those R consecutive time periods,

[18] $[\textbf{SALIENCE}_{\textbf{spi}} = 0] \rightarrow \textbf{ANM}_{\textbf{spi}} = \textbf{0}.$

MEASURES OF EFFICIENCY

Four measures of efficiency will be presented—two structural and two political in nature. These four measures—E1, E2, E3, and E4—are based on the program chiefs' access structure, the AEOs' access structure, the salience of the issues to the AEOs and the salience of the issues to the CEO, respectively. Each of the efficiency measures is a time average.

The first two measures, E1 and E2, are structural; that is, they are gaged relative to inherent access structure of the specific organization under study. Structural inefficiencies may be difficult to eliminate without altering the structure of the organization. The second two measures, E3 and E4, are political in nature; that is, they relate to specific executives (the AEOs and the CEO) working in the organization and not to the organizational structure. Political inefficiencies may be difficult to eliminate without altering the political impressions of the executives. In both cases, it would be expedient in the short run if one could find a managerial solution for decreasing these inefficiencies, for example, by altering the personnel transfer mechanism.

All four measures—E1, E2, E3 and E4—are normalized measures of rising efficiency, with a range from 0 to 1. When multiplied by 100, they can be thought of as the percentage of that type of efficiency achieved by the organization. Essentially, these measures are normalized by the organization's size so that they are comparable across organizations. These measures are referred to as measures of rising efficiency, as a 0 represents total inefficiency and a 1 represents perfect efficiency. Each of the four measures is a moving time average; that is, they measure how efficient that particular garbage can hierarchy was on average, up to the time period chosen.

All four measures are based on a comparison between a valuation of a particular spot and whether or not there is actually a staff member in that spot. All four measures of efficiency are essentially measuring the prevalence of *bad spots* in the organization. We can think of a *bad spot* as a spot in the organization where the person making the decision does not have access to, or does not consider salient, the issue.

E1: Structural Efficiency—Program Chiefs' Access

Structural efficiency relative to the program chiefs' access structure is essentially measured by a counting procedure, which looks for staff members in inaccessible spots. This procedure counts for each time period, the number of staff members in the entire organization that are analyzing the information that comes in on a particular issue; such that the issue is not accessible by the program chief under which the staff member is working. When this count is divided by the number of time periods, it yields a 0 to 1 measure of inefficiency; dividing by time gives the average number of structural inefficiencies that occur over time due to the program chiefs' access structure. Subtracting this from 1 produces the measure E1.

Let **TIME** be the number of time periods for which the simulation was run or, alternatively, for which one has data. Then, given this and the fact that a logical operator used on a matrix operates element by element, we are ready to look at the mathematical definition of E1. E1 as presented here ranges from 0 to 1 and thus needs to be multiplied by 100 to turn it into a percentage.

$$[19] \quad E1 = 1 - \sum_{t=1}^{\text{TIME}} \frac{\sum_{s=1}^{\text{AEOS}} \sum_{p=1}^{\text{PCV}_s} \sum_{i=1}^{\text{ISSUE}} (\text{ANM}_{spit} > \text{PCACCESS}_{spi})}{\dfrac{\sum_{s=1}^{\text{AEOS}} \sum_{p=1}^{\text{PCV}_s} \sum_{i=1}^{\text{ISSUE}} (\text{PCACCESS}_{spi} = 0)}{\text{TIME}}}$$

E2: Structural Efficiency—AEO's Access

Structural inefficiencies can also occur at the AEO's level, in a manner similar to that in which they occur at the program chief level. Structural inefficiency relative to the AEO's access structure is measured via a counting procedure. This procedure counts, for each time period, the number of staff members in the entire organization who are analyzing the information that comes in on some issue, where the AEO above that staff member does not have access to the issue on which that staff member is working. Knowing the nature of this matrix, we can now understand the mathematical definition of E2. Again, like **E1**, the measure ranges only from 0 to 1.

$$[20] \quad E2 = 1 - \sum_{t=1}^{\text{TIME}} \frac{\sum_{s=1}^{\text{AEOS}} \sum_{p=1}^{\text{PCV}_s} \sum_{i=1}^{\text{ISSUE}} (\text{ANM}_{spit} > \text{SACCESS}_{spi})}{\dfrac{\sum_{s=1}^{\text{AEOS}} \sum_{p=1}^{\text{PCV}_s} \sum_{i=1}^{\text{ISSUE}} (\text{SACCESS}_{spi} = 0)}{\text{TIME}}}$$

E3: Political Efficiency—Assistant Executive Officer

One way in which political efficiency can occur at the AEO's level is for there to be staff members working on issues that the AEO does not consider to be salient for the program whose program chief that staff member is under. Like structural inefficiency, political inefficiency can be measured via an accounting mechanism. This mechanism simply counts the number of such staff members working on issues that are not salient to the AEO. Note, AEO's salience changes with time. Given this, E3, with a range of 0 to 1, is measured as follows:

$$[21] \quad E3 = 1 - \sum_{t=1}^{TIME} \frac{\sum_{s=1}^{AEOS} \sum_{p=1}^{PCV_s} \sum_{i=1}^{ISSUE} (ANM_{spit} > ASALIENCE_{spit})}{\sum_{s=1}^{AEOS} \sum_{p=1}^{PCV_s} \sum_{i=1}^{ISSUE} (ASALIENCE_{spit} = 0)} \Big/ TIME$$

E4: Political Efficiency—Chief Executive Officer Salience

Similarly, at the top executive level, political inefficiency arises when there is a staff member working on an issue that the CEO does not consider germane to that program. Like the previous measures, E4 measures this type of inefficiency via a counting procedure. This procedure counts, for each time period (t), the number of staff members in the organization that are analyzing the information that comes in on issue (i) for program (p), such that the CEO does not consider issue (i) to be salient to program (p). Thus, E4 is a time average of this count: political inefficiency relative to political salience is the average over time of the number of staff members analyzing nonsalient issues in that organization. Given this, we can state that

$$[22] \quad E4 = 1 - \sum_{t=1}^{TIME} \frac{\sum_{s=1}^{AEOS} \sum_{p=1}^{PCV_s} \sum_{i=1}^{ISSUE} (ANM_{spit} > PSALIENCE_{spit})}{\sum_{s=1}^{AEOS} \sum_{p=1}^{PCV_s} \sum_{i=1}^{ISSUE} (PSALIENCE_{spit} = 0)} \Big/ TIME$$

LONG-RUN EFFICIENCY

This section is divided into two parts. The first contains a mathematical analysis of the four measures of efficiency relative to each of the personnel transfer criteria suggested in the second section. This analysis is done in terms of the probabilities of the underlying comparisons. This analysis is summarized in Tables 8.5 and 8.6. The second part contains an analysis of the effect of changing the delay period, **R**, on whether or not there is a staff member in a particular spot.

Spot Filling as Independent of Spot Valuation

Central to each of the four measures of efficiency suggested previously is a comparison of a particular valuation of an issue against whether or not there is a staff member working on that issue **ANM**. Specifically, each measure of efficiency **(E)** is a function of the form

[23] **E = f(ANM > VALUATION)**.

When looking for the expected value of each of the measures of efficiency, we must be concerned with the expected value of these comparisons. Further, since this is an element-by-element comparison, we can look at the comparison being made for a single spot **(ANM$_{spi}$)** and generalize to the other spots. Note that the form of the comparison being made is the same for all spots. Further, since all five of the relevant matrices consist of just 0s and 1s, then

[24] $E\{ANM_{spi} > VALUATION_{spi}\} = 1 - E\{ANM_{spi} = 1$ & $VALUATION_{spi} = 0\}$.

When **ANM** is independent of the comparison matrix,

[25] $E\{ANM_{spi} > VALUATION_{spi}\} = 1 - Pr(ANM_{spi} = 1) \times Pr(VALUATION_{spi} = 0)$.

The personnel transfer mechanism always affects whether or not there is a staff member in a particular spot, **ANM$_{spi}$**. The question is, does it affect the other matrices? As we shall presently see, the answer is no—that is, not in such a way as to make these dependent on which spot which staff member is in (**ANM$_{spi}$**). Thus, for our purposes, **ANM** and these other matrices are independent.

It turns out that under all of the personnel transfer mechanisms suggested, these matrices are, in fact, independent. This independence arises from the way in which the personnel transfer mechanisms affect these matrices. The personnel transfer mechanism always affects whether or not there is a staff member in a particular spot (**ANM$_{spi}$ = 1**) at any particular time greater than the delay (**t > R**). The program chiefs' access structure (**PCACCESS**), the AEO's access structure (**SACCESS**) or AEO's salience (**ASALIENCE**) are exogenous variables; that is, they are not affected by the personnel transfer mechanism chosen. Therefore, **ANM** is independent of **PCACCESS**, **SACCESS**, and **ASALIENCE**.

While it also turns out that **ANM** is independent of **PSALIENCE**, the reasoning behind this is not quite as straightforward. Now, when the personnel transfer mechanism is based on either the amount of information (**AMOUNTINFO**) that comes in on a particular issue at time (**t**) or the content of that information (**CONTENT**), the personnel transfer mechanism does not affect political salience (**PSALIENCE**). Therefore, under these two mechanisms **ANM** is independent of **PSALIENCE**.

It turns out that even when the personnel transfer mechanism is based on political saliency, **ANM$_{spi}$** is independent of **PSALIENCE**. For at time (**t**) efficiency is calculated first and then staff members are transferred. That is, where **ANM(t)** is the value of **ANM** after it is updated using the information gathered during period **t**, then

[26] **ANM(t) = f(PSALIENCE(t))**

and

[27] $E\{E4(t)\} = 1 - E\{ANM(t - 1) > PSALIENCE(t)\}$.

Even though **PSALIENCE** is not independent of **ANM(t)**, it is independent of **ANM(t − 1)**. Recall that **PSALIENCE(t)** is independent of **PSALIENCE(t − 1)** as **PSALIENCE** for any particular spot is reassigned randomly each time period.

Given these considerations, equation 19 is valid for the following analysis. Therefore, let us consider the value of the resulting five probabilities: *Pr*(**ANM** = 1), *Pr*(**PCACCESS** = 0), *Pr*(**SACCESS** = 0), *Pr*(**ASALIENCE** = 0) and *Pr*(**PSALIENCE** = 0).

There are an infinite number of ways to model each of the five main probabilities mathematically. Some of these models are independent of the staff members' location, spot, (**ANM$_{spi}$**), others are not. When the staff members' locations are homogeneous, the comparisons are independent of location and can thus be pulled outside of the corresponding sums. As the counting procedures produce a normalized output, these sums without the internal comparison are 1. That is, when *Pr*(**ANM** = 1) and the **VALUATION** matrices—*Pr*(**PCACCESS** = 0), *Pr*(**SACCESS** = 0), *Pr* (**ASALIENCE** = 0) and *Pr*(**PSALIENCE** = 0)—are independent of the staff members' position (the spot **spi**), then the expected value of each measure of efficiency is found by

[28]
$$E\{E\} = 1 - \lim_{TIME \to \infty} \sum_{t=0}^{TIME} \frac{Pr(ANM = 1) \times Pr(VALUATION = 0)}{TIME}$$

In this study, such homogeneity is assumed to be the case, therefore, the form of the above equation suffices to define the efficiency of the organizations. Exactly how these five probabilities are measured will be discussed in the next five subsections. How the corresponding matrices are modeled in the simulation program GARCORG is also discussed. Numerical examples are drawn from the data used in the simulation analysis in a later chapter. The effect of the personnel transfer mechanism on this probability is also discussed in the case of the likelihood of having a staff member in a particular spot.

Transfers—Probability of a Filled Spot

The probability of having a staff member in a particular spot **Pr(ANM$_{spi}$ = 1)** is dependent on the personnel transfer mechanism. If for all spots (**spi**) the flow on which the personnel transfer criteria is based is deterministic, and if after a deterministic number of time periods there are no changes in the **ANM** matrix, the final personnel transfer decision for each of the spots will have been made. For example, if the criteria is amount, and the amount of incoming information is constant, then after **R** time periods there will be no changes. On the other hand, if the flow on which the personnel transfer criteria operates is stochastic, then the expectation of whether or not there is a staff member in a particular spot can be modeled as a Markov process.

As previously mentioned, there is a plethora of ways in which the probability of having a staff member in a particular spot could be modeled. The important thing to note here is that whether or not there is a staff member in a spot depends on the criterion used for transferring personnel. The three criteria discussed analytically here are amount of information, content of information and political saliency.

TRANSFER CRITERION IS AMOUNT OF INFORMATION

Constant   Under this option, **AMOUNTINFO** is fixed for all time periods. In this case, after **R** time periods, all the personnel transfer decisions will be made in one fell swoop. Until $t > R$, until the first delay period is over,

[29]   **ANM = ANMINITIAL**.

And, at time $t = R$, if

[30] $[\textbf{AMOUNTINFO}_{\textbf{spi}} > \textbf{THA}] \rightarrow \textbf{ANM}_{\textbf{spi}} = 1$

or if,

[31] $[\textbf{AMOUNTINFO}_{\textbf{spi}} \leqslant \textbf{THA}] \rightarrow \textbf{ANM}_{\textbf{spi}} = 0$.

Hence, for any time $t > R$,

[32] $\textbf{ANM(t)} = \textbf{ANM(t} = \textbf{R})$.

On average, for all spots combined, after **R** time periods,

[33] $Pr(\textbf{ANM} = 1) = Pr(\textbf{AMOUNTINFO} > \textbf{THA})$.

In GARCORG, this is interpreted as

[34] $Pr(\textbf{ANM} = 1) = \dfrac{100 - \textbf{THA}}{101}$.

Increasing Amount   In this case, since the amount of incoming information for each issue is increasing, eventually a staff member will be transferred into every spot. Eventually, $Pr(\textbf{ANM} = 1) = 1$. When this occurs depends on the threshold and the rate of increase; that is, the maximum amount of time that it will take for **ANM** to reach steady state is simply the threshold divided by the rate of increase **B** plus the delay period:

[N + E] $MAX\text{t} = (\textbf{THA} \div \textbf{B}) + \textbf{R}$.

Recall that for a linear change the amount of incoming information is found to be some base amount plus a fixed increase (**AINIT** + **Bt**) from the initial amount of information **AINIT**. Thus, for cases of fixed increase, the time by which all of the personnel transfer decisions are made for a particular spot, where the matrix of such time is *M*t, is found by using the following equation:

[35] $M\text{t} = \textbf{R} + \dfrac{\textbf{THA} - \textbf{AINIT}}{\textbf{B}}$

Since the for **AINIT** are chosen randomly from the uniform distribution over the integers 0 to 100, the average value of **AINIT** is 50. Then, on average, at most 25% of the spots will be unfilled at time $t = 0$, and only 1% will take the full maximum time periods to be filled.

Random Amount In this case, since the amount of incoming information for each issue is determined each time period in a stochastic fashion, for any given spot staff members will keep being transferred in and out. Recall that the stochastic process used was one where, for each time period, the amount for each issue is rechosen at random from a uniform distribution over the integers 0 to 100. This is the same as having a mean that is constant over time at 50 pieces of information. In this case, the value of the amount of information can be described as a base (**AINIT**) plus a choice from a zero mean distribution (**C(t)**).

In this case, the probability that there is a staff member in a particular spot can be modeled by a Markov process based on the probability of transferring in a staff member and the probability of transferring out a staff member. Let the probability of transferring a staff member into a spot be denoted by $\mathbf{H}^R$, where **H** is the probability that the criterion will be above the threshold for transferring into a spot at a particular time. Similarly, let the probability of transferring out of a spot be denoted by $\mathbf{F}^R$, where **F** is the probability that the criterion will be below the threshold for transferring out of a spot at a particular time. Since the threshold for transfers into a spot is equal to that for transfers out of a spot,

[36] $\mathbf{H} + \mathbf{F} = 1$

As long as neither of these probabilities goes to zero, a steady state equilibrium is reached where

[37] $Pr(\mathbf{ANM} = 1) = \dfrac{\mathbf{H}^R}{\mathbf{H}^R + \mathbf{F}^R}$

or in reduced form,

[38] $Pr(\mathbf{ANM} = 1) = \dfrac{1}{1 + (\mathbf{F} \div \mathbf{H})^R}.$

Thus,

[39] $\mathbf{H} = Pr(\mathbf{AMOUNTINFO} > \mathbf{THA}) = (100 - \mathbf{THA}) \div 101$

and

[40] $\mathbf{F} = Pr(\mathbf{AMOUNTINFO} \leqslant \mathbf{THA}) = (1 + \mathbf{THA}) \div 101.$

Therefore,

[41] $Pr(\mathbf{ANM} = 1) = \dfrac{1}{1 + ((1 + \mathbf{THA}) \div (100 - \mathbf{THA}))^R}.$

Note, if **R** is 1, then equation 41 reduces to equation 39—that is, choosing the option *random* produces the same effect as choosing the option *constant*, on average.

TRANSFER CRITERION IS CONTENT OF INFORMATION

Constant Average   Similarly, when the personnel transfer criterion is content, and the content of incoming information changes over time, staff members will keep being transferred to the same spot. Like the case of random amounts of information, the case where the average content of the information is constant inhibits the user from achieving a state where no staff members are transferred. Since content is always modeled as a stochastic process, the probability that there is a staff member in a particular spot can be modeled by a Markov process, as was done for the amount of incoming information when it was modeled as random. As before, there is a particular probability of a staff member being transferred into a spot (**H**) and of being transferred out of a spot (**F**). Since the content is chosen from a mean centered distribution, where the mean is drawn at random from a uniform distribution over the integers 0 to 100, scaled to lie between 0 and 1

[42] $\mathbf{H} = Pr(\mathbf{CONTENT} > \mathbf{THC}) = (1 - \mathbf{THC}) \div 1.01$

and

[43] $\mathbf{F} = Pr(\mathbf{CONTENT} \leq \mathbf{THC}) = (0.01 + \mathbf{THC}) \div 1.01.$

And

[44] $Pr(\mathbf{ANM} = 1) = \dfrac{1}{1 + ((0.01 + \mathbf{THC}) \div (1 - \mathbf{THC}))^{\mathbf{R}}}.$

The threshold, **THC**, has a range of 0 to 1. Placing these limits into equations 42 and 43 limits **H** and **F** to

[45]   if **THC** = 1, then **H** = 0 and **F** = 1

and

[46]   if **THC** = 0, then **H** = 0.99 and **F** = 0.0099.

In the first case

[47] $Pr(\mathbf{ANM} = 1) = 0,$

and in the second case

[48] $Pr(\mathbf{ANM} = 1) \rightarrow 1.$

Moving Average   When a moving average type is chosen using GARCORG, the user can choose to have the average increase linearly, decrease, or a mixture of the two. Note, as the average content for any particular issue increases, new staff members are transferred in, and the staff size approaches its maximum; that is,

[49] $[B > 0] \rightarrow \underset{\mathbf{T} \rightarrow \infty}{limit} \; Pr(\mathbf{ANM} = 1) = 1.$

Similarly, when the option chosen is decreasing, then as the average content for any particular issue decreases, staff members are transferred to other programs or even divisions, and the project grinds to a halt as the staff size approaches 0; that is,

[50] $[B < 0] \rightarrow \underset{T \to \infty}{limit}\ \mathbf{Pr}(\mathbf{ANM} = 1) = 0.$

The probability of a staff member being in a particular spot is still modeled as a Markov process, such that the probability of being transferred changes over time. Recall that the stochastic process used to calculate content, in effect, creates a mean centered distribution where the mean is equal to **CINIT** plus a rate of increase (**Bt**). Thus,[8]

[51] $\mathbf{H} = \dfrac{1 - (\mathbf{THC} - \mathbf{Bt})}{1.01}$

and

[52] $\mathbf{F} = \dfrac{0.01 + (\mathbf{THC} - \mathbf{Bt})}{1.01}.$

Therefore,

[53] $\mathbf{Pr}(\mathbf{ANM} = 1) = \dfrac{1}{1 + ((0.01 + \mathbf{THC} - \mathbf{Bt}) \div (1 - \mathbf{THC} + \mathbf{Bt}))^{\mathbf{R}}}.$

TRANSFER CRITERION IS CEO SALIENCY

Criteria salience when the transfer criteria is political salience, the only thing that will affect whether or not there are staff members in a particular spot is the level to which the CEO's salience is set (**PSP**). Recall that political salience is a stochastic process; that is, at any time period salience is reassigned to each spot at random. However, the level of salience (**PSP**) as defined by the user determines the fraction of issues which will be considered salient. Thus, the probability of there being a staff member in any spot can be modeled as a Markov process such that

[54] $\mathbf{H} = \mathbf{Pr}(\mathbf{PSALIENCE} = 1) = \mathbf{PSP} \div 100$

and

[55] $\mathbf{F} = \mathbf{Pr}(\mathbf{PSALIENCE} = 0) = (100 - \mathbf{PSP}) \div 100,$

in which case,

[56] $\mathbf{Pr}(\mathbf{ANM} = 1) = \dfrac{1}{1 + ((100 - \mathbf{PSP}) \div \mathbf{PSP})^{\mathbf{R}}}.$

Valuation—Probability of a Bad Spot

The probability that a spot is bad is based on the valuation measure. Herein, four such measures have been proposed: (1) program chief access; (2) AEO access; (3) AEO saliency; and (4) CEO saliency. The first two of these can be thought of as structural valuation measures having to do with the organizational structure; and the second two can be thought of as political valuation measures having to do with the personnel preferences and political structure.

PROGRAM CHIEF ACCESS

The probability that any particular program chief does not have access to the information on a particular issue, $Pr(\textbf{PCACCESS} = 0)$, is a function of both the number of potential issues that the program chief might have access to (**ISSUE**) and the specified access structure. Four such structures are considered: *total, random, specialized* and *quasi-specialized*. This probability is computed for a single organization as the average, over all of the program chiefs in the organization, of the percentage of potential issues that each of them do not have access to. When several organizations are looked at, this probability is just the average over the organizations of each of their individual averages.

For a particular organization,

$$[57] \quad Pr(\textbf{PCACCESS} = 0) = \frac{\displaystyle\sum_{s=1}^{\textbf{AEOS}} \sum_{p=1}^{\textbf{PCV}_s} \sum_{i=1}^{\textbf{ISSUE}} (\textbf{PCACCESS}_{spi} = 0)}{\textbf{ISSUE} \times \displaystyle\sum_{s=1}^{\textbf{AEOS}} \textbf{PCV}_s}.$$

Given the particular access structures, this form can be reduced.

Total Access   When the access structure is one of total access, then every program chief has access to every issue; therefore,

$$[58] \quad Pr(\textbf{PCACCESS} = 0) = 0.$$

Random Access   When the access structure is random, then the probability that a program chief does not have access to any particular issue is dependent on the characteristics of the random distribution. In GARCORG, a uniform white noise source is used; that is, 1s and 0s are distributed with equal likelihood over the access structure. Under these conditions,

$$[59] \quad Pr(\textbf{PCACCESS} = 0) = 0.5.$$

Specialized Access   For specialized access structures, the calculations become more complex. In GARCORG, each program chief has access to as many issues as every other program chief (**I** issues). However, no two program chiefs have access to information on the same issue. Further, each division has as many potential spots for staff members, as many issues to be worked on as the next (**ISSUE**). This reduces equation 57 to

$$[60] \quad Pr(\textbf{PCACCESS} = 0) = \frac{(\textbf{AEOS} \times \textbf{ISSUE}) - \textbf{I} \times \sum_{s=1}^{\textbf{AEOS}} \textbf{PCV}_s}{\textbf{AEOS} \times \textbf{ISSUE}}.$$

The structure of the organization, its size and its differentiation level affect this calculation. One has to take into account the total number of program chiefs (**NUM PC**), the number of AEOs (**AEOS**) and the information on issues. For an example of the range available, refer to Table 8.1, where the data for the organizations simulated in a later chapter are gathered.

Quasi-Specialized Access For a quasi-specialized program chief access structure, the calculations depend on the degree of overlap. In GARCORG, each program chief has access to as many issues as every other program chief (**I** issues). However, each program chief shares a certain number of these issues with another program chief (**OVERLAP**). Otherwise, the situation is set up identically to the way it was set up for specialized access. Thus,

$$[61] \quad Pr(\textbf{PCACCESS} = 0) = \frac{(\textbf{AEOS} \times \textbf{ISSUE}) - (\textbf{OVERLAP} + (\textbf{I} - \textbf{OVERLAP}) \times \sum_{s=1}^{\textbf{AEOS}} \textbf{PCV}_s}{\textbf{AEOS} \times \textbf{ISSUE}}.$$

In GARCORG, for a quasi-specialized access structure, **I** is set to 3, and the degree of overlap (**OVERLAP**) to 2; hence,

$$[62] \quad Pr(\textbf{PCACCESS} = 0) = \frac{(\textbf{AEOS} \times \textbf{ISSUE}) - (2 + \sum_{s=1}^{\textbf{AEOS}} \textbf{PCV}_s)}{\textbf{AEOS} \times \textbf{ISSUE}}.$$

For an example of the available range, refer to Table 8.2.

AEO ACCESS

Recall that AEO's access is just the anding over the program chief access structure of those program chiefs under that AEO. Thus, the probability that

Table 8.1: *Pr*(**PCACCESS** = 0) Under Specialized Access					
STRUCTURE	**NUM PC**	**1**	**AEOS**	**ISSUE**	**Pr(PCACCESS = 0)**
small differentiated	7	2	3	8	0.4167
small undifferentiated	5	2	2	8	0.375
large differentiated	34	2	8	12	0.2917
large undifferentiated	11	3	3	12	0.0833

| Table 8.2: *Pr*(PCACCESS = 0) Under Quasi-Specialized Access ||||||
STRUCTURE	NUM PC	1	AEOS	ISSUE	Pr(PCACCESS = 0)
small differentiated	7	3	3	8	0.625
small undifferentiated	5	3	2	8	0.5625
large differentiated	34	3	8	12	0.625
large undifferentiated	11	3	3	12	0.6389

no AEO has access to a particular issue is equivalent to the probability that no program chief has access to a particular issue.

AEO SALIENCE

AEO salience is assumed to be distributed randomly. For any particular issue, whether or not the AEO considers it to be salient is redetermined each time period. However, the user sets the level of saliency (**ASP**); that is, the user sets the percentage of issues which the AEO will consider salient each time period.[9]

[63]   *Pr*(**ASALIENCE** = 0) = 1 − (**ASP** ÷ 100).

CEO SALIENCE

CEO salience is assumed to be distributed randomly. For any particular issue, whether or not the CEO considers it to be salient is redetermined each time period. However, the user sets the level of saliency (**PSP**); that is, the user sets the percentage of issues which the CEO will consider salient each time period.[10]

[64]   *Pr*(**SALIENCE** = 0) = 1 − (**PSP** ÷ 100).

Summarizing and Combining Filled and Bad Spots

The following tables summarize the predicted long-run efficiency in terms of the foregoing subsections. By way of example, exact values are also calculated for the long-run levels of these likelihoods, based on the parameters used in the simulation analysis in a later chapter. These values are listed in brackets "[ ]." In Table 8.3, the parameter values used in that simulation analysis are listed.

| Table 8.3: Simulation Parameters ||
PARAMETER	VALUE
delay period **R**	3
amount threshold **THA**	25
amount rate of change **B**	3
content threshold **THC**	
content rate of change **B**	0.01
CEO saliency level **PSP**	50%
AEO saliency level **ASP**	50%

In Table 8.4, the likelihoods that there is a staff member in a particular spot, relative to the three personnel transfer mechanisms (or criteria), are summarized. Note, none of the parameters, other than those listed, affect the *Pr*(**ANM** = 1), the likelihood of there being a staff member in a particular spot.

In Table 8.5, the relationship between relevant GARCORG parameters and the associated underlying probabilities are summarized. None of the parameters other than those listed affect these probabilities. For both the probability of **PCACCESS** and that of **SACCESS**, the predicted values for the four different organizational structures simulated are presented. These are small differentiated (SY), small undifferentiated (SN), large differentiated (LY) and large undifferentiated (LN).

In Table 8.6, the relationship between various parameters in GARCORG and the predicted long-run efficiency values are summarized. Note, the values listed for efficiency are the expected values. For the structural measures of efficiency, data for the four different organizational structures simulated are presented, and all organizations are assumed to be quasi-specialized. These are small differentiated (SY), small undifferentiated (SN), large differentiated (LY) and large undifferentiated (LN). In most cases, what is presented is the long-run efficiency value.

Table 8.4: GARCORG and *Pr*(**ANM** = 1)	
PARAMETER AND HIRING/FIRING MECHANISM (HF)	*Pr*(**ANM** = 1) =
HF = AMOUNT, AMOUNT is	
constant	$(100 - \mathbf{THA}) \div 101$ after $\mathbf{t} = \mathbf{R}$ [0.7426]
linear	1 after $\mathbf{t} > \mathbf{R} + (\mathbf{THA} + \mathbf{B})$ [1 after $\mathbf{t} > 12$]
random	$1 \div (1 + ((1 + \mathbf{THA}) \div (100 - \mathbf{THA}))^{\mathbf{R}})$ [.96]
HF = CONTENT, CONTENT is	
constant	$1 \div (1 + ((0.01 + \mathbf{THC}) \div (1 - \mathbf{THC}))^{\mathbf{R}})$ [0]
increasing	$1 \div (1 + ((0.01 + \mathbf{THC} - \mathbf{Bt}) \div (1 - \mathbf{THC} + \mathbf{Bt}))^{\mathbf{R}})$ [1 after $\mathbf{t} > 26$]
decreasing	$1 \div (1 + ((0.1 + \mathbf{THC} - \mathbf{Bt}) \div (1 - \mathbf{THC} + \mathbf{Bt}))^{\mathbf{R}})$ [0 after $\mathbf{t} > 26$]
HF = SALIENCY, CEO SALIENCE	
PSP level	$1 \div (1 + ((100 - \mathbf{PSP}) \div 100))^{\mathbf{R}})$ [0.5]

PARAMETER	PROBABILITY
Table 8.5: GARCORG and Underlying Probabilities	
Program Chief access and AEO access	$Pr(\textbf{PCACCESS} = 0) =$ $Pr(\textbf{SACCESS} = 0)$
total	0 [no effect due to structure]
specialized SY SN LY LN	$1 - ((\textbf{I} \times \textbf{NUM PC}) \div (\textbf{AEOS} \times \textbf{ISSUE}))$ [0.4167] [0.375] [0.2917] [0.0833]
quasi-specialized SY SN LY LN	$1 - ((\textbf{OVERLAP} + (\textbf{I} - \textbf{OVERLAP}) \times \textbf{NUM PC}) \div (\textbf{AEOS} \times \textbf{ISSUE}))$ $[1 - ((2 + \textbf{NUM PC}) \div (\textbf{AEOS} \times \textbf{ISSUE}))]$ [0.625] [0.5625] [0.625] [0.6389]
random	0.5 [no effect due to structure]
AEO salience	$Pr(\textbf{ASALIENCE}) = 1 - (\textbf{ASP} \div 100)$
ASP 50%	[0.50]
CEO salience	$Pr(\textbf{PSALIENCE}) = 1 - (\textbf{PSP} \div 100)$
PSP = 50%	[0.50]

With regard to Table 8.6, having a total program chief access structure is clearly the most efficient. However, a random program chief access structure leads to a more efficient organization than either a specialized or a quasi-specialized access structure.

Effect of Delay Period, R

The delay period, **R**, is the number of time periods that the transfer criterion has to be met in order to transfer a staff member. Examples include the number of "goofups" someone gets before he is demoted or the number of times a particular skill is required before someone who has that skill is hired. In the simulation analysis presented in Chapter 9, **R** is set to 3. The exact effect that **R** will have on the measures of efficiency is dependent on the model used for the probability that there is a staff member in a particular spot ($Pr(\textbf{ANM} = 1)$). Now, unless this probability is defined stochastically, the size of **R** serves only to delay the time at which all the transferring in and out will occur, but it will not have an effect on whether or not the changeovers occur. In such cases, the larger **R** is, the longer it takes the system to reach its final state, but that state remains the same. However, when this probability is defined stochastically, **R**

	EXPECTED EFFICIENCY					
PARAMETER AND HIRING/FIRING MECHANISM	*E1 = E2*				*E3*	*E4*
	SY	*SN*	*LY*	*LN*		
HF = AMOUNT, AMOUNTINFO is						
constant	0.536	0.582	0.536	0.526	0.629	0.629
linear after t>12	0.375	0.4375	0.375	0.3611	0.5	0.5
random	0.4	0.46	0.4	0.387	0.52	0.52
HF = CONTENT, average CONTENT is						
constant 1 after t>3	1	1	1	1	1	
increasing after t>26	0.375	0.4375	0.375	0.3611	0.5	0.5
decreasing after t>26	1	1	1	1	1	1
HF = SALIENCE						
CEO SALIENCE **PSP** level [50] **ASP** level [50]	0.688	0.719	0.688	0.681	0.75	0.75

Table 8.6: GARCORG and Expected Efficiency

has a more complex role. Recall in the Markov examples suggested in the last subsections that

[65] $\quad Pr(\mathbf{ANM} = 1) = \dfrac{\mathbf{H}^R}{\mathbf{H}^R + \mathbf{F}^R} .$

Differentiating this with respect to **R** gives

[66] $\quad \dfrac{d}{dR}[Pr(\mathbf{ANM} = 1)] = \dfrac{(\mathbf{F} \div \mathbf{H})^R \times ln(\mathbf{F} \div \mathbf{H})}{[1 + (\mathbf{F} + \mathbf{H}^R)^2]} .$

Thus, when the probability of transferring a staff member out of a spot is greater than the probability of transferring someone into a spot, then $(\mathbf{F} > \mathbf{H})$—an increase in the delay period $(\mathbf{R})$ results in a decrease in the probability that there is a staff member in a particular spot $(Pr(\mathbf{ANM} = 1))$. And, as the probability of transferring a staff member into a spot increases over the probability of transferring a staff member out of a spot, an increase in **R** results in an increase in $(Pr(\mathbf{ANM} = 1))$. This is represented pictorially in Figure 8.2.

SUMMARY

Combining the organized-anarchy model and the more familiar social-structural model led to several results. First, this combination provides a

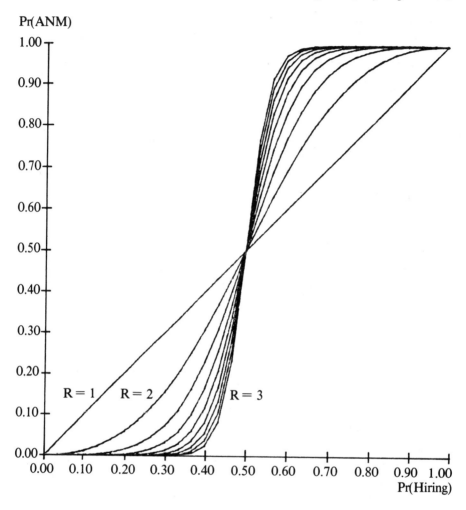

Figure 8.2   Altering the delay period. The effect of changing **R**, the grace or delay period for hiring and firing, on the value of **PR(ANM)**. Recall that **PR**(HIRING) + **PR**(FIRING) = 1.

framework in which the garbage can hierarchy can be viewed as "one type of organization" relative to other organizations. That is, organizations are seen as being more garbage-can-like the more ambiguous the flow of information, the flow of personnel and the decision technology. Herein, a set of models for information flow (content and amount), personnel flow (personnel transfer mechanisms) and aspects of the decision technology (access structures and saliency) are presented. In the GARCORG program the user can set these parameters as desired; this allows one to test theses about, for example, whether or not "garbage can hierarchies" are more or less efficient than other organizations, or which problematic flows have the highest impact on efficiency.

A second item due to the combination of the anarchy model and the hierarchy model is the development of the notion of *spots* in the organization. In specific, the notion of *bad spots* in an organization has been presented. A *bad spot* is basically a position or job that does not contribute to the overall effectiveness of the organization, a spot that has a negative valuation on some criteria. There are many ways in which a spot can be *bad*. Herein, two different types of criteria for *bad spots* have been suggested—structural ineffectiveness (measured as lack of access) and political ineffectiveness (measured as lack of saliency).

A final result due to placing the organized anarchy within the hierarchical structure is that it creates a framework in which efficiency can be measured. Herein, inefficiency has been defined in terms of having staff members working in bad spots. This is just one way in which efficiency could be modeled. Alternate measures might be percentage of decisions that are pushed up to the CEO for final approval, time before a decision is made and so on. The point here is that although placing the organized anarchy into a hierarchical structure admitted the possibility of measuring efficiency, the measure of efficiency chosen determines the nature of the results.

NOTES

1. The term *garbage can hierarchies* was coined by Cohen, March and Olsen (1972) to describe organizations where the goals and technology are unclear.

2. In GARCORG, **B** is set to 3; however, this can be changed at the user's discretion.

3. Note, in GARCORG, the level of change **B** is set internally to 0.01 when the *increasing* option is chosen and to −0.01 when the *decreasing* option is chosen. However, this can be changed by the user.

4. For a more detailed description, the reader is referred to either the GARCORG program or the paper by Padgett (1980).

5. Differentiation is a measure of the spread of the organizational hierarchy. There are many potential measures, of which this is just one. Another might be the number of branches.

6. Note, the AEO (**s**) has access to issue (**i**) just in case at least one of the program chiefs (**p**) under AEO (**s**) has access to issue (**i**). A result of this is that the AEO access structure is identical vis-à-vis the program chiefs. The "***" indicates that for all program chiefs under AEO (**s**) for issue (**i**), **SACCESS** is set as indicated. In other words, the "***" indicates identity across that dimension.

7. Note, in the simulation program different transfer criteria can be used for bringing staff members in than are used for transferring staff members out. Also, the in-transfer threshold can be set independently of the out-transfer threshold in GARCORG.

8. Recall that content is never allowed to go outside the range 0 to 1. Therefore, if the sum of **Bt** and **THC** is greater than 1, the content level for that issue is set to 1 if **B** is positive, and 0 otherwise.

9. Note, the user is asked for a percentage and can give any number between 0 and 100 for **ASP**. To convert **ASP** into a percentage for this analysis, simply divide it by 100.

10. Note, the user is asked for a percentage and can give any number between 0 and 100 for **PSP**. To convert **PSP** into a percentage for this analysis, simply divide it by 100.

REFERENCES

Cohen, R. M., March, J. G., and Olsen, J. P. "A Garbage Can Model of Organizational Choice." *Administrative Science Quarterly* 17 (1972): 1–25.

Padgett, J. F. "Managing Garbage Can Hierarchies." *Administrative Science Quarterly* 25 (1980): 583–604.

Perrow, Charles. "Review of Ambiguity and Choice in Organizations." *Contemporary Sociology* 6 (1977): 294–298.

9

Efficiency in a Garbage Can: Implications for Crisis Management

KATHLEEN CARLEY

INTRODUCTION

The navy, considered at as a decision-making organization, presents us with a set of interesting and difficult parameters according to which important decisions must be and are made. These parameters are interesting because they are somewhat different from those artificially imposed on theoretical models of decision making; and they are difficult in that they (the parameters) are the result of real-world phenomena and not the simplifying assumptions so often characteristic of science. Let me identify a few of these parameters, suggest how they might be modeled and then examine whether there are any implications for decision making in the navy.

- *Multiplicity of objectives:* The navy wants to be ready, on the one hand, for the "big one," World War III, and at the same time be able to manage individual crises like Grenada or the Jordanian Crisis. One goal might be to set up an organization that can efficiently handle crises without impinging on its efficiency to maintain a global ready state during long periods of peacetime activity.

Kathleen Carley is Assistant Professor in the Department of Social Sciences at Carnegie-Mellon University.

- *Hierarchical structure:* Within the navy there is a definite chain of command; for example, lieutenant, second lieutenant, ensign and so on. Different responsibilities, different training and different objectives correspond to each level in this hierarchy.

- *Mobile salience:* The navy, being subject to the commander-in-chief, is not immune to the wiles of politics. In fact, at any level in the chain of command, different problems will be more salient for some leaders or executives than for others. Further, this saliency may change not only across people but over time. The political environment, the state of world affairs and the economic setting affect the degree of importance attached to a particular problem.

- *Changing technology:* Tactical readiness at the decision level requires up-to-date knowledge of currently available technology. However, with the present rate of change in technology, officers need to be constantly retrained just to keep abreast of currently available devices. Rapidly changing technology also means that appropriate manpower may not be available, that people will have to be retrained and that staff members will have to be moved about in order to utilize their knowledge or talents. This is especially so when relatively new or unique technologies are used in novel situations. For example, in the bid to free the hostages in Iran, the task force was forced to look to all the services to find the right kind of pilots to fly the navy's mine sweeping helicopter, the MH-53, since mine war pilots are not trained for assault missions.

- *Rapid-event theaters:* Escalation occurs rapidly, and the time during which a crisis can be contained is often relatively short. For example, the entire Grenada incident lasted less than a week.

- *Volatile information flows:* When a situation arises that has potential crisis ramifications, the information flow increases. In a relatively short time, a great deal of information comes in, and it comes in very quickly. Once the crisis is abated, the information flow basically returns to normal, the rate of incoming information decreases and the amount of information decreases.

- *Incomplete information:* Intelligence reports are often incomplete. For example, during the Grenada invasion, one of the problems facing the admiral was the lack of a current topological map of the island.

- *Unreliable information:* Not only is the information provided by intelligence reports incomplete, but it is sometimes wrong. Information can be unreliable for a variety of reasons, including human error, misrepresentation or datedness. For example, it is often claimed that unreliable information led to the Bay of Pigs incident.

- *Unclear decision technology:* One of the first steps in crisis management is often the establishment of a joint task force. Often, the members of this task force have not previously worked together, they have different backgrounds and goals, are from different military branches and so forth. They are not an established decision team with practice making decisions together; hence, the technology of working as a team and making a decision is undefined. This lack of joint decision training forces the joint task force to face two problems: management of the crisis and team coordination.

Admittedly, these parameters do not cover all aspects that affect decisions in the navy (for example, the impact of peacetime activities and the role of leadership). Further, the interaction between the DoD, the White House, the OMB and organizational staffs is mentioned only insofar as it looks like a hierarchy; hence, many of the important nuances of this organizational structure have been left out. Nor have I spoken of the impact of investment strategies and various bureaucratic issues important during peacetime. For the nonce, however, let us consider those parameters suggested as sufficient. One further point is that not all of the parameters listed are unique to the navy; and to the extent that these parameters affect other organizations the results presented will be applicable there as well.

Let us consider now a simulation model, GARCORG, which takes into account at least some of those parameters suggested as important to naval decisions. Since GARCORG can simulate organizations with parameters like those identified for the navy, the results are potentially relevant to crisis management. This model is based on recent advances in decision theory centered around what has been referred to as garbage can models of organizations. Recall that garbage can organizations, as described by Cohen, March and Olsen (1972) are characterized as organized anarchies beset by (1) problematic information flows, (2) unclear decision technology and (3) fluid personnel flows. These characteristics are strikingly like the parameters of decision making identified for the navy, the main difference being the existence of a hierarchical chain of command in the navy, and its absence in the garbage can model. The Cohen, March and Olsen model of garbage can organizations can be combined with hierarchical models or organizational structure (Padgett, 1980) thus creating a system in which it is possible to measure organizational efficiency (see Chapter 8 in this volume).

A program for simulating organizational behavior based on such a system was developed—GARCORG. The mathematical underpinnings of this model are discussed in Chapter 8. GARCORG can be used to simulate the behavior of various types of garbage-can-like organizations and emulate their efficiency levels in both the short and the long run. GARCORG was not designed specifically with the navy in mind; rather, it was designed as a general-purpose tool for testing theories about the impact of organizational structure and information flows on organizational efficiency. However, due to the inherent flexibility in the GARCORG system, it can be used to test out ideas about organizational efficiency in the navy by simply setting the appropriate parameters to resemble those previously suggested.

Let us turn now to a description of the way in which organizations can be simulated using GARCORG. Some of the limitations and features of this simulation program will be examined. Then, to illustrate one of the ways in which GARCORG can be used, a set of results from simulating a wide range of organizational structures using GARCORG will be presented. The results also serve as an exploratory study of the impact of organizational structure and decision flows on organizational efficiency. In turn, the results of this study have important implications for crisis management.

GARCORG is a simulation model, designed to do preliminary explorations of the relationship between various organizational features and efficiency, to study short-term effects of changing various structural and nonstructural features of the organization. Because it was hoped that this, or later expanded versions, would be used as a classroom or analytic tool, the program was written in a user-oriented, interactive, friendly fashion. The program is written in APL on an IBM 370. It allows the user to test the efficiency of organized anarchies by altering various features—for example, size and amount of incoming information. The information flow and the decision structure used for a single time period as currently implemented in GARCORG are similar to the analytic model as developed by Padgett (1980). The efficiency measures used are those discussed in Chapter 8. The organizational model used in this program departs from Padgett's in that it incorporates feedback into the system in terms of processes for transferring lower level personnel, staff members, in and out of various positions.[1] Staff members are not expected to be always available; that is, the composition of the staff is not fixed, new staff members may be added, old ones transferred and so on.

GARCORG allows the user to model a particular organization or set of organizations and the information flows that affect decision making in this organization. The user is asked to specify various structural features of the organization and aggregate flows. Using GARCORG, the user can study the impact of various managerial solutions on the organization's efficiency level simply by testing out different sets of features.

In this paper the GARCORG simulation model is used to explore the causes of inefficiency by looking at the effects of altering various organizational features on the level of organizational efficiency. Note that this paper is not an exhaustive report on all of the capabilities of the GARCORG system, nor a critique thereof. Rather, it is an introduction to an exploratory simulation model, including an investigation of some causes of inefficiency through using this model. In the following section, the organizational structures that can be studied using the GARCORG program will be discussed. First, there will be a brief introduction to the general model used for information and decision flow. Then those features used in the GARCORG program to define an organization will be presented, as will all available options. In a way, this subsection can be thought of as a codebook for using GARCORG. In the following section, short-run organizational behavior will be looked at via computer simulation, thus illustrating some of the capabilities of the GARCORG program. That section can be viewed as an exploration of the causes of inefficiency. Note, although all of the options and features of GARCORG are presented in the second section, they are not all used in the analysis in the third section. Symbols used in analysis and in the computer code are represented by names in bold face type; for example, the number of AEOs is referred to as **AEO** in the calculations. Finally, in the conclusion, the implications of these exploratory findings for crisis management will be considered.

GARCORG—AN OVERVIEW

Garbage Can Hierarchies—The General Model

We will refer to organizations as *garbage can hierarchies*—garbage cans because they are organized anarchies with problematic flows, and hierarchies due to the fact that the people who work in an organization are organized in a hierarchical fashion. The hierarchical form used, like that suggested by Padgett (1980) is set to four tiers. There is a chief executive officer (CEO) in charge of an organization which is composed of several divisions. In charge of each division is an assistant executive officer (AEO) who oversees numerous programs. Each program is run by its own program chief. Under each program chief are a number of staff members who analyze the information that comes in on a particular issue. The chain of command and the decision flow are illustrated in Figure 9.1.

Associated with each division is a particular set of potential issues. This set is time invariant in the short run—for example, the length of the crisis. Associated with each of these issues, in a particular program, is a particular position for a staff member whose job would be to analyze all the information that comes in on that issue. That is, under each program chief, there are as many positions available for staff members (spots) as there are potential issues. Each staff member analyzes information on only one issue, and handles only one aspect of a problem.

The decisions of concern are, for example, of the form *what units should comprise the assault force* or *what equipment should be used to rescue hostages*. Taking this latter example, the CEO in charge of the rescue operation might place a particular assistant (AEO) in charge of determining what type of equipment should be used. The AEO would have each program chief under him give him a recommendation for a particular type of equipment. Then each program chief might request a recommendation from each staff member under him.

The program chiefs make recommendations to the AEO on their programs based on the analyses of the staff members under them for only those issues to which they have access. Thus, there are as many recommendations to the AEO as there are programs. Similarly, the AEO makes one recommendation to the CEO for each of the programs under his jurisdiction based upon the recommendations of the program chiefs under him and, hence, the analyses of all the staff members for each of the programs under him. Then the CEO makes a final decision regarding each of the programs based on the recommendations of the AEOs and, hence, the analyses of all of the staff members in the entire organization.

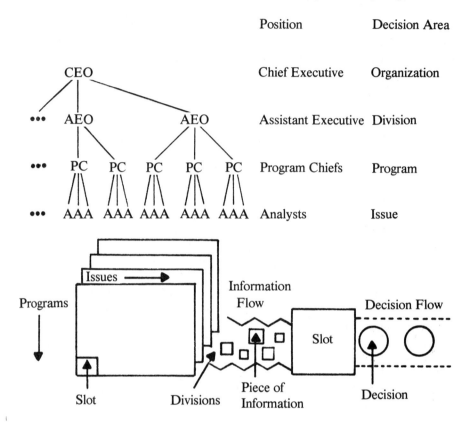

Figure 9.1   Chain of command.

Each AEO can rubber stamp program chief recommendations, thus proposing them as the final decision. Similarly, the CEO can simply rubber stamp the AEO's decision, making it the final decision.[2] In this paper, we will be concerned not so much with the decision-making process per se as with the process by which the staff members are transferred, and the impact of such movement on the organization's efficiency.

Aside from the hierarchical flow, the garbage can hierarchy can be uniquely described for the purposes of simulation by a limited set of features. Each of these features has several possible values that it can take on; for example, the feature *program chief access structure* can take on values like *specialized* or *quasi-specialized*. Each garbage can hierarchy has a level of efficiency that it is achieving, and this level is specific to the features that describe that organization. Further, there are several different ways in which efficiency can be measured, some based on structures and others based on political salience, thus allowing the researcher to use GARCORG to test various theories about the causes of inefficiency. These measures were described in Chapter 8.

Organizational Features

In the GARCORG program, the organizations are described by a set of eleven features (see Table 9.1), each of which can take on several values. By choosing a particular value for each of these features, the user can simulate a particular organization. Each of these features and their values will be described in turn.

SIZE

The size of an organization is simply the total number of people who have "jobs" or positions in that organization [**TOTAL**]. There are four types of "jobs," in hierarchical order the CEO, the AEOs, the program chiefs and the staff members.

With GARCORG, the user can set the initial size of the organization to be *small* (26 people), *medium* (50 people) or *large* (100 or 112 people). Setting the size of the organization also sets the number of divisions (equal to the number of AEOs [**AEOS**]), the number of programs in each division (equal to the number of program chiefs under that AEO) and the number of potential issues per program [**ISSUES**]. The number of staff members can change throughout the course of the simulation; however, this number for any one program chief can never exceed the number of issues. Note, the number of issues denotes the number of "spots" or positions that can be filled by staff members. It is assumed that for the period of interest this number is fixed.

DIFFERENTIATION

Differentiation refers to the width of the organizational tree, the breadth of the product line, or the range of projects. The larger the size of the organization, the greater the effect of differentiation on the overall organizational structure. At higher or executive levels in the organization a differentiated organization will have more slots available than will an undifferentiated organization; as there are more projects, there are more directors or program chiefs (see Figure 9.2). As differentiation is a relative measure, its greatest use is in distinguishing between organizations of nearly the same size.

Table 9.1: Possible Organizational Features

1. size
2. differentiation
3. amount of information per issue over time
4. content of information per issue over time
5. CEO salience assignment
6. AEO salience assignment
7. program chief access structure
8. delay or grace period
9. criterion for transferring staff in
10. criterion for transferring staff out
11. the personnel transfer cutoff level

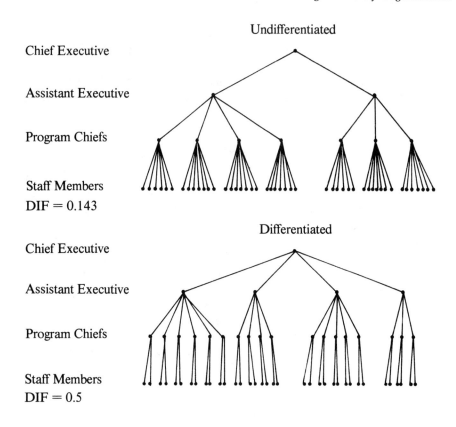

Figure 9.2 Examples of differentiation structures.

For organizations of the same size, a higher level of differentiation leads to a higher executive/staff ratio [**DIF**]. **DIF** measures the level of differentiation as the ratio of program chiefs to staff members. A **DIF** of 0 indicates that the organization is totally undifferentiated, all staff members are under one program chief; and a **DIF** of 1 indicates that there is complete differentiation, one program chief per staff member. In practice, any ratio over one-third is considered to have a high degree of differentiation. Note, the two structures displayed in Figure 9.2 have a **DIF** level of 0.14 and 0.5, respectively.

In **GARCORG**, the differentiation levels are fixed, so the organizations are distinguished as being either differentiated (YES) or undifferentiated (NO). Refer to Appendix A for the exact structures.

AMOUNT OF INFORMATION

During each time period [**t**], for example, a day or a week, a certain amount of information [**AMOUNTINFO**] is acquired by the organization on each issue known to be of potential interest to one of the programs in the organization (a potential issue). This information is acquired whether or not there is a staff member in the organization studying that issue [$\mathbf{ANM_{spi}} = 1$ or 0]. That is, information comes in on a particular issue, to a particular spot, whether or not there is a staff member in that spot. The exact amount of information that comes into an organization for a particular issue at any given time is dependent on the pattern of flow chosen by the user. Regardless of the pattern of flow chosen, for a particular issue [$\mathbf{i}$], for example, rescuing the students in Grenada, at a particular time [$\mathbf{t}$], say June 1983, there is a particular amount of information that comes in to the organization, such as reports from intelligence operatives, orders, political objectives, availability of equipment and so forth.

In theory, there are many ways in which the amount of information that comes in on a specific issue may vary over time, and there are many different patterns possible for the flow. For example, the amount of information may stay constant over time, increase linearly, increase exponentially or decrease in some fashion. Moreover, it may be sinusoidal or have an even more complex pattern. To simplify matters, in the GARCORG program all issues, are treated as the same type of phenomena; that is, for all issues the information flow in terms of the amount of information has the same pattern over time. However, the exact amount of information that comes in on all issues is not equivalent.

Regardless of the time pattern, each issue starts out with a known amount of information, **ANINT**. That is, each issue has its own *initial value* for the average amount of information that came in on that issue at time ($\mathbf{t} = 0$). The initial value, the initial amount of information for each issue, is chosen at random from a uniform distribution over the integers 0 to 100. The pattern for amount of information that is chosen will affect the range of the amount of information that is available during later time periods.

In **GARCORG**, there are four options for information flow available to the user. These options are *constant, linearly increasing, exponentially increasing* and *random*. These options allow the user to model the flow of the amount of information in two ways: as a product of a deterministic process (first three options) or as a stochastic process (last option).[3] For a pictorial representation of these choices, see Figure 9.3.

Deterministic Flow One can argue that the flow of information is deterministic, that at a specific time a certain amount of information comes in on a particular issue. All we know about this piece of information is that x amount came in. Under these circumstances, the amount of information that comes in on a specific issue at a particular time can be modeled as

[1] $\mathbf{AMOUNTINFO} = \mathbf{AINIT} + \mathbf{Bt}$,

where **AINIT** is the initial or base rate at which information comes in, and **B** is a fixed degree of change.

When the user chooses the option *constant*, then $\mathbf{B} = 0$ and $\mathbf{AMOUNTINFO} = \mathbf{AINIT}$. If the option chosen is *linear*, then $\mathbf{B} = 3$. If the option *exponential* is chosen, then the amount of information that comes in is calculated as

[2] $\mathbf{AMOUNTINFO} = \mathbf{e^{t\ +\ AINIT}}$.

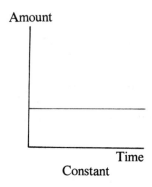

Constant

The amount of information for each issue is set to a random number, 1 to 100

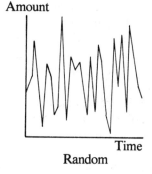

Random

The amount of information for each issue is drawn each time period from a random number, 1 to 100

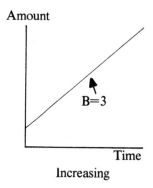

Increasing

The amount of information for each issue is drawn at time (T=O) as a random number, 1 to 100, and increases by 3 each time period

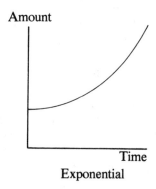

Exponential

The amount of information for each issue is drawn at time (T=0) as a random number, 1 to 100, and increases as . (AINIT)

Figure 9.3   Information flow (amount).

Stochastic Flow   As previously mentioned, another way to view this flow is as the result of a stochastic process; that is, at a certain time there is a distribution for the amount of information that may come in on a particular issue. At a particular time, the amount of information that does come in on a specific issue looks as though it has been chosen at random from a distribution that has a particular mean and variance. The mean of this distribution is allowed to vary over time. In this way, the amount of information that comes in at a particular time on any issue is stochastically determined. Here, the amount of information that comes in on a specific issue at a particular time can be modeled as

[3]   **AMOUNTINFO = AINIT + Bt + C(t)**,

where **AINIT** is the level at which the mean amount of information starts (**t** = 0), **B** is the rate at which the mean changes over time, and **C** is the 0-mean distribution from which the amount of information for that particular spot is chosen for the organization.

In GARCORG, **B** is set to 0, and thus the amount of information is chosen from a distribution (**C**) with a constant mean over time (**A**); that is, the mean amount of information that comes in on that issue is constant over time. However, the actual amount of information that comes in on any issue during any particular time period is random. The constant mean (**A**) is set to 50 pieces of information, and the distribution (**C**) is uniform over the integers 0 to 100.

CONTENT OF INFORMATION

Each piece of information that comes into the organization is of some value. We can think of this value as either the degree of reliability of this piece of information or its degree of content or importance. The point here is that *content* serves to capture the qualitative value-oriented aspect of information, whereas *amount* serves to capture the quantitative aspect of information. Unlike the amount of information that comes in on any particular issue, the content for any particular issue is always assumed to be stochastic. Like amount of information, there are many ways in which the content of the information may vary with time. Content, for any particular issue, is modeled as a random variable with a known mean and variance. The mean is assumed to be a function of time, whereas the variance is not.

The quantitative/qualitative difference between the amount and the content of information is reflected in the measurement scales used. The amount of information, the number of pieces of information, can range from 0 to infinity,[4] whereas the content of information is treated as a percentage, with numeric values ranging from 0% to 100%. A common view of content is in terms of things like value and reliability, on which bounds from 0% to 100% can be placed. For example, one might think of content in terms of the percentage amount of useful information that a particular piece of information has relative to the "ideal" piece of information. A result of this approach is that in terms of content there are end or limiting effects; for example, one sees in increasing/decreasing the average content of information over time that in the long run ($t = \infty$), on average, the content of a particular piece of information for a particular issue will become as good or bad as it can be 100% or 0%.

The content of the information can be viewed as the result of a stochastic process; that is, at a certain time, for a particular issue, there is a distribution for the content of information that may come in on any particular piece of information. At a particular time, the content of information that does come in on a specific issue looks as though it has been chosen at random from a distribution that has a particular mean and variance. The mean of this distribution is allowed to vary over time. In this way, the content of information that comes in at a particular time on any issue is stochastically determined. Here, the content of information that comes in on a specific issue at a particular time can be modeled as

[4]   **CONTENT** = **CINIT** + **Bt** + **C(t)**,

where **CINIT** is the level that the mean amount of information starts at ($\mathbf{t} = 0$), **B** is the rate at which the mean changes over time, and **C** is the 0–mean distribution from which the amount of information for that particular spot is chosen for the organization. **CINIT** + **Bt** is the mean of the content of that information at time **t**.

Regardless of the time pattern, each issue starts out with a known average content of information, **CINIT**. That is, each issue has its own *initial value* for the average content of information that came in on that issue at time ($\mathbf{t} = 0$). The initial value, the initial content of information for each issue, is chosen at random from a uniform distribution over the integers 0 to 100 and scaled to lie between 0 and 1. The pattern for content of information that is chosen will affect the exact range of the content of information that is available during later time periods; however, this range will never lie outside the bounds 0 to 1.

In **GARCORG**, the user can choose one of three ways in which to vary with time the average content of information for any particular issue: *constant* (time invariant), *increasing*, and *decreasing*. These are represented pictorially in Figure 9.4.

Regardless of the option chosen, $\mathbf{C}(t)$ is basically chosen each time period at random from a uniform distribution with a maximum range from $-\,0.25$ to $+\,0.25$. The exact range is different for each issue and is constant over time. The absolute end point of this range is set at time ($\mathbf{t} = 0$) by a random choice from a uniform distribution over 1 to 100, scaled to 0.0025 to 0.25.

If the user chooses the option *constant*, **B** is set to 0, and the mean content of that information is equal to the initial value

[5]   **CONTENTMEAN** = **CINIT**.

Whereas, when the option chosen is *increasing*, **B** is set to 0.01, and

[6]   **CONTENTMEAN** = **CINIT** + 0.01 **t**.

Similarly, when the option chosen is *decreasing*, **B** is set to $-\,0.01$, and

[7]   **CONTENTMEAN** = **CINIT** $-$ 0.01 **t**.

In terms of actual calculation, the following fact was utilized. All the information that arrives on a particular issue is assumed to come from the same distribution in terms of content. Therefore, the distribution of the sum of n samples, the distribution of the total content of information for that issue, has a mean that is also n times the distribution mean and a variance that is also n times as large. This simplifies calculation of content, since to determine the total incoming content we need choose only once from this summed distribution. In essence, the equations previously presented were used with the appropriate scaling by the amount of information.

CEO SALIENCY ASSIGNMENT

For a particular issue, CEO salience (**PSALIENCE**) is simply the answer to the question "Does the CEO consider this issue to be salient to this program?" (**PSALIENCE** = 1 if the answer is yes, and **PSALIENCE** = 0 if the

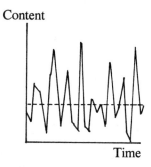

Content

Time

Constant Average

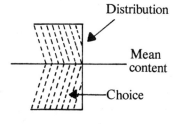

Distribution

Mean content

Choice

Content Distribution

The mean content of information for each issue is drawn at random from a uniform distribution over 1 to 100

The content is set by a random choice from a distribution. The mean is set by the pattern chosen. The range is set at time (T=O) to at most -0.25 to +0.25

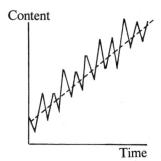

Content

Time

Increasing Mean

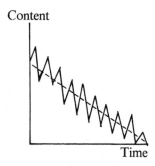

Content

Time

Decreasing Mean

The mean content of information for each issue is drawn at time (T=O) at random from a uniform distribution and increases by 0.01 each time period

The mean content of information for each issue is drawn at time (T=O) at random from a uniform distribution and decreases by 0.01 from each time period

Figure 9.4 Information flow (content).

answer is no.) It is expected that the CEO will change his mind over which issues are salient. However, the mechanism behind this change, or for that matter even the pattern of change, is unclear. This makes it difficult to model saliency. To allow change over time and yet retain some user control, the following scheme was used.

Political saliency is assigned at random each time period. This is done by choosing for each spot an integer chosen at random from the uniform distribution over the integers 0 to 100. Then this number is compared against the saliency level (**PSP**) provided by the user. If the integer is less than the saliency level, it is set to 1, otherwise to 0. The result of this comparison determines whether or not that issue is considered salient by the CEO (1 yes, 0 no). This process assures that, on average, the percentage of issues considered salient by the CEO will be equal to the level set by the user (**PSP**). That is, during each time period the CEO reevaluates the salience of each particular issue to the respective program. Over time the salience of a particular issue this appears as a random sequence of *yesses* and *nos* (1s and 0s).

The user sets the level once and it remains fixed throughout the simulation. For example, if the user sets the salience level at 0.7, then each time period 70% of the issues would be considered salient by the CEO, although exactly which 70% are decided at random. By setting the saliency level high, the user makes it less likely that a particular issue is not salient at a particular time. In effect this increases the length of a saliency assignment, whereas by setting a lower level of saliency, the user effectively increases the rapidity with which the CEO changes his mind.

AEO SALIENCY ASSIGNMENT

Salience for the AEOs is assigned in the same manner for the CEO. As the user first sets up the organization using GARCORG, he is asked for the level of AEO saliency (**ASP**), an integer between 0 and 100. This then sets the percentage of 1s in the AEO saliency matrix, which is redefined each time period.

THE PROGRAM CHIEF ACCESS STRUCTURE

An access structure, as one might expect, simply describes who has access to what information. In this case, we are interested in that information to which the program chiefs have access. The information is the analysis or recommendation made by the staff members who analyze issues that are relevant to the program chief's program. The decision the program chief makes is dependent on which of these analyses he has access to. Access, in this case for the program chief (**PCACCESS**), is simply the answer to the question "Does the program chief have access to this issue?" (**PCACCESS** = 1 if the answer is yes, and **PCACCESS** = 0 if the answer is no.)

An interesting point is that a program chief may not have access to the analyses of all the staff members working under him. For example, one of the staff members might have been told by one of the AEOs to work on project x, but the staff member's immediate superior may not have the right security clearance to look at that staff member's report. Clearly, this would be inefficient. The program chief access structure (**PCACCESS**) simply defines which program chief in any given division has access to which of the potential issues for that division. Thus, if the personnel transfer criterion, the job assignment criterion, does not take into account the program chief access structure, it is likely that staffs will be transferred in and put to work on issues such that the analyses are inaccessible by the staffs' immediate superior.

In **GARCORG**, four types of access structures for the program chiefs are available: *random, specialized, quasi-specialized*, and *total*. The access structures mentioned are illustrated in Figure 9.5.

A *random access* structure is one where the issues that a program chief has access to are assigned at random. There is no structural design as to which program chief, or how many of them have access to a given information.

A *specialized access* structure means that no two program chiefs in the same division have access to the same issue. This corresponds to a matrix of 0s with 1s along the diagonals.

A *quasi-specialized access* structure allows two program chiefs to have access to some of the same issues, but each program chief has some issues that are peculiar to him.

All program chiefs have access to information on all issues in the *total access* structure. This corresponds to a matrix of all 1s.

Each AEO is assumed to have access to all the information available to the program chiefs under his direction. Logically, this is the anding of the rows for each column. Only where the program chief access structure is total is it guaranteed that the AEO access structure will be total. Further, under

Total

1	1	1	1	1	1	1	1	1
1	1	1	1	1	1	1	1	1
1	1	1	1	1	1	1	1	1
1	1	1	1	1	1	1	1	1

Specialized

1	1	0	0	0	0	0	0	0
0	0	1	1	0	0	0	0	0
0	0	0	0	1	1	0	0	0
0	0	0	0	0	0	1	1	0

Random

1	0	0	1	1	0	1	0	0
0	0	1	1	0	1	0	0	1
1	0	0	0	0	0	0	1	0
1	0	1	0	1	0	1	1	0

Quasi-Specialized

1	1	1	0	0	0	0	0	0
0	0	1	1	1	0	0	0	0
0	0	0	0	1	1	1	0	0
0	0	0	0	0	0	1	1	1

Figure 9.5 Examples of program chief access structures.

a random access structure for the program chiefs, it is possible that there will be some issues to which no AEO has access.

PERSONNEL TRANSFERENCE CRITERIA AND CUTOFF

The personnel transference criterion is simply the answer to the question "On what criteria are staff members moved in or out of a particular position in this garbage can hierarchy?" Criteria for transferring staff members in or out of a particular "spot" can be defined separately or jointly, although identical options are available. Obviously there are many reasons why one might transfer staff members: incompetence, lack of money, lack of work, political value and so on. In GARCORG there are three criteria: amount of information available *(amount)*, content of information available *(content)* and political salience *(salience)*.

Associated with each criterion for transferring personnel is a cutoff level or threshold **(TH)**. Should the value of the criterion for a particular issue be above or below the cutoff level (threshold) for that criterion during a certain number of consecutive time periods (**R**, the grace period) the staff member is transferred in or out of that spot.[5] Recall that there is at most, at any one time, one particular staff member associated with each issue; that is, each issue defines a particular spot in the organization. Therefore, a staff member's transfer into a spot means that someone will be working on that issue; whereas a staff member's transfer out of a spot means that no one will be working on it. In GARCORG the user is asked to set the length of the grace period **[R]**. The grace period can be any number of time periods. The three transference criteria result in a total of 9 personnel transfer schemes. With the ability to adjust cutoff levels, and the length of the grace period, they create an environment in which the user can test a variety of managerial schemes.

Criterion Based on Amount When the criterion is *amount*, a staff member is transferred in or out of a position involving analysis of a particular issue because the amount of information (**AMOUNTINFO**) arriving over for the last **R** time periods on that issue is higher or lower than the established threshold (**THA**). If the user chooses the option *amount* for transfers, GARCORG prompts him for the cutoff level, the threshold. This can be any number between 0 and 100. Since the amount of information generally tends to stay between 0 and 100,[6] the most likely value for the amount of incoming information for a particular issue is 50. In this case, if the threshold is set above 50, most of the staff will be transferred out. The project, in other words, would be aborted.

Criteria Based on Content When the criterion is *content*, then staff members are transferred in or out if the average content of all information arriving on that issue for the last **R** time periods is higher or lower than the cutoff level, the established threshold (**THC**) for the content of information. If the user chooses the option *content* for transfers, then GARCORG prompts the user for the cutoff level for content. This can be any number between 0 and 100. But where the threshold for amount (**THA**) is interpreted as the number of units of information, the threshold for content (**THC**) is treated as a percentage. In this case, if the user specifies a content cutoff level equal to 50%, then staff members are transferred out if the average content of information arriving during each of the **R** time periods is less than 50%.

Criteria Based on Political Saliency   Finally, when the criterion is *political saliency*, staff members are transferred based on whether or not the CEO, for the last **R** time periods, considered that issue to be salient to the program for which it was being analyzed. For example, the CEO can assign a staff member who specializes in designing assault forces to a crisis management team if he feels that having an assault force is necessary to the management of the crisis. Here there is no cutoff per se. An issue either is considered to be salient by the CEO or it is not. For example, consider when the grace period is set to 3 (**R** = 3) and there is a staff member working on an issue that the CEO does not consider to be salient during this time period. If he does not consider it to be salient during the next two time periods, then that staff member will be transferred out, and vice versa for transfers.

SIMULATION ANALYSIS

The GARCORG system can be used to study the relationship between various features of garbage can hierarchies and the levels of efficiencies that these organizations achieve. In this section, GARCORG is used to study the effect of changing various organizational features on the efficiency levels of the organization in the long and short run. The following analysis is not intended to be definitive; rather, it is presented as indicative of the type of analyses that can be done using the GARCORG program. One way to view this section is as an exploration of the causes of efficiency.

Method

In GARCORG, assigning a value to each of the features discussed in the previous section uniquely identifies an organization. In this way, GARCORG can simulate as many organizations as there are combinations of these features. This allows the user to simulate 2,592 organizations without even altering the grace period (**R**), the AEO's saliency level (**ASP**) or the CEO saliency level (**PSP**), let alone the thresholds for personnel transfer (**THA** and **THC**).

To study efficiency by focusing on the comparison of changes in structural features and flows versus changes in managerial parameters like the personnel transfer criteria, a limited set of values was assigned to the features (see Table 9.2). This allows the simulation of 36 organizations, whose behavior is averaged for a particular type of organization to produce the "behavior" of one *well-behaved* organization of that type. Of these 36 organizations, half of them (18 organizations) are small and half are large, half of them are differentiated and half are undifferentiated. All the organizations have a quasi-specialized

Table 9.2: GARCORG Features Used in Simulations		
PARAMETERS	*VALUES*	*NUMBER*
size	small large	2
differentiation	yes no	2
amount of information	constant linear random	3
content of information	constant	1
criteria for transferring in =		
criteria for transferring out	amount content saliency	3
amount threshold	25	1
content threshold	0.25	1
program chief access structure	quasi-specialized	1
AEO's saliency level	50	1
CEO saliency level	50	1
grace period	3	1
total organizations		36

program chief access structure. Further, one-third of the organizations (12) have a constant flow for the amount of incoming information, one-third have an increasing flow, and one-third have a random flow. Finally, the criteria for transferring staff members in and out of a particular spot are set to amount in a third of the organizations, to content in another third and to salience in the final third. In these simulations the criterion for transferring staff members into a spot is the same as that for transferring a staff member out of a spot.

The total number of time periods analyzed for each of the organizations simulated was 20—**TIME** = 20. If we think of these time periods as months, then what is being simulated is the organization's macrobehavior over a 20-month period, a year and three-quarters. All four efficiency measures were calculated for each of the simulated organizations for each of the 20 time periods. GARCORG is designed so that features of the organizations are functionally independent—that is, no feature is a function of another. Thus, the data on each organization can be thought of as independent random samples. Therefore, the data can be combined for all organizations of a particular type,[7] time period by time period. This allows the calculation of a mean efficiency for a particular type of organization at a particular time, as well as the standard deviation and other statistics. In the following figures, the average behavior of a particular type of organization for a particular measure of efficiency is presented versus the average behavior of another type of organization.

The statistical test to compare the effect of organizational type for a particular category of efficiency is simply the difference-of-means test (Beals, 1972).[8] This is a two-tailed test. The significance level was set at 0.05. The null hypothesis, H_o, is that the difference between the two means is zero (0). In other words, if the two means are significantly different, we can be 95% confident in saying that the organizational type with the higher mean promotes more efficiency in a garbage can hierarchy than does the type with the lower mean, ceteris paribus.

In the following figures, each line represents the average value for that measure of efficiency of all organizations with that particular feature value. For example, in Figure 9.6, the top line is the average level of structural efficiency at the program chief level for all the small organizations simulated.

The data gathered allow comparisons over the effects of size, differentiation, amount flow and personnel transfer criteria. The effect of each of these features will be considered separately, and in some cases in pairs. For the organizations examined, structural efficiency at the AEO's level (E2) tended to behave as did structural efficiency at the program chief level (E1), as AEO's access is defined in terms of program chief access. Due to the way efficiency is measured, the organization will be inefficient at the AEO's level in the case it is inefficient at the program chief level. In the following simulations, that political efficiency at the AEO's level (E3) also tended to behave like political efficiency at the CEO level (E4). This is an artifact arising because the level of AEO saliency was set equal to the CEO saliency level. Due to these considerations, in the following subsections only the data on the measures E1 and E4 will be presented.

Efficiency Due to Size—Questionable

In Figure 9.6, the effect of size on organizational efficiency is presented. Note, small organizations are both structurally (E1) and politically (E4) more efficient than are large organizations. This difference can be explained by the bad spot syndrome. Because the measures of efficiency are based solely on the number of bad spots that are filled by staff members—positions for staff members where the issue worked on is either inaccessible by their superior or not salient to the superior—the more bad spots there are, the more inefficient the organization. This is the effect referred to as the *bad spot syndrome*.

Larger organizations have more spots, more positions available for staff members, than do small organizations; hence, all else being the same, large organizations have a greater potential for bad spots than do small organizations. Thus, at least in the short run, large organization will be much less efficient than small organizations, both politically and structurally. Referring to Figure 9.6, we see that this is, in fact, the case.

The bad spot syndrome should be mitigated by time. Basically, because small organizations have fewer spots, and hence fewer bad spots, they also have a greater likelihood of having staff members assigned to any particular spot, including the bad spots. This is especially true if the personnel transfer criterion does not take the value of the spot into account[9]—that is, if staff members are allowed to be transferred into bad spots, then over time the effect of size will be diminished. Thus, in the long run, there should be less difference between large and small organizations. The data in Figure 9.6 support this argument; although the efficiency levels for small and large organizations start out being significantly different, they rapidly converge.

Recall that none of the personnel transfer criteria take the program chiefs' access structure into account. Thus, as more staff members are transferred about, there is an increasing potential that the issues they are analyzing are not

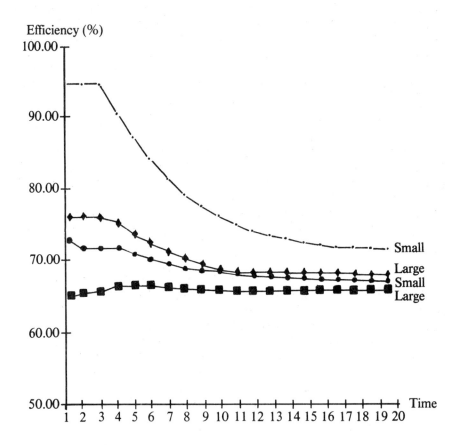

Figure 9.6 Efficiency by size.
Changes in efficiency levels over time as the size of the organization changes. Difference in means for structural efficiency is significant at the 0.05 level for only the first 8 time periods, and only for the first time period for political efficiency. Number of Organizations = 18 of each size. Structural efficiency (E1), small; structural efficiency (E1), large; political efficiency, (E4), small; political efficiency (E4), large.

those to which the program chief over them has access; therefore they are in a bad spot. Thus, one expects the level of structural efficiency to drop, as it in fact does.

The bad spot syndrome will also be mitigated by scaling. That is, to the extent that the ratios of executives to accessible issues in the case of structural efficiency, and executives to salient issues in the case of political efficiency, remain constant across size, the size of the organization will have little effect on overall efficiency. (In the organizations studied, the level of accessibility was not held constant across size, but the level of political saliency was. Thus, we would expect a greater difference in the level of structural efficiency by size than we would in the level of political efficiency. As was expected, the difference in size is negligible with respect to the political efficiency measure (E4) during all but the first time period.)

This analysis suggests that in the short run small organizations will be more efficient than large organizations, especially structurally. However, in the long run size does not appear to have a significant effect on organizational efficiency.

Differentiated Organizations Are Most Efficient

Differentiated organizations tend to be more efficient than undifferentiated ones, both structurally (E1) and politically (E4), as shown by Figure 9.7. Note that undifferentiated organizations relative to differentiated organizations of the same size have more staff members. Hence, they have a higher likelihood of having staff members working on issues to which their superiors do not have access or which are not considered salient.

If the personnel transfer criterion does not maintain the ratio of executives to staff members (**DIF**), then over time the effect of differentiation should be mitigated. As the ratio of managers to staff members increases, as the organization becomes more differentiated, more potential locations for staff members open up; hence, the number of potentially bad spots both politically and structurally increases. Further, the more differentiated the organization, the more potential spots there are, and, for the same size organization, the fewer staff members. While this leads to efficiency in the short run, in the long run it means that there are more openings for staff members. Given a personnel transfer policy such that staff members are more likely to be moved in than out (as was the case for two-thirds of these simulations) the more likely it is both that staff size will increase and also that the net effect will be a decrease in the overall level of efficiency. For undifferentiated organizations, the situation starts out worse, with more staff members and fewer potential spots because of the low number of available positions, however, there are relatively few positions for new staff members, the size of the staff cannot increase as much, and therefore the efficiency level will remain unchanged or might even improve.

Structurally, this trend is exacerbated by the fact that there are fewer executives in undifferentiated organizations than in differentiated organizations, each executive has more responsibility, and has access to a wider range of issues. Thus, vis-à-vis the available positions, there are relatively fewer potentially bad spots. Note that, in the simulation results in Figure 9.7, by the 19th time period, differentiation no longer has a significant effect on the structural efficiency level. However, in terms of political efficiency, although both differentiated and undifferentiated organizations are becoming similar by time 20, it is still the case that differentiated organizations are significantly more politically efficient.

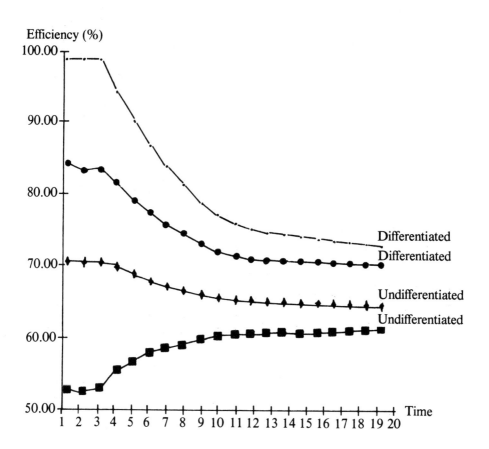

Figure 9.7 Efficiency by differentiation. Changes in efficiency levels over time as the differentiation of the organization changes. Differences in means are significant at the 0.05 level during all but the last two time periods for structural efficiency and for all time periods for political efficiency. Number of Organizations = 18 of each type. Structural efficiency (E1), differentiated; structural efficiency (E1), undifferentiated; political efficiency (E4), differentiated; political efficiency (E4), undifferentiated.

Information Format Has Little Effect on Efficiency

Changes in the pattern of the amount of incoming information appear to have little or no effect on either structural (E1) or political (E4) efficiency (see Figure 9.8). Admittedly, as the pattern for the amount of incoming information shifts from constant to random to increasing, the organizations become less efficient, both structurally (E1) and politically (E4). While these differences increase over time, at no time are they statistically significant.

When the amount of incoming information increases linearly over time, then if the criterion for personnel transfer has anything to do with information,

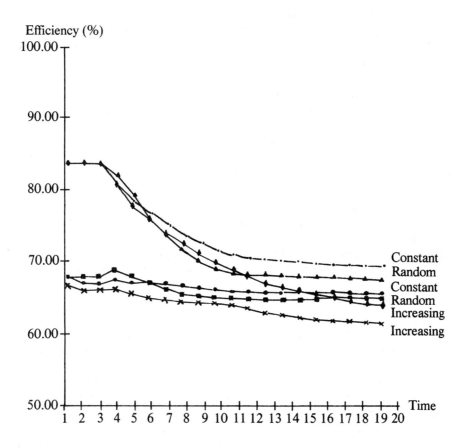

Figure 9.8 Efficiency by amount of information. Changes in efficiency levels over time as the amount of information that comes into the organization changes. Differences in means for each of the efficiency measures are not significant at the 0.05 level for any time period. Number of organizations = 12 for each amount type. Structural efficiency (E1), constant amount; structural efficiency (E1); increasing amount; structural efficiency (E1), random amount; political efficiency (E4); constant amount; political efficiency (E4), increasing amount; political efficiency (E4), random amount.

more staff members will be transferred in than out.[10] The larger the number of staff members, the greater the potential for transfer into bad spots, to work on issues that are not salient to the CEO or accessible to the program chief. This would be why, given a flow of information with the amount increasing linearly over time, the organization would be less efficient. This suggests that an exponential distribution for the amount of incoming information over time would have led to even more inefficiency.

Multiple Managerial Solutions

The personnel transfer criterion utilized has a dramatic effect on the efficiency of the organization both structurally (E1) and politically (E4). As can be seen in Figure 9.9, although all the organizations tend to start out with similar levels of efficiency, they quickly disperse according to the personnel transfer scheme chosen. For the organizations simulated, this meant that those organizations where the criterion was content were the most efficient, those where the personnel transfer criterion was saliency were second, and those where the criterion was amount were the least efficient.

The important point here is not that a particular personnel transfer criterion produces a more efficient organization but that the personnel transfer criterion used has a greater effect on organizational efficiency than either the structural features—size and differentiation—or the problematic flows—amount and content of information. This means that the efficiency of the organization can be tuned by the manager by altering the way in which the staff members are transferred and that such changes will be not only easier to implement but more effective than making changes in the organization per se. Another point is that such changes will quickly alter the organization's efficiency. For example, in Figure 9.9, in roughly two full personnel transfer cycles ($2\mathbf{R}$) the organizations are fairly close to their final values.

As to the exact simulated results, the high efficiency levels of organizations where the personnel transfer is based on content results from the fact that the threshold is set so high ($\mathbf{THC} = 1$) that eventually all the staff members will be fired. The organizations will be efficient only because with no one working, no one can be working on an issue to which his superior does not have access or does not consider salient. Organizations with a personnel transfer criterion based on saliency are next in terms of efficiency because the particular level of saliency chosen resulted in a higher level of transfers off the staff than did the personnel transfer criteria based on amount. An interesting future study would be one where the criteria were set such that the level of transfers in or out were equivalent regardless of criteria; that is, $\mathbf{H}$ and $\mathbf{F}$ are constant across criteria. In a sense, the CEO can only get involved in an arbitrary fashion, as his involvement is based on how salient he believes an issue to be, and this salience is time variant. The question is whether intervention in this arbitrary fashion is worse than no intervention or intervention in a controlled fashion (e.g., based on content or amount). The study proposed above would allow this question to be tested.

Another important point is that having a criterion for personnel transfer that takes into account the value of the spot does not guarantee efficiency. (In the cases where the personnel transfer criterion was based on saliency, the organizations were still not very efficient politically. The manager could do better by choosing another personnel transfer scheme.)

Value of Results

The simulated results tend to approach asymptotically the expected values calculated in Chapter 8 for the respective measures of efficiency. Therefore,

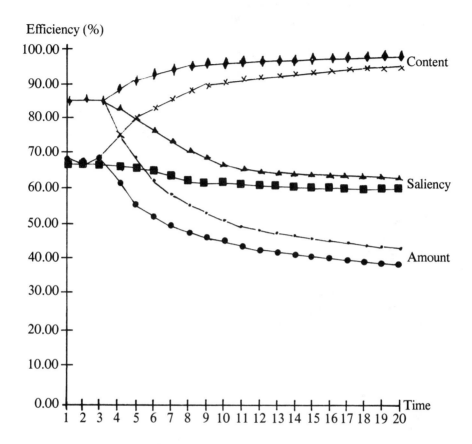

Figure 9.9 Efficiency by transfer criteria. Change in efficiency levels over time as the personnel transfer mechanism used by the organization is altered. Differences in means for both types of efficiency are significant at the 0.05 level after the third or fourth time period. Number of organizations = 12 of each type. Structural efficiency (E1), hiring/firing based on amount of information; structural efficiency (E1), hiring/firing based on content of information; structural efficiency (E1), hiring/firing based on saliency to CEO; political efficiency (E4), hiring/firing based on amount of information; political efficiency (E4), hiring/firing based on content of information; political efficiency (E4), hiring/firing based on saliency to CEO.

the simulation model can be used to predict organizational behavior accurately in both the long and short run. As to the robustness of the results, it should be noted that multiple simulations of the same organization do produce slightly different empirical results, although they have the same quantitative behavior.

For example, in Figure 9.10 the same organization has been simulated six times, and its behavior in terms of political efficiency at the CEO level (E4) is plotted. In Figure 9.11 the structural efficiency levels (E1) for that organization

are plotted. The organization simulated was a small, undifferentiated organization where the amount of incoming information and average content of that
information are constant over time. Further, the organization has a quasi-
specialized program chief access structure, schemes based on amount for
transferring in and out, the CEO saliency level and AEO's saliency level set
to 50, the threshold to 25 and the delay period to 3.

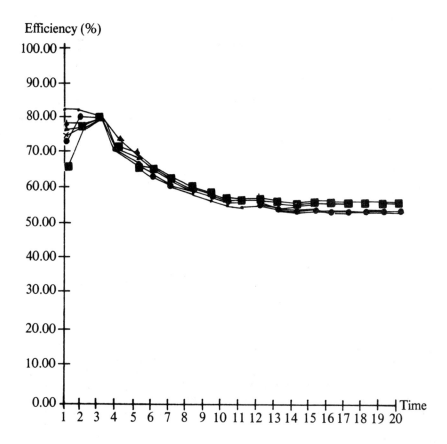

Figure 9.10 Example of political efficiency range. Changes in political efficiency at
the CEO level over time for the same organization. This shows the deviation in
efficiency that can occur for a small, undifferentiated organization where the amount of
incoming information and the content is constant over time. The hiring/firing scheme
is based on the amount of information. Six simulations are shown.

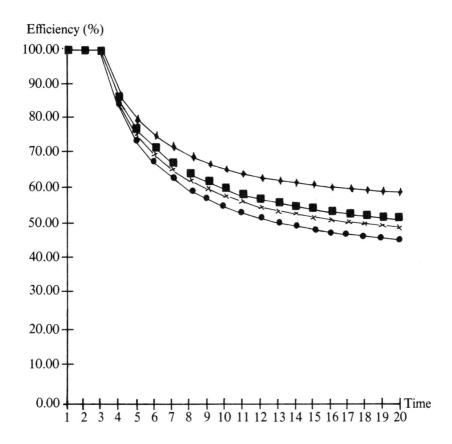

Figure 9.11 Example of structural efficiency range. Changes in structural efficiency at the program chief level over time for the same organization as in Figure 9.10. This shows the deviation in efficiency that can occur for a small, undifferentiated organization where the amount of incoming information and the content is constant over time. The hiring/firing scheme is based on the amount of information. Six simulations are shown.

Note, for political efficiency the simulated runs begin much more dispersed than they finish, moving from a 17.3-point spread to a 3-point spread. For structural efficiency, the simulations start out identical and then disperse to a 12.39-point spread. Referring back to some of the earlier figures, the reader will see that the average difference in types of organizations was often smaller than these spreads.

In the current study, the organizational behavior looked at was an average over a large number of different organizations. It is not clear that this averaged behavior is a true indicator of organizational behavior. As the above figures indicate, the degree of difference among organizations with the same characteristics is small. However, it is still within the same range as the differences in behavior for particular types of organizations. Thus, a more thorough analysis would be one in which the effect of organizational type on efficiency level is checked against differences in efficiency level for the same organization. For example, an ANOVA could be performed to see if the deviations among simulations of the same organization are greater or lesser than deviations across types of organizations.

Short-Run versus Long-Run Efficiency

In terms of the time trends, organizations asymptotically approach equilibrium. For that matter, the equilibrium they approach is the analytically predicted value. Exactly when equilibrium is reached is dependent on the type of organization. For the organizations simulated, most have basically reached equilibrium by 20 time periods.

Short-run behavior tends to be somewhat different than long-run behavior. For example, organizations where the amount of incoming information is random or increasing are slightly more efficient in the short run but less efficient in the long run than organizations where the incoming information is constant. Undifferentiated organizations tend to become more efficient over time, especially politically. This is probably due to the transferring out of excess staff members. If the personnel transfer criterion is based on amount, then those organizations where the amount of arriving information is random are the most efficient in the short run.

The smaller the organization, the more efficient it is in the short run. However, in the long run size basically does not alter the level of efficiency achieved. Similarly, differentiated structures tend to be more efficient in the short run; but over time the behaviors converge. This suggests that to make long-term changes in efficiency levels, structural alterations are not necessary. Rather, they will only lead to short-term changes in efficiency. The problematic data flows that characterize garbage can anarchies are like the structure in which they are embedded, ineffective in terms of altering efficiency levels.

CONCLUSIONS

There are several general policy considerations that can be drawn from this analysis. First, if one is setting up an organization where the technology will be unclear (i.e., a garbage can hierarchy) then the preferred structure for minimizing overall inefficiency is a small, highly differentiated organization where the program chiefs' access structure is quasi-specialized. Moreover, the number "overlaps" in the access structure should be as high as other cost considerations allow, so as to minimize structural inefficiency relative to program chief access.

Second, if the organization is faced with problematic data flows, it will not necessarily be inefficient. If the data flows are extreme—for example, incredibly high rates of information or extremely low density or reliability—the flows, in the long run, will affect the organization's efficiency levels if the criterion for transferring personnel takes these flows into account. The simulations suggest that, regardless of the flow, the manager should be able to increase overall efficiency without altering the data flows per se.

Given an existing organization, it should be possible to increase overall efficiency by changing the criterion on which the staff members are transferred, or even just the threshold used in making the changeover decision. Which scheme for transfers in and out is best for which organization, and whether or not such schemes should be mixed, is a point for further research. In the meantime, however, it should be noted that a personnel transfer scheme based on political saliency does not guarantee high levels of efficiency in terms of saliency.

Further, if the data flows are stochastic, altering the delay period can have a major effect on the efficiency levels. To begin with, the length of time that it takes to reach equilibrium is, to an extent, a function of the delay period (R). The longer the delay, the longer it will take to reach equilibrium. However, the actual effect of R is dependent on the probability of being greater than, less than or equal to the threshold for personnel transfer. Thus, the actual effect of R is, in part, dependent on the level at which the threshold is set. The threshold levels can be set as high or as low as one desires in order to achieve the desired level of efficiency. An interesting future study would be a comparison study of the effects of changing the criterion threshold versus changing the delay period.

As a final note, both the structural and the political measures of efficiency were based on "bad spots," on knowing the number of staff members working on issues to which their superiors did not have access or did not consider salient. These particular measures of efficiency have the disadvantage that organizations with no staff members are perfectly efficient, as are organizations with staff members only in the "good spots." Another notion of inefficiency would be based on knowing the number of "good" spots in which there were no staff members. It would be interesting to check the personnel transfer criteria against each other in terms of these two, in a sense, competing measures of efficiency. An important point to remember is that different personnel transfer criteria may increase or decrease different types of organizational efficiency. Thus, the way in which one defines efficiency becomes a critical factor.

Implications for Crisis Management

The movement from a general peacetime situation to a crisis situation provokes many changes in the environment that the navy, as an organization, must deal with. Let us assume that, from an organizational standpoint, the goal of the navy is to establish and maintain an organization that can deal with crises and yet maintain a global ready state during peacetime. We can view general peacetime activity and the state of being ready for World War III as being the long-run behavior of the military organization. Crisis management can be viewed as the short-run behavior, due to the explosive nature and short time frame of crises. Thus, the dual objective of crisis management and global readiness can be met if we can create an organization that exhibits high levels of short-run efficiency without dramatically lowering its long-run efficiency levels.

As noted earlier, one of the parameters of naval decision making is the presence of volatile information flows; for example as a situation reaches crisis proportions, the information flow will change its characteristics, going perhaps from a flow that is constant or linear in both content and amount of information to a flow with perhaps very ambiguous content and extremely high amounts of information. Another parameter, unreliable information, is also exacerbated during a crisis. The information may not actually be more unreliable, but there is certainly less time to check it out, and it is therefore effectively viewed as more unreliable. Further, during a crisis situation personnel are transferred, joint task forces are established, and so forth. Thus, the personnel flows parameter becomes increasingly volatile. The technology of decision making becomes increasingly unclear. During crises, saliencies appear to shift radically. This may just be due to differences in the perceived political objective and the actual political objective, or it may be due to real changes in objectives. In either case, the point remains that saliences may be unstable during a crisis. Finally, the short time frame of a crisis often makes retraining and equipment testing unfeasible, thus increasing the impact of rapidly changing technology. Taken together, these parameter changes suggest that the movement from a peacetime situation to a crisis situation is one that thrusts the military organization from acting in a standard organizational arena to acting in a garbage can arena. From an organizational standpoint, to effectively deal with crises we want to structure the organization such that it can rapidly move from a peacetime configuration to a crisis management configuration, and the configuration chosen for crisis management should exhibit high levels of short-term efficiency regardless of what its long-term efficiency profile looks like. Assuming reconfiguration is impossible, then we want to utilize that organizational structure that is highly efficient in the long run for very steady flows, and yet highly efficient in the short run for extremely altered information flows.

In the long run, size makes little difference on efficiency; however, in the short run small organizations are more efficient than large organizations. Differentiated organizations are more efficient in the short run, and might be a little more efficient in the long run. A possible reason here is that in a highly differentiated organization the chain of responsibility has been established such that most problems are dealt with at the lowest possible level, thus reducing the number of problems that the CEO and AEOs have to deal with. Thus, if an organization is to deal with crises efficiently, it should be structured as a small, highly differentiated organization.

Recall that the impact of the information flow on organizational efficiency could be moderated by the personnel transfer criteria. While the results presented herein are only exploratory, they do suggest that if the CEO is given control over transfers, if he is allowed to adjust his staff as he sees fit, if the task force or the navy as a whole is not locked into a particular method for moving personnel, then high efficiency levels can be maintained by simply altering the criteria for transference as the characteristics of the information flows change. This does not mean that the transference criteria should be based on saliency, how important a particular issue is to the CEO; recall from Figure 9.9 that CEO saliency does not guarantee efficiency. Rather, the point is that by promoting management flexibility by, for example, allowing the CEO to switch the criteria for transferring from one based on content of information to one based on amount of information, the navy creates an organizational structure that has the flexibility to deal efficiently with crises.

To summarize, to create an organization that is capable of dealing efficiently with crises without impairing its long-run capabilities, the navy should be structured as a flexible organization where it is possible to establish task forces rapidly. To maintain long-run efficiency, the peacetime organization should be structured as a highly differentiated unit. The task forces should be structured as small, highly differentiated units, with maximum flexibility for the CEO. The CEO should be given complete control over personnel transfers.

It is provocative to note that this is essentially the organizational structure of the joint task force that Admiral Metcalf commanded in Grenada. There are many reasons for the success of his mission, among which I would suggest is the fact that he, as CEO, had a great deal of flexibility over personnel and commandeered an organizational structure with a high short-run efficiency portfolio. Other reasons for his success seem to include an equivalence of perceived and actual political objectives, the movement of responsibility and authority to the lowest reasonable level (the decisions of "on the spot" commanders were backed up), the establishment of strong lines of communication and personal leadership. While the current GARCORG program does not have the flexibility or power to model these last two items, it can be used to model the first two. That is, the equivalence of perceived and actual political objectives can be roughly modeled as having a constant saliency matrix. Similarly, the movement of responsibility and authority to lower levels can be modeled as high levels of "rubber stamping." Hence, GARCORG could be used to model the impact of these parameters on the crisis management behavior, on the short-run efficiency of the organization.

NOTES

1. This can be thought of either as personnel transfers or as the actual hiring or firing of individuals.

2. For a more detailed description, the reader is referred to either the GARCORG program or the paper by John Padgett (1980).

3. For more details on the actual formalization, see Chapter 8.

4. Only the *linear* and *exponential* options allow the amount of information per issue per time period to exceed 100.

5. The grace or delay period allows the user to eliminate minor fluctuations. Note, the effect of **R**, the delay or grace period, on organized efficiency is analyzed in Chapter 8.

6. This would not be true if one is using either of the *increasing* options, in which case, eventually, a staff member would be transferred into every spot.

7. A particular type of organization has the same value for one feature regardless of the values used for the other features. For example, all small organizations are of one type.

8. No tests were done to estimate whether or not some average type of organizational efficiency was different from zero, because all efficiency measures were constrained to lie between zero and one. Statistical tests on means tend to require that the distribution of the means is normal at least in the limit. For the case in hand, the central limit theorem does not apply due to the boundary conditions. Thus, the test used for differences in means cannot be considered conclusive (see Beals, 1972).

9. In two-thirds of the organizations simulated, the personnel transfer criterion did not take spot into account.

10. As the amount of information increases, then even if the average content is low per piece of information, the total incoming content will be higher. Therefore, whether the personnel transfer criterion is based on amount or content, staff size will increase. Now, if the mean of the content of the information is also increasing, even more staff members will be transferred in, whereas if the mean of the content is decreasing, then fewer staff members will be transferred in.

REFERENCES

Beals, R. E. *Statistics for Economists.* New York: Rand McNally, 1972.

Cohen, Michael R., March, James, G., and Olsen, Johan P. "A Garbage Can Model of Organizational Choice." *Administrative Science Quarterly* 17 (1972): 1–25.

Padgett, J. F. "Managing Garbage Can Hierarchies." *Administrative Science Quarterly* 25 (1980): 583–604.

APPENDIX A
ORGANIZATIONAL STRUCTURES USED IN GARCORG

Structure 1—Small, Undifferentiated

CEO	1			
AEOs	2			
Program Chiefs	2	2		
Staff	4	6	6	5

Structure 2—Medium, Undifferentiated

CEO	1	
AEOs	2	
Program Chiefs	4	3
Staff	6 7 7 8	6 7 8

Structure 3—Large, Undifferentiated

CEO	1		
AEOs	3		
Program Chiefs	4	3	4
Staff	8 9 6 8	8 7 8	8 10 7 6

Structure 4—Small, Differentiated

CEO	1		
AEOs	3		
Program Chiefs	2	3	2
Staff	2 3	3 3 2	2 2

Structure 5—Medium, Differentiated

CEO	1			
AEOs	4			
Program Chiefs	6	4	5	3
Staff	2 2 2 2 2 2	2 2 2 2	2 2 2 2 2	2 2 2

Structure 6—Large, Differentiated

CEO   1

AEOs   8

Program Chiefs   4   4   5   3   6   5   3

Staff   3 2 2 2   2 2 2 2   2 2 2 2   2 2 2   2 2 2 2 2 2 2   2 2 2 2 2 2   2 2 2

APPENDIX B
EXAMPLE SESSION WITH GARCORG

GARCORG
What is the size of the organization
The options are> small, medium, or large
Small
Is the organization differentiated, yes or no
Yes
Amount of information
The options are> constant, linear, exponential, and random.
Constant
Content of information
The options are> constant, increasing, and decreasing,
Constant
What is the hiring mechanism dependent on
The options are> amount, content, and salience.
Salience
What is the firing mechanism dependent on
The options are> amount, content, and salience.
Salience
Program chief access structure
The options are> total, specialized, quasi-specialized, and random.
Specialized
What percentage of the issues are salient to the assistant executive officer, 0 to 100
L>
        30
What percentage of the issues are salient to the chief executive, 0 to 100
L>
        60
How long is the grace period for hiring and firing
L>
        3
Do you want just final results (y) or a time plot (n)?
n
How many time periods do you want to run for
L>
        20

efficiency — percentage

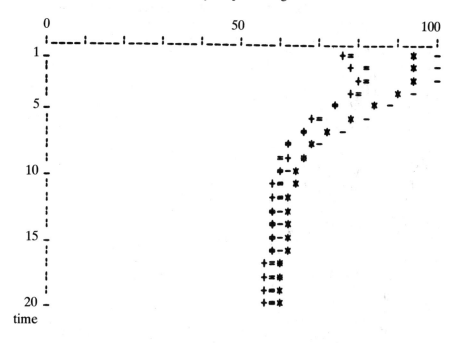

time

The organization's features are

size .... small   26
differentiated .... yes
amount of information over time .... constant
average content of information over time .... constant
hiring mechanism is dependent on .... salience
firing mechanism is dependent on .... salience
program chief access structure .... specialized
issues salient to CEO (percent) 60.00
issues salient to AEO (percent) 30.00
cutoff levels .... tha   .00 thc   .00
hiring/firing grace period 3.00
run length is 20

*************************** the results ***************************
long-run average amount of information/issue 41.26
long-run average content of information/issue .... .19
percentage pcrec rubber stamped by AEO over time ... 42.86
percentage AEOrec rubber stamped by CEO over time   .00
long-run analytic bias> efficiency .... .00 var   .00
structural efficiency> program chief's access 59.91
structural efficiency> AEO access 58.13
political efficiency> AEO salience 56.52
political efficiency> CEO salience 57.29

***end

10

Exploration of Staff and Line Relationships Using the Garbage Can Model

PAUL GRAY

INTRODUCTION AND OVERVIEW

The computer implementation developed by Stahr (1978) of the classic garbage can model assumed that organizations consist of a fixed number of decision makers who are either working on a decision or are idle. Stahr explored the garbage can model under a variety of assumptions about the rules for decision making, including variations in access by participants to choices (unsegmented, hierarchical, and specialized), the access of problems to choices, the assignment of participants and problems, the entry sequence of problems and choices, the accumulation of energy and the difficulty of choices. One of the principal results was that large numbers of decision makers are idle for long periods of time under a variety of perfectly plausible scenarios.

It is the contention of this chapter that real organizations do not work in this way. The old bromide that idle hands do the devil's work is ingrained in American managerial thinking, and as a result managers do, indeed, do something when they are not taking decisions.

This observation is certainly true in the U.S. Navy. Navy officers spend their time in both line (i.e., decision-making) and staff (i.e., study and support)

Paul Gray is a Professor at the Claremont Graduate School, Claremont, California.

Alexander J. Annala provided invaluable help throughout this project, particularly in the hand solution of the model. I am indebted to Dr. Roger Weissinger-Baylon for getting me interested in the garbage can model and for the discussions that led to the present work.

positions. Even under battle conditions, senior officers seek staff advice. In the language of the garbage can model, the staff applies energy to problems. Staff energy can be applied whether or not there is a choice to be made. The question to be asked, therefore, is what is the effect of this expenditure of energy? The contention here is that putting staff work into a problem changes (hopefully, reduces) its difficulty and, hence, the amount of energy still required to solve the problem when it is attached to a choice. As will be discussed below, the garbage can model is sufficiently robust that the energy resulting from a unit of staff work need not be equal to the energy resulting from a unit of work by a line officer.

In observing organizations, we see that some operate with very large staffs, while others have little or no staff. The problem of optimal staff size and use has long engaged organizational theorists. In the navy context, "staff" is an ephemeral concept, since officers may move between staff and line roles depending on current conditions.

This chapter will explore the relations between line and staff in an organization based on the garbage can model. The basic approach is twofold:

- To develop a set of assumptions about the relations between line and staff and translate these assumptions into the garbage can framework
- To modify the relatively simple simulation model developed by Stahr (1978) to include these additional hypotheses

To illustrate the effects of staff work, we will work out an example in detail.

HYPOTHESES

We begin with the assumption that large organizations do generally try to work within Simon's (1960) framework of "bounded rationality." Managers like to think that their efforts are rational and that they follow a reasonable set of guidelines for creating and allocating work to staff. It is in this spirit that we state the following set of hypotheses.

Hypothesis 1:   Staff work changes the energy required to solve a problem.

Organizations contain both staff and line people. In many organizations, the same individuals move between these two roles. During normal times, staff work is done by staff people on problems that are anticipated to be available for choice opportunities at a later time.

The effect of the staff work is to reduce the energy required to solve a problem. Thus, if staff work has been done on problems attached to a choice, less energy is required to make the choice; that is, it makes the choice easier. Hence, it is our hypothesis that staff work results in more problems being resolved by the choice process.

(Note that in the model it is also possible to consider staff work to have a negative effect, that is, that staff work increases the amount of energy required to solve the problem when it is attached to a choice.)

Hypothesis 2:   The amount of energy expended on a problem by staff and line per unit time need not be equal.

Work on a problem by a decision maker (that is, work on a problem when it is attached to a choice) may be carried out at a higher energy level per period than work on the same problem by the staff because of the greater sense of urgency of decision makers. One variant, therefore, is to introduce a "presure coefficient" to reflect higher energy input by decision makers working on a choice. Such a situation can occur, for example, during a crisis.

Hypothesis 3:   Conservation of energy.

The amount of energy required to solve a problem when it attaches itself to a choice is the total energy required to solve the problem less the work already expended during staffing.

This hypothesis assumes that no energy is lost when a problem is
· transferred from line to staff. In fact, there are usually "frictional" losses in the transfer as decision makers are brought up to speed by their staff. These frictional losses can be modeled by adding a term that represents such losses.

Hypothesis 4:   Individuals can move between line and staff as work fluctuates.

The people available for staff include those "not working on a choice." That is, we assume sufficient rationality that decision makers are detailed off to do staff work if they do not have access to a decision but do have access to a problem.

Conversely, as the number of choices to be made increases, people can be reassigned to decision making from staff work. However, there may be a lag (or lead) in this assignment. That is, the partition between choice and staff people changes over time.

We assume that the total number of participants is fixed (e.g., the table of organization remains unchanged); however, individual participant roles as line and staff can change over time. Our concept that people float between decision making and staff is observed in both military and corporate organizations. It is also true in hierarchical organizations that the higher the individual is in the organization, the less time spent on staff, the more on choice.

Hypothesis 5:   Even if staff solves a problem, the solution is not implemented until the problem is attached to a choice and that choice is made.

Staff work builds up a reservoir of information, contingency planning and alternative options to be used in choice making. It is this reservoir that reduces difficulty level. It is possible for a problem to have staff work completed on it (i.e., enough energy to be spent on it so that it is "solved") but no choice to be available to which the problem can attach itself. However, when a suitable choice arrives, the problem is solved with the choice. That is, the choice is easy and the problem is also solved.

An example of such a choice occurred in drug regulation. For years, the Kefauver Committee heard testimony about problems in the drug industry and drafted legislation. However, there was no choice available to which this program could attach itself, and the legislation died in committee. After the thalidomide scandal, the pressure for drug regulation provided the needed choice, and it was made quickly because the staff work had been done. Similar arguments apply to military choices where extensive planning has already been done.

Hypothesis 6:   Staff work sometimes creates choice situations.

Staff work can lead to new choice situations. That is, completion of staff work on a problem can create the opportunity for management to make a choice. However, management need not make a choice.

Presidential commissions are a classic example. When they issue their reports (usually with public fanfare), they create a choice opportunity. Usually, the report generates expenditure of energy but no immediate choice.

It is possible for a problem to be sent to staff and never be attached to a choice and, conversely, for a problem to be attached to a choice and never staffed. An example of the former is a bill sent to an unfriendly committee which goes through the motions of holding hearings but never prepares a bill. Similar burying of problems by keeping them in staff is not unknown in military organizations. Modern battles in a "come as you are" war are examples of problems that engage decision makers without having gone through staffing.

Hypothesis 7:   Feedback between line and staff eventually stabilizes the allocation between line and staff.

The flow between being a decision maker involved in choices and being a staff member can create a feedback mechanism. For example, for a fixed population, if the number of decision makers is too large, the number of staff is too small, and, hence, the amount of staff work decreases. Therefore, the amount of energy that decision makers have to expend on problems attached to choices increases. That is, the problems faced by decision makers increase in difficulty. According to garbage can theory, the number of choices made by flight and oversight increases. Within the framework of bounded rationality, senior managers respond to such situations by detailing decision makers off to staff so as to reduce the complexity of the situations they face. The same argument, in reverse, leads to the conclusion that if there is too large a staff, some of the people in staff roles are pulled out and put in line (i.e., combat command) positions.

Additional Modeling Considerations

An important modeling consideration is how staff is to be allocated to problems, that is, how to represent the scheduling of staff work. Alternatives include the following:

1. Staff works on problems closest to completion irrespective of whether decision makers are involved in making choices on the problem or not.

2. Staff works on problems with the least done on them (i.e., the staff attempts to equalize the amount of energy expended on each problem). The choice could be based on the absolute amount of energy or the percentage of energy still left to be applied.

3. Staff works on problems currently involved in choices wherever possible. If additional time is available, it chooses those problems that are closest in time to being able to attach themselves to a choice. (This alternative implies that intelligence information is available on coming choices or crises.)

4. As new problems enter the arena, they may or may not be staffed. One policy might be to attach at least one staff person to each problem so that "something is being done about it."

A natural extension is to consider a multistage decision process in which there is staff, line and command. A choice made by line must be approved (or at least is subject to review either ex ante or ex post) by command.

MODIFYING THE STAHR MODEL FOR LINE AND STAFF

To examine the effects of considering both line and staff functions, we now discuss how the Stahr (1978) model could be modified to take this change into account. What follows is one set of rules that could be used. This set of rules is not unique; other conditions could be imposed. However, we believe the following set of rules to be in the spirit of the garbage can.

To define a model, we begin by considering the information and rules needed as input data for problems and choices. For each problem, we need to specify

- The total energy required to solve the problem.
- The energy spent thus far.
- To which choices the problem has access.
- To which choice (if any) the problem is currently attached.
- To which staff person(s) the problem is attached.

For each participant, we need to specify

- Is the participant working in a staff or choice role?
- To which choices the participant has access.

- To which problems the participant has access.

The following assumptions are made:

1. The total number of individuals is fixed. Therefore,

   - Staff + decision makers = 100%.
   - The float is between staff and decision makers.

2. The percentage of staff runs from 0 to 100%.

   - At 100% all individuals are staff and choices are never made.
   - At 0% the model reduces to the original Stahr model.
   - We postulate that the maximum number of problems is solved at some staff level between 0% and 100%.

3. There is an energy trade-off between staff and line work.

   Energy spent on solving problems in staff changes the energy required by line to make the choice when these problems are attached to a choice. (Note that this assumption as stated allows a broad range of conditions. The simplest case is one in which there is perfect transfer of information from staff to line and the amount of energy input by staff is used to reduce the energy required to solve the problem. In the real world, however, there are frictional losses resulting from such factors as the learning curves of new individuals brought into a problem. Thus, the energy provided by staff may not transfer fully. In the worst case, staff may have a negative influence; that is, they may make the problem more difficult by providing incorrect or unacceptable solutions. This case results in the line having to expend more energy than they would have if no staff work had been done. In terms of the model, staff energy is multiplied by a constant in determining what fraction of the energy expended is transferred from staff to line. In the example of the next section, this constant is taken to be one for simplicity.)

4. When a problem arrives, if it cannot attach itself to a choice, it is sent to staff if staff is available.

   Work is performed on it in staff mode until either sufficient energy has been expended on it to solve it or it attaches itself to a choice. At that point, energy is expended in trying to make the choice. In the example of the next section, we assume that staff work continues while the problem is attached to a choice, if staff is available. This approach is consistent with commanders or chief executive officers using their staffs as assistants while they work on making choices. A variant of this assumption would be to assume that staff work stops when the problem is presented for choice. This variant corresponds to a staff that prepares a report or action paper and goes on to other problems.

5. Staffing a problem can create a choice situation.

   That is, when the energy spent on staffing a problem is equal to the energy required to solve the problem, the problem is brought to the decision level for choice. The decision level can make the choice or defer it. (For example, a congressional subcommittee drafts a bill after lengthy hearings; however, the parent committee or the rules committee or the House as a whole tables the bill for later consideration.) A problem on which staff work has been completed but on which action has been deferred can have three outcomes:

- It can be brought up for choice again later.
- It can attach itself to some other choice.
- It can disappear from the system.

HAND SOLUTION OF THE MODEL WITH BOTH LINE AND STAFF

To illustrate how the garbage can model can be operationalized on the computer, we present a hand solution for the modified Stahr model. To allow comparison with Stahr's (1978) paper, we create an example that is similar to Stahr's but which embeds both line and staff.

We make the following assumptions:

- The organization consists of 5 decision makers and 5 staff people. These people will work for a total of 10 periods. During this time, the organization is presented with 10 problems and 5 choices. Problems arrive in pairs for each of the first 5 periods, and choices arrive one at a time for the first 5 periods. Problems require 5 units of energy for solution.
- All problems and all choices have access to all decision makers.
- If a choice is not scheduled to be completed during the period, the problems attached to it can also receive staff work.
- Each problem that is at a choice that is not scheduled to be completed during a period receives at least one staff member to work on it, up to the total number of staff available.
- If several problems are attached to a choice, they each receive the same amount of energy. That is, a decision maker's energy is divided equally among the problems attached to the choice he is working on.
- The energy spent by decision makers on problems is recorded and, like staff work, helps reduce the energy required to solve the problem.
- Only one problem is handled by a staff person at a time, whereas, since they work on choices, decision makers work on all the problems attached to a choice.
- A decision maker expends one unit of energy/period. A staff person expends less than or equal to one unit per period. In the example below, we assume that the staff person provides one-half unit of energy.

A three-stage process is used to decide on how problems attach themselves to choices:

1. Choices arrive first. They look for problems to which they have access and which are not currently attached to choices.

2. New problems come in. They look for choices to which they have access, and each problem attaches itself to the choice which has the lowest energy requirement. (Notes: First, in this implementation, we assume that if the energy required is the same for an existing choice or one that arrived in stage 1, the stage 1 choice will be selected. Second, this is done "simultaneously" by all new problems, based on the energy requirements at the end of stage 1.)

3. Problems attached to choices in the previous period select the choice to which they have access that has the least energy requirement and migrate to it. (This is done "simultaneously" by all "old" problems based on the energy requirements at the end of stage 2.)

If the problems attached to a choice are being worked on by both staff and line in a given period, it is possible for enough energy to be expended by this combination to solve all the problems at that choice. However, the choice is not made during the period in this case because it is assumed that the staff work is not completed until the end of the period; in effect, this assumption results in a lag in communications of staff work to decision makers.

Period 1

Problems 1,2 arrive.
Choice 1 arrives.
Problems 1, 2 attach to choice 1.

All decision makers attach themselves to choice 1.
Problems 1,2 each receive 2.5 units of energy from decision makers.

Problem 1 receives $4/2 = 2$ units of energy from staff.
Problem 2 receives $1/2$ units of energy from staff.
(This division of staff assumes that we assign at least one staff member to each problem and that we try to put as much energy as possible into the problem closest to solution.)

Period		Decision Makers						Staff			
		1	2	3	4	5	6	7	8	9	10
1	Problem	1,2	1,2	1,2	1,2	1,2	1	1	1	1	2
	Decision	[1]	[1]	[1]	[1]	[1]					

(Here, 1,2 denotes problems 1 and 2; [1] denotes choice 1 and I divides the decision makers from the staff.)

Summary:

Choice 1 requires 10 units of energy at start of period 1 since problems 1 and 2 are attached to it. Five units of energy are expended by decision makers. Because the choice will not be made during this period based on decision maker energy, the staff works on the problems associated with choice 1. Four staff members are assigned to problem 1, and one staff member is assigned to problem 2.

At the end of period 1, problem 1 has 4.5 units of energy expended on it; problem 2 has 3 units of energy expended on it.

Period 2

At the beginning of period 2,

- Problems 3 and 4 arrive.
- Choice 2 arrives.
- Choice 1 requires $10 - 7.5 = 2.5$ to complete.
- Choice 2 requires 0 units to complete.

Problems 3 and 4 attach themselves to choice 2 since this choice has the least energy requirement. As a result, choice 2 requires 10 units to complete. Problems 1 and 2 at choice 1 do not move since choice 1 has only 2.5 units required to complete, whereas choice 2 requires 10 units.

Three of the five decision makers continue to work on choice 1 and it is made. The remaining two decision makers work on choice 2. Staff works on problems 3 and 4.

Period		Decision Makers						Staff			
		1	2	3	4	5	6	7	8	9	10
1	Problem	1,2	1,2	1,2	1,2	1,2	1	1	1	1	2
	Decision	[1]	[1]	[1]	[1]	[1]					
2	Problem	1,2	1,2	1,2	3,4	3,4	3	3	3	3	4
	Decision	[1]	[1]	[1]	[2]	[2]					

(Here 1,2 denotes problems 1 and 2; [1] denotes choice 1.)

Summary:

Choice 1 required 2.5 units of energy at the start of period 1. It continues to have problems 1 and 2 attached to it. Three units of energy are expended on this choice. Choice 1 is made and problems 1 and 2 are solved.

At the end of the period, choice 2 has accumulated 2 units of energy from decision makers and 2.5 units of energy from staff. Problem 3 has 3 units of energy and problem 4 has 1.5 units of energy.

Period 3

At the start of period 3,

- Problems 5 and 6 arrive.
- Choice 3 arrives and requires 0 units to complete.
- Choice 2 now requires $10 - 4.5 = 5.5$ units of energy to complete.

Problems 5 and 6 attach themselves to choice 3, which now requires 10 units to complete.

Problems 3 and 4 stay with choice 2.

All five decision makers attach themselves to choice 2, since it is closest to being made.

Since problem 3 had 3 units of energy expended on it during period 2, the energy to be expended on it by the decision makers will be sufficient to solve it. However, since problem 4 only had 1.5 units of energy during period 2, the 2.5 units of energy will not be sufficient to solve it. As a result, 2 staff are put on this problem.

Problems 5 and 6 are assigned to staff.

Period		Decision Makers					Staff			
		1	2	3	4	5	6	7	8	9	10
1	Problem	1,2	1,2	1,2	1,2	1,2	1	1	1	1	2
	Decision	[1]	[1]	[1]	[2]	[2]					
2	Problem	1,2	1,2	1,2	3,4	3,4	3	3	3	3	4
	Decision	[1]	[1]	[1]	[2]	[2]					
3	Problem	3,4	3,4	3,4	3,4	3,4	4	4	5	5	6
	Decision	[2]	[2]	[2]	[2]	[2]					

(Here, 1,2 denote problems 1 and 2; [1] denotes choice 1.)

Summary:

Choice 2 requires 5.5 units of energy at the beginning of the period. Only 5 units are available. However, there is enough staff available to reduce the energy required to 0. This choice is ready to be made next period.

Choice 3 receives no decision maker energy. However, 1.5 units of staff work reduce the energy required for this choice to 8.5.

Period 4

At the start of period 4,

- Problems 7 and 8 arrive.
- Choice 4 arrives and has 0 energy required.
- Choice 3 has 8.5 units of energy required.
- Choice 2 has 0 units of energy required.

Problems 7 and 8 attach themselves to choice 4, which now requires 10 units. Problems 3 and 4 migrate to choice 2, which now has 8.5 units required. Choice 3 has 0 units required.

Decision maker 1 works on choice 3.
The other decison makers work on choice 2, which has problems 3, 4, 5 and 6 attached. Staffing is begun on problems 7 and 8.

Period		Decision Makers					Staff			
		1	2	3	4	5	6	7	8	9	10
1	Problem	1,2	1,2	1,2	1,2	1,2	1	1	1	1	2
	Decision	[1]	[1]	[1]	[1]	[1]					
2	Problem	1,2	1,2	1,2	3,4	3,4	3	3	3	3	4
	Decision	[1]	[1]	[1]	[2]	[2]					
3	Problem	3,4	3,4	3,4	3,4	3,4	4	4	5	5	6
	Decision	[2]	[2]	[2]	[2]	[2]					
4	Problem	—	3,4,5,6	3,4,5,6	3,4,5,6	3,4,5,6	7	8	5	5	6
	Decision	[3]	[2]	[2]	[2]	[2]					

(Here, 1,2 denote problems 1 and 2; [1] denotes choice [1]; 3,4,5,6 indicates problems 3, 4, 5 and 6, with the bold face indicating that a problem was completed previously and, hence, required—and used—no additonal energy.)

Summary:

Choice 2 required 0 units to complete at the start of the period. However, this requirement jumped to 8.5 units because of the migration of problems 5 and 6.

The migration of 5 and 6 resulted in choice 3 being made by flight.

Four units of energy were expended on choice 2 by decision makers, resulting in two units of energy each on problems 5 and 6 by the decision makers. Combining decision maker and staff energy expenditures, 4 units had been spent on problem 5 and 3 units on problem 6. At the end of the period, choice 3 required 3 units. The problems attached to choice 4 (i.e., problems 7 and 8) each had 1/2 unit of energy spent on thcm by staff.

Period 5

At the start of period 5,

- Problems 9 and 10 arrive.
- Choice 5 arrives and requires 0 energy.
- Choice 2 requires 3 units to complete.
- Choice 4 requires 9 units of energy.

Problems 9 and 10 attach themselves to choice 5, which now requires 10 units of energy.
Problems 3 through 6 remain at choice 2.
Problems 7 and 8 move to choice 2, which now requires 12 units of energy.
Choice 4 requires 0 units of energy.
One decision maker is assigned to choice 4, the others to choice 5, since choice 5 is closest to completion.
Since problems 9 and 10 are at choice 5, they receive staff work. Problems 5, 6 and 7 being closest to completion also receive staff work.

Period		Decision Makers					Staff				
		1	2	3	4	5	6	7	8	9	10
1	Problem	1,2	1,2	1,2	1,2	1,2	1	1	1	1	2
	Decision	[1]	[1]	[1]	[1]	[1]					
2	Problem	1,2	1,2	1,2	3,4	3,4	3	3	3	3	4
	Decision	[1]	[1]	[1]	[2]	[2]					
3	Problem	3,4	3,4	3,4	3,4	3,4	4	4	5	5	6
	Decision	[2]	[2]	[2]	[2]	[2]					
4	Problem	—	**34**56	**34**56	**34**56	**34**56	7	8	5	5	6
	Decision	[3]	[2]	[2]	[2]	[2]					
5	Problem	—	9,10	9,10	9,10	9,10	7	9	10	5	6
	Decision	[2]	[5]	[5]	[5]	[5]					

(Here 1,2 denotes problems 1 and 2; [1] denotes choice 1; 3, 4, 5, 6 indicates problems 3, 4, 5 and 6, with the bold face indicating that a problem was completed and, hence, used no additional energy.)

Summary:

Choice 2 requires 12 units of energy at the beginning of the period because of migration. Active decision work on this choice stops during the period. However, since problems 5 and 6 are nearest to completion, they receive staff effort. This results in reducing the energy required for choice 2 to 11.
Choice 4 is made by flight.
Choice 5 is worked on by both decision makers and staff. The energy still required by this choice is 5 units.

Period 6

At the start of Period 6,

- By our assumptions, no new changes or problems arrive.
- Choice 2 requires 11 units of energy to complete.
- Choice 5 requires 5 units of energy to complete.

Problems associated with choice 2 migrate to choice 5, since choice 5 requires less energy.
Choice 5 now requires 16 units of energy. Choice 2 is solved as a result of the flight.

Because enough energy is expended on Problem 5 by the decision makers to solve it, it receives no staff work. All other problems receive staff work.

Period		Decision Makers					Staff				
		1	2	3	4	5	6	7	8	9	10
1	Problem	1,2	1,2	1,2	1,2	1,2	1	1	1	1	2
	Decision	[1]	[1]	[1]	[1]	[1]					
2	Problem	1,2	1,2	1,2	3,4	3,4	3	3	3	3	4
	Decision	[1]	[1]	[1]	[2]	[2]					
3	Problem	3,4	3,4	3,4	3,4	3,4	4	4	5	5	6
	Decision	[2]	[2]	[2]	[2]	[2]					
4	Problem	—	**3456**	**3456**	**3456**	**3456**	7	8	5	5	6
	Decision	[3]	[2]	[2]	[2]	[2]					
5	Problem	—	9,10	9,10	9,10	9,10	7	9	10	5	6
	Decision	[4]	[5]	[5]	[5]	[5]					
6	Problem	—	3.10	3.10	3.10	3.10	7	9	10	8	6
	Decision	[2]	[5]	[5]	[5]	[5]					

(Here 1,2 denote problems 1 and 2; [1] denotes choice 1; 3,4,5,6 indicates problems 3, 4, 5 and 6, with the bold face indicating that a problem was completed and, hence, used no additional energy; 3,10 denotes problems 3 through 10.)

Summary:

Choice 2 is made by flight.
Choice 5 has a total of 6.5 units of work put into it and now requires 10.5 units to complete.

Periods 7 through 10

The foregoing example can easily be run out the full 10 periods. However, not much of interest happens, since only choice 5 remains and its remaining 10.5 units of energy can be applied in periods 7 and 8.

Note that in the course of this example, three choices were made by flight. We also saw how staff work supplemented choice 2 to the point where the choice was ready to be made but, because it had not yet been made, new problems came in and attached themselves to that choice.

COMPARISON OF HAND SOLUTION TO THE CASE WITH NO STAFF

The following table shows the sequence of problem allocations that would be made in the original Stahr (1978) model if there were only five decision makers and no staff. Note that Stahr assumes that energy is attached only to choices, whereas we assume that the staff and line energy is conserved, that is, that energy expended on a problem serves to reduce its difficulty.

Period	Decision Makers				
	1	2	3	4	5
1	1,2	1,2	1,2	1,2	1,2
2	[1]	[1]	[1]	[1]	[1]
3	[2]	[2]	[2]	[2]	[2]
4	[3]	[3]	[3]	[3]	[3]
5	[4]	[4]	[4]	[4]	[4]
6	1..10	1..10			

In period 1, all five decision makers work on choice 1, which has problems 1 and 2 attached.

In period 2, choice 2 comes in. Problems 1 and 2 as well as new problems 3 and 4 migrate to choice 2. Choice 1 is made by flight. This pattern repeats; the problems, including the new problems, move en masse from choice to choice. Choices 2, 3 and 4 are made by flight. In period 6, only choice 5 remains, but it has all 10 problems attached to it. Fifty units of energy are still needed to make the choice, since each of the 10 problems requires 5 units of energy. If no new problems or choices come in then 10 periods are needed before the problems are solved and the choice made.

Note that adding staff hastens the decision process, particularly if the energy accumulated on problems stays with the problem.

CONCLUSIONS

In this paper we have introduced the concept of staff and line into the garbage can model. We have made the assumption of bounded rationality to argue that managers try to behave rationally by creating and using a staff to work on problems to reduce the difficulty of choices. One can speculate that managers may, in fact, make many individual choices within a rational framework but that the observed garbage can behavior comes about because managers treat problems and choices individually without considering systemic impacts.

The example worked through in detail indicates the role of staff work in changing the pattern of choice. Staff work does not, however, eliminate choice by flight (or by oversight, for that matter). Although it was not shown in the example, staff work can create choice opportunities by presenting problem solutions to management for their consideration.

The line-staff relationships are particularly important in thinking about the garbage can model in a navy context. In the navy, officers move between staff and line positions continually, particularly in peacetime. Furthermore, the role of a particular individual may change over time. When there are a lot of decisions to be made, an individual officer may be put into the command chain. However, as the backlog of decisions is worked down, individuals can be assigned to staff roles. In the staff roles, they in fact help reduce the energy that has to be put into decision making when a choice opportunity occurs. An example of this occurred in the 1973 Arab-Israeli war. When the Egyptian commanding officer was asked how his army, long known to be inferior to the Israelis, was able to cross the Suez Canal, he indicated that they had practiced it and practiced it until it was second nature. Thus, by doing the preparatory staff work, the energy that had to be put into decision making when a choice opportunity arose was much reduced.

The present research was designed to be indicative of the staff-line relations within the garbage can framework. The next step in exploring the line-staff relation is to run an extensive set of cases by computer, as was done by Stahr (1978) Anderson and Fischer (1986) and Carley (1986). These computer explorations should include consideration of alternative staff-line relations implied by the specific assumptions used here.

REFERENCES

Anderson, Paul A., and Fischer, Gregory W. "A Monte Carlo Model of a Garbage Can Decision Process." In *Ambiguity and Command: Organizational Perspectives on Military Decision Making*, edited by James G. March and Roger Weissinger-Baylon. Marshfield, Mass.: Pitman Publishing: 1986.

Carley, Kathleen. "Efficiency in a Garbage Can: Implications for Crisis Management." In *Ambiguity and Command: Organizational Perspectives on Military Decision Making*, edited by James G. March and Roger Weissinger-Baylon. Marshfield, Mass.: Pitman Publishing, 1986.

Simon, Herbert A. *The New Science of Management Decision*. New York. Harper & Row, 1960.

Stahr, Walter. "Further Exploration of the Garbage Can", Unpublished Manuscript, Graduate School of Business, Stanford University, June, 1978.

THE MILITARY
PERSPECTIVE

11

Garbage Cans at Sea

WAYNE P. HUGHES, JR.

This paper is concerned with U.S. Navy combat decision making at sea. Other defense decisions are more likely to be vulnerable to the incoherence of garbage cans. Washington, with its committees, briefings and conferences, all thought necessary to allow diverse representation of authority, interest and expertise, more obviously fits either the "bureaucratic-administrative" or the "bargaining-political" paradigms of choice. I will, however, limit this discussion to operational decision making in the U.S. fleet; first, because there may be more relevance of the garbage can model than meets the casual glance, and second, because a modification of the model may lead to especially revealing investigations.

THE PEACETIME NAVY

Striking similarities between the three conditions which, according to Cohen, March and Olsen (1972), are conducive to a garbage can environment seem consonant with conditions that exist in the U.S. Navy *peacetime* fleet operations. What are the organizational circumstances that breed a garbage can environment?

Wayne P. Hughes, Jr., Captain, USN (Ret.), is a Professor in the Department of Operations Research at the Naval Postgraduate School, Monterey, California.

- First, when the organization does not have clear goals, there is no clear statement of preference.
- Second, when the organization's decision makers come and go from the decision process, there is an unstable allocation of labor.
- Third, when the organization's operating procedures are poorly defined and ad hoc, technology fails to associate alternatives with outcomes.

Unclear Goals in Peacetime

There is a disconcertingly close fit between the above conditions and our fleet in peacetime. Observe any fleet readiness exercise. Its goal is training to improve combat readiness. Beyond that single consensus, we rarely see agreement on training objectives among the participants either within exercises or between exercises. One may find reasonably clear objectives stated, but in general they are belied in execution. It is easy to understand why. The navy's wartime missions for which we train are variegated, depending on geography: consider the difference between Sixth Fleet (Mediterranean) and Seventh Fleet (North Pacific) environments, for example. "Projection" operations dominate the thinking of some naval officers, "sea control" operations dominate others. Consciously or not, some participants would emphasize presence and crisis containment, others conventional theater war, others global nuclear war. Some players focus on the crucial first salvo problem and rules of engagement, others on a hot war. The navy's prospective wartime roles are so diverse that it is exceedingly difficult to establish peacetime objectives that are unambiguous.

Unstable Group of Participants

Second, the peacetime navy is constantly struggling to overcome the distractions of administrative inspections, repairs and maintenance, cultural problems associated with drugs or equal opportunity and, sometimes it seems, everything but readiness. A worthwhile study to examine how many hours a day our flag and commanding officers—the bosses—devote to tactical thinking and battle planning would be most revealing. The fleet environment had become so polluted with noncombat problems, real or imagined, that five years ago Admiral Hayward, then the chief of naval operations, established the improvement of tactical competency as one of a handful of his major objectives. He did so because our peacetime leaders mentally "come and go" from their primary task: preparing to fight.

What is worse, they also "come and go" physically. Command tours for senior officers at sea last a short time, one or two years. Our task forces suffer tremendous turnover of the attached ships and air squadrons. The situation is not ameliorated by the turnover of staffs, nor of ship's officers, nor of enlisted complements. A few years ago, when Admiral Small was commander of the Sixth Fleet in the Mediterranean, he was invited to comment on the proposed (since adopted), new Composite Warfare Doctrine. He said, in effect, that any reasonable command organization could be made to work if forces could be kept together and trained; no command organization would work when forces and people were coming and going at such a furious pace. To the extent that commanders are mentally and physically coming and going, for good reason or bad, then a garbage can environment ensues.

Poorly Defined Operating Procedures

Third and last, the U.S. Navy in peacetime suffers a lack of coherent definitive operating procedures—what we call doctrine. How this came to be is a subject unto itself. Suffice it to say that compared with either the U.S. Army or the U.S. Air Force, or with any segment of the Soviet armed forces, the peacetime U.S. Navy places enormous responsibility and authority on its commanders to draft and execute their own tactics. The definitive rules for maneuver—for explicit formations and for operational evolutions that were our inheritance from World War II—have withered away without adequate replacement. If garbage cans are fostered by ad hoc operating rules, then our peacetime navy is prone to garbage can decision making.

WARTIME: AN END TO GARBAGE CAN DECISION MAKING?

The next thing to observe is how these garbage can circumstances will correct themselves in wartime.

First, there is a firm objective for each operation. It is called the mission, and it is clear and unambiguous.

Second, combat leaders are selected in the crucible of battle. Continuity of command is retained for the duration. Crews are frozen in place. Squadrons and battle groups retain their unit integrity. As a result, the cast of players is no longer in the flux of change so characteristic of the peacetime navy.

Third, doctrine firms up around the weapons in hand. Tactics that succeed endure. And specific plans may be layed against an enemy who is known in a geographical location that is case-specific.

All three garbage can characteristics fade away in wartime, partly because they can now be dealt with, partly because, to win battles, they must.

Worrisome, however, is that these stabilizations do not occur at the first salvo. In fact, history shows a shakedown of leaders and crews at war's onset, the violence of surprise attacks, and the radical surgery undergone in tactics and doctrine as the lessons of war unfold. Thus, after the war starts it may be too late. Former Chief of Naval Operations Admiral Thomas Hayward's admonition that next time it will be a "come as you are war" exhibits the hazard.

So there are good reasons for us to look more closely at the weaknesses and the strengths of the garbage can paradigm as it relates to military decision making and command at sea in wartime.

Special Treatment of Combat is Required

First, there are four weaknesses. Any suitable model of combat at sea must capture its essential force-on-force nature. Perhaps even more than in the past, sea battle is a process of stalking the enemy, culminated by the deadly delivery of decisive attack. Sudden ship and aircraft losses in the Falklands war are only a foretaste of what we will see in future sea battle. Now, the garbage can model includes a penalty in that problems not solved in a timely way disappear. But in naval combat, when the problems of how, and especially when, to attack are not solved in a timely way, there *are* no more problems—except how to succor the survivors. So the garbage can model must be fixed, first, to reward the timeliness of problem solving and, second, to emphasize that there is a hierarchy of problems: little solutions contribute to major solutions all leading to one (or conceivably two or three) decisions to launch the decisive attack. We may surmise that this model defect may be eliminated.

The Form of Combat Decision Making

The second defect is more difficult to correct. It also stems from the force-on-force nature of warfare and the importance of attacking effectively first against an enemy who has the same objective, as both sides grope in the fog of war. Commanders making decisions in any battle when the outcome is in doubt must make a commitment of force—launch aircraft or fire a decisive missile strike—based on incomplete information. The implication for modeling, as well as for the construction of decision support systems, is suitably expressed in a way first brought to my attention by Ervin Kapos. Hypotheses may be formed consciously or unconsciously, but are subject to reevaluation and revision as more information becomes available. The ability to formulate hypotheses early is essential for positive commitment. The ability to synthesize available information to formulate the right hypotheses is a key element in how successful a commander will be.

Command logic is more subtle than machine logic; it is not "if A do Z," but rather "if A then assume P or Q for the time being and do X to temporize." The genius of combat decision making is knowing when (neither too early nor too late) to commit: *when to take step Z*. A garbage can model modification will not easily handle this mode of decision making. Nor will any other model; nevertheless it is important. A good battle model concerns itself with not only the timeliness of decisions and the fact that decisions tend to be interrelated, but the texture and quality of decisions as well. An inferior timely decision is better than a perfect decision taken too late. A useful model should reflect the properties of battlefield decisions: sequential, correlated, cumulative and climactic.

The Energy Core of Decisions

The third deficiency has to be treated carefully because it gets to the heart of the garbage can model's philosophy, namely, that authority and choice are fuzzier than tables of organization and charters that vest responsibility would have us believe. Nevertheless, commanders do tend to command; and, especially in combat, committee actions by garbage can groups will be fatally inept. This strikes at the heart of the garbage can model concept that a group has a total energy level represented by those present—a power of decision that accrues from the aggregate wisdom of diverse or competing persons. In battle, good and timely decisions result when essential information is focused into one mind which decides in solitude. Now, if that mind is inferior, there is not much help for it; a brilliant staff cannot save a bumbling commander. Our navy believes this is because of the force-on-force nature of battle; the only salvation for poor decision making is a bumbling enemy commander. In business or government, poor corporate choices will also probably eventually overtake inferior group decisions, but it takes longer and the cause-and-effect relationships are less obvious.

Since a commander's span of control is not unlimited, battle organizations are arranged hierarchically. But at each level some large fraction of the energy of decision—which is the subject of this third deficiency—resides in the commander at that echelon. How might the garbage can model be modified for fleet decision making so that "good" choices will occur when problems are directed to the right person and the quality of the decision will depend on the amount (quantity and quality) of relevant information that reaches that person? The model I have described brings to mind a lecture at the Naval Postgraduate School by Eberhardt Richten (1983). He said one recent development in intelligence analysis has the information for decision seeking the user instead of the other way around. I can envision a new model in which "committees" of information (with their associated energy) are the essential ingredients of problem solving, instead of committees of persons (with their collective personal energy).

The Foresight of Decision Making

The fourth and last concern may not turn out to be a problem at all. Let us, however, consider the anticipation required of a decision. Timeliness, ever present timeliness, intrudes on the commander because decisions made are not decisions effected. At Midway, it took two-and-a-half hours for Spruance's aircraft to reach the Japanese carriers after he had made an irrevocable decision to launch them. If one were making decisions at chess the way commanders must make battle decisions, then each player would make his move the turn before it was executed. White would write "P-K4" on a piece of paper, Black would write down his move, and only then, while White was writing his second move, would White be allowed to advance his pawn to king-four. The game would be entirely different, full of subtlety and traps. This delay in the execution of decisions is a problem that haunts commanders, even before taking into account the wicked effect of garbled, lost or misinterpreted orders that our co-editor Roger Weissinger-Baylon (1986) has emphasized.

The Strength of the Garbage Can Model

Having considered four inadequacies of the garbage can model for fleet decision making, let us turn to its strengths.

The first point is that the obvious solution, one which corrects all the above inadequacies, namely war gaming, would be the wrong solution in the following sense. Within its own limitations, gaming is another useful tool that social scientists and naval officers employ. Indeed, U.S. naval officers have rediscovered war gaming in the past five years. But each kind of model has its limitations, because all models are abstractions and, in one way or another, are simplifications of reality. War gaming is manpower intensive and time consuming. It is also very tricky to use the quantitative output of war games. Replication is a difficult problem. Fixing the variables and correlating the variables is an even more difficult problem. Obtaining subjects in the experiment that think and decide as they should is an almost insurmountable problem, when the purpose is for research (that is, to "learn lessons") rather than simply for training. The distinction between gaming for investigation rather than training is not our subject. Nevertheless, the difference between *modeling* for research and for training is vital and relevant. War gaming, despite its attractiveness for the investigation of decision making, is necessary but not sufficient; analytical techniques are also indispensable. This brings me back to the garbage can model and its strengths.

First and most important, the garbage can model is analytical and quantitative. Hence, it can be manipulated to yield quantitative results in the form of if-then statements. While I believe the model structure itself (not merely the inputs or applications) must be changed, nevertheless the very fact that the garbage can decision process can be described, understood and criticized is a salient and uncommon strength, characteristic of analytic models and, by contrast, difficult or impossible with war games, fleet exercises or even historical research. Does the model incorporate the important characteristics of combat decision making? It does not yet. Might it do so and still retain its transparency, unlike our attempts to understand decision making in "realistic" and complicated simulations? This is still an open question.

Like war gaming, an analytic model of combat decision making is necessary but not sufficient. Unlike war games or fleet exercises, analytic models of decision making are rare, indeed, and a good one will be a precious asset.

ADDITIONAL GOOD FEATURES OF THE GARBAGE CAN MODEL

There are at least six other virtues of the garbage can model that a good analytic model of operational decision making should preserve:

- The model explicitly incorporates the competition between problems for the attention of "decision makers." At sea, a superabundance of problems seek command attention and the model can treat the effects of the loading.
- The model permits investigation of how organizational structure influences the kinds of decisions with which the organization can

deal, the rates with which decisions can be made and the relative numbers and complexities of aggregate decisions that different organizational structures can make (though not, it seems, the quality of the decisions that are made).

- The model is sensitive to and affected by the flow patterns of participants, problems, solutions and choice opportunities (though it is not yet sensitive to the flow of essential external information that military reconnaissance, surveillance and intelligence provide).

- The model permits exploration of how organizational structure affects the propensity of decision makers, solutions and even the problems themselves to "participate" in choice opportunities.

- The characterization of player participation in choice making as (1) unsegmented, (2) hierarchical or (3) specialized seems to capture three of the most vital decision-making alternatives.

- The idea of solutions looking for questions is one of the most engaging features of the model. There must be something in this. Some officers will never rest until they can apply air power to "do the job." Others are convinced that over-the-horizon radar or radar satellites or some other "surveillance" system is *the* way to scout the enemy. History teems with military solutions seeking problems. The most famous is the vision in 1939 of a line of battleships stalking an enemy. It was a vision that never materialized.

In summary, garbage can models have these virtues, and perhaps others, that should be retained.

- They are analytical and, hence, flexible and transparent.
- They describe parametrically the plethora of problems seeking decision-maker attention.
- They describe flow patterns of most (not yet all) of the combat decision ingredients. More generally, a garbage can model incorporates more than principles; it also includes the dynamic *processes* of decision making.
- They explore the influence of organization on patterns of choice.
- They permit the "solutions" of predisposition to compete for attention.

These are all properties of battlefield decision making that warrant study.

SOME ATTRIBUTES OF A GOOD MODEL OF COMBAT DECISION MAKING

The next suggestion came from mulling over a model that the three communities—social scientists, operations analysts and military officers—all would be about equally familiar with. It had to be "real" command, it had to involve pretty high stakes, evoke strong passions and embody the properties of timeliness and force-on-force competition, with defined, quantitative, explicit outcomes. Peacetime naval operations fail, to a greater and lesser extent, in each of these criteria.

Usually, meetings of the Operations Research Society of America have sessions on sports. Sports competition, notably football, is using computers increasingly as decision aids. Professional football uses computers in many ways, but the most fascinating way is helping coaches plan their game strategy against an opponent and prepare batteries of situational play-calling alternatives. San Francisco 49er coach Bill Walsh is reported often to script the first 20 offensive plays of a game before he goes to the stadium (Business Week, 1983). It is interesting that an NFL rule bars computer terminals from the sidelines or press boxes on the basis that the hometown advantage would be too great for teams that use complex computer systems for play-calling assistance. Wayne Winston at Indiana University has assisted the Indiana coach in trying a system he has worked out that gives play sets and associated frequencies for each down, position on the field, time to play and other key parameters (Winston et al., 1983). In view of Indiana's reputation in the Big Ten, the coach has little to lose.

The significance is the tremendous contribution analysts have brought to one form of real competition, involving high stakes, plenty of uncertainty and yet highly measurable results on the scoreboard.

Let us be clear. Football competition is not like war. Unlike warfare, in football one starts and ends the game with eleven players on the field. And there is little of the fog of war in football; it is a game of relatively complete information, because the "commander" can see the field.

Still, there are striking parallels with combat in the *command* aspects. Decisions are made on the spot in real time by men under mental stress directing men under physical stress. Decisions are communicated from the bench, but plays can be changed by the quarterback's audibles. Each coach has a staff that plays different roles for different teams. The coach blends raw player material with an operational plan and training to match. He gains strategic intelligence from game movies and tactical intelligence both from spotters sited remotely at the top of the stands and player debriefs on the sidelines. Operations are plotted in advance of the game, and tactics (the plays) are communicated by compact signals. If we constructed an analytic model of the processes of football leadership, then we would probably have a better paradigm of wartime decision making as it *ought* to be than either the garbage can model in its present form or decision making in a naval training environment.

SUMMARY: A VITAL NEED AND ITS CHARACTERIZATION

Whether or not we take choice in a football game as an enlightening subject, it is a suitable way to begin summing up. Consider the words "*ought* to be," just above. It is abundantly clear that an understanding of how people make choices goes deeper, by several layers of excavation, than, say, the operations analysts' rational models. Some decisions are made, other decisions happen. In war or football, the "*ought* to be" of the choice process is really a process which "*must* be in order to win." Whether the choice process is rational or irrational or something else too difficult to describe, war time operations offer the behavioral scientist an enticing laboratory to investigate patterns of choice, because there is a clear-cut measure of successful choice—namely, battles won when the issue was in doubt—and unsuccessful choice—namely, battles lost when the issue ought not to have been in doubt, as at Pearl Harbor in December 1941, or on any Saturday afternoon when Indiana University wins a football game.

Let us return to what was referred to as "step Z," and the problem of understanding the process by which a naval commander makes his decision to commit his whole force, in which process the texture and quality and especially timing all are important. For studying the Z decision, the football paradigm loses much of its power. The garbage can model also fails, and even our peacetime exercises in the fleet do not serve our needs very well. In describing the "Z decision," I mentioned the banality that a timely decision is better than a perfect decision taken too late. As to the principle of making timely decisions, everyone believes it; but as to the process of arriving at timely decisions, no one understands it. That is why an analytic model of the navy decision processes will be so valuable.

REFERENCES

Cohen, Michael D., March, James G., and Olsen, Johan P. "A Garbage Can Model of Organizational Choice." *Administrative Science Quarterly* 17 (1972): 1–26.

"The Computer Scores Big on the Gridiron." *Business Week*, October 24, 1983, pp. 185–188.

Richten, Eberhardt. "The Technology of Command." The Charles H. Davis Lecture Series, National Academy Press, Washington, D.C., Fall 1983.

Weissinger-Baylon, Roger. "Garbage Can Decision Processes in Naval Warfare." In *Ambiguity and Command: Organizational Perspectives on Military Decision Making*, edited by James G. March and Roger Weissinger-Baylon. Marshfield, Mass.: Pitman Publishing, 1986.

Winston, Wayne, L., Sagarin, Jeffrey S., and Cabot, Victor A. *A Stochastic Game Model of Football Play Selection*. School of Business, Indiana University, Bloomington, Indiana, November 1983.

12

An Ex-CNO's Reflection on the Garbage Can Theory of Naval Decision Making

THOMAS B. HAYWARD

In decision making, there always exists a huge gulf between the perceptions and misperceptions of the different communities involved, as between the naval operator and the knowledgeable decision theorist, or the military and the academic community. Since each community holds quite different viewpoints, arising mainly from the fact that they confront problems and choices of a different order, it follows that they tend to seek totally different objectives. The purpose of this paper is to examine, with concrete examples, the relationship of the "garbage can" theory to the process of practical decision making as it pertains to the U.S. Navy, and to see whether the addition of a theoretical perspective to such practical decision making (through the introduction of formal decision-making theory into the curriculum at the Naval Academy and into advanced leadership courses) would improve the efficiency of our present system.

In examining this issue from the practical standpoint, there are essentially three quite different environments involved in defense decision making: (1) decisions related to a major war that might involve the superpowers; (2) tactical decisions confronted in crisis management; and (3) bureaucratic issues in peacetime, largely related to investment strategies.

Admiral Thomas B. Hayward, USN (Ret.), is a former chief of naval operations.

Before turning to actual examples, it is important to stress the unique differences that exist between, on the one hand, the decision-making process used to arrive at crisis management and bureaucratic solutions to peacetime problems and, on the other hand, the decision-making process used in actual wartime situations. In both these contexts, however, peacetime and wartime, many aspects of garbage can decision making will be found.

EXAMPLE 1: A MAJOR U.S.–SOVIET WAR

In discussing the decision-making processes that might be applied in a major war against the Soviets today, one of the major problems to be confronted is the virtual absence of experience among senior naval officers in other than the kind of limited engagements of the Korean or Vietnam wars, in which, due to our total domination of the sea, battles at sea were essentially nonexistent. Furthermore, suppose that the senior admirals who were involved in the major decisions of World War II were to be exposed to the sophisticated threat envelope of this decade or the next. Despite their extensive experience in the last war, which involved numerous naval engagements, they would have every bit as much difficulty defining the decision aids and the appropriate decisions to be made as we who lack their "at-sea" battle exposure. It is clear that in this century, the theory-relevant combat management information system appropriate to the next war is now and will be more extraordinarily complex, will involve voluminous quantities of data (both good and bad) and a command line from the National Command Authority (NCA) to the commander at sea that will be both unpredictable and uncontrollable. In addition, there has been such an extraordinarily rapid rate of change in technology over the last twenty years that our frames of reference have been altered frequently and are subject to constant and rapid obsolescence. Technology is moving so fast today that naval commanders at senior levels must be continually retrained, as never before. Their knowledge of the threat and knowledge of the total combat system must be frequently updated. If not, they are going to be outdated in wartime in both the tactical and strategic decision-making sense. On account of this, the demand for extraordinary professionalism has never been higher.

EXAMPLE 2: TACTICAL DECISION MAKING

The Libyan "Shootdown"

The tactical decision processes related to the very unique circumstances surrounding the Libyan "shootdown" were substantially different from those that would have been used in wartime. For very obvious reasons, political factors and civilian leaders played major roles in framing the constraints to be observed by the on-the-scene commander in developing and exercising tactical control.

In the Libyan situation, a two-star admiral in charge of the operation was called to Washington before the "exercise" to sit with the Joint Chiefs of Staff and explain, in detail, how he intended to conduct a mission designed to demonstrate our right to free access in the Gulf of Sidra, knowing full well that there was more than inconsequential probability of an interaction of one kind or another with an unpredictable adversary. This potential interaction had to be so well understood by all, in advance, that the commander proceeded to the White House and briefed both the National Security Staff and the commander in chief, the president. Only when everyone was satisfied that the admiral had matters fully in hand was he allowed to go back to his theater, rejoin his force and initiate the operation. The outcome of this highly unusual decision-making process (which did not reflect conventional decision-making theories) was to insure that everyone had a sense of confidence that, were a situation to develop into a crisis where there might be some interaction, the right decision would be made, and at a relatively low tactical level. And, to everyone's satisfaction, as events turned out, this was precisely what did happen. The uniqueness of this decision-making process, however, was one that would provide very little assistance with, for example, the development of futuristic combat information systems or the design of the Tactical Flag Command Center. However, in this instance, tactical doctrine prevailed, and with highly favorable results.

The Iranian Crisis

The decision-making process of the Iranian hostage recovery operations involved one of the more obvious kinds of decision-making problems at the limited-war threshold. In this example, I will recount my own involvement—as a member of the Joint Chiefs of Staff. I will not attempt to make any excuses for the outcomes attained or not attained. The account will be limited to what happened and how decision points were addressed. Hopefully, this approach will both provide descriptive material for those interested in developing a theory of alternative outcomes and test further the applicability of the garbage can model to real-life events.

On November 4, 1979, the Iranian crisis confronted us abruptly. The underlying reasons why the situation erupted will not be discussed here. Suffice it to say that a series of prior decisions had already been made by a variety of Americans, and others, which may have been right or wrong, but regardless which helped to create the circumstances that brought us to the crisis point. At that particular point in time, we were caught in a crisis situation that we had not anticipated in any sense, and we had little understanding of how to deal with it. Therefore, we had to begin by devising a crisis decision process at various levels of government—at the White House, the secretary of defense, the Joint Chiefs of Staff (JCS) and the commanders-in-chief (CINCs). Without preparation, we were confronted with several very unique problems. First, we did not have the proper forces available to react promptly to the crisis, nor did we possess an appropriate operational organization. Second, we were seriously lacking in useful intelligence. Before we could deal realistically with reasonable options, these initial deficiencies had to be met and corrected. This took a period of time to accomplish.

Nevertheless, despite these particular deficiencies, our overall system had its strengths. We did have in place an organization that knew how to deal with decision making. The Joint Chiefs of Staff were able to go instantly to work, without having to concern themselves with the political factors that inevitably would preoccupy the White House. It was not up to us to decide whether a logical option might be for the United States to sit back and wait for our allies to put enough pressure on the Iranians to release the hostages before deciding to take military action. Our job was to develop feasible plans, identify logical force components and get on with the necessary training.

We had hardly embarked on this task when another major crisis occurred, a garbage can exigency of the first order—the Soviets invaded Afghanistan and altered the dimensions of the initial problem. On account of this, the U.S. fleet was promptly steamed to the Indian Ocean in large numbers. To provide the required strength, we took ships from the Mediterranean forces of the Sixth Fleet and also from the Seventh Fleet in the Pacific. We literally created a new fleet for the Indian Ocean, structured around forces that were forward deployed and available. This new force certainly was not structured around any preconceived plan. We had to be flexible and imaginative in our use of available resources, yet the process of arriving at such decisions was very easy. The existing military operational decision tree is made to order for this kind of flexible reaction.

For the following few months, we continued to develop our Iranian options while remaining highly sensitive to what the Soviets were doing in Afghanistan and to the troubling intelligence that we were getting on Soviet preparedness to exploit the situation in Iran. With the help of the television media's nightly dramatization of the hostage situation in Tehran, this issue soon escalated to an event of overwhelming national concern. Without such overexposure, events might have retained a better sense of proportion and been less a national or even a military problem to the Joint Chiefs of Staff. Nevertheless, a decision was made by the Joint Chiefs to proceed with the development of the critical intelligence necessary for us to simultaneously develop the force structure capable of handling a hostage rescue option while preparing to confront any Soviet adventurism. Our task was demanding in the extreme: on the one hand, to meet the Carter Doctrine and, on the other, to develop believable hostage rescue options.

This was a good test of the military decision tree, and it proved to be well suited to this kind of crisis demand. Obviously, we had not anticipated the simultaneous crises, but with the available time and resources at our disposal, we put into motion the creation of an operational organization for a rescue attempt, with the appropriate forces selected from each service. We developed a plan and started to practice it, until we reached the point where we were ready to make a major decision—to go or not to go.

At this point, I would like to dispel the belief that has been held by a number of critics that all four services were involved because each service had to have its role and that, somehow, one of the major causes of the failure of the mission was that each service demanded to be there, ultimately leading to a failure of leadership at the critical moment. This was not the case. The operation was highly professional and run by real professionals. They were chosen from different services for the simple reason that we did not have an in-place, single-service organization available. And, in the evaluation following this crisis, one of the principal conclusions of the Holloway Commission was that we should create a dedicated force for such contingencies. This recommendation was implemented, and such a force now exists, so that if a similar situation were to happen again, we would have better options to choose from and would be able to move out much faster.

On the general issue of overall decision making, there are a number of examples in the Iranian case study that I would like to touch upon briefly—for example, the use of mine warfare helicopters in this mission. The decision that led to the employment of these helicopters was an interesting one that certainly fits the "garbage can" theory well. But an equally interesting question was how did it come about that U.S. Navy MH-53s were selected?

When one looks at the various ways one might have gone about rescuing the hostages, there were a number of problems to consider. First, we did not know precisely where the hostages were, how they were being treated or where they were incarcerated. Second, the general location and surroundings were extraordinarily hostile. Third, the crisis was taking place in the middle of a capital literally thousands of miles away from the nearest U.S. or other friendly support base. From this set of factors, one quickly concludes that this was certainly not an Entebbe type of situation.

Given the above factors, however, we immediately began to analyze various options and soon discovered that this mission was no place for paratroops. We would have to use helicopters. We then looked at the available choices in helicopters to make this very demanding flight. It came down to only one type—the U.S. Navy's mine-sweeping helicopter, the MH-53. Of all the services' helicopters, it alone could handle the mission.

Fortuitously, the rhetoric emanating from the Iranians, who were threatening to mine the Strait of Hormuz, provided us with an ideal cover to rationalize the "trans-pacing" of the mine sweep helicopters to the carriers that we had deployed to the area in response to the intensity of Soviet action in Afghanistan. In this enterprise, secrecy and surprise were paramount. Without surprise there could be no mission! What could be more logical than to call upon our best mine-sweeping equipment to handle the Iranian threat to the strait?

Frequently we are criticized for being too secretive, and on some occasions I think that the criticism is valid. But, in this instance, absolute secrecy was necessary. We had to take every available precaution. If too many people had known about an operation like this one, which involved continuous planning for months ahead, a leak would have certainly occurred. It did not, and our total success in maintaining such tight security was a credit to all commands.

On the issue of managing the helicopter assets, several other problems confronted us. Almost every available mine-sweeping helicopter was on the ships. The analysts said that it would take about eight helicopters to execute the mission successfully. We had nine. In retrospect, we now know we should have had twelve or thirteen, but it is not clear that we could have made that many available. However, it is reasonably clear that we would have had much more difficulty rationalizing a force that large for the supposed mine-sweeping contingency. As it was, the helicopters sat out on the carrier decks for about three months, during which time the operational commanders became more and more irate at the presence of these big "whales" on their flight decks, because of their constant interference with the daily operational flying directed at Soviet naval presence in the area. These operational flights were an ongoing necessity to prepare for potential Soviet action/reaction. Even the carrier commanders did not know the real reason why the mine forces were there, which shows the degree to which secrecy added to the effectiveness of the plan. No small concomitant task was to create a logistics system to support the helicopters, a type known to be difficult to support. This task was executed to perfection.

Another problem related to this decision-making process was selecting and training the right helicopter pilots. It must be kept in mind that mine warfare pilots are not trained for this kind of assault and rescue mission! After an initial couple of months spent unsuccessfully trying to train enough of these pilots, it was clear we needed to widen the pool and draw from all the services—air force, navy and the marines. Of the final pilot group selected, only one navy lieutenant in the mine warfare force qualified for the mission. Tragically, the major who had the task of choosing the other helicopter pilots—a first rate, well-experienced special forces helicopter pilot—was the pilot who himself crashed into the C130 on the ground, creating the terrible inferno that contributed to the ultimate abort of the mission.

Examining the problems encountered in this mission in light of the garbage can decision model, it must be noted that, even if the model includes these kinds of uncertainties, which are a frequent occurrence in military operations, it will still be the case that the decision maker, although he thinks he has planned for the unexpected, will not have covered all the available options. In this instance, we preplanned a series of abort decision criteria, which were analyzed, generated, practiced and executed. But, at the critical moment, we ran into unforeseen circumstances that decimated the number of helicopters available and reduced them to our preordained abort decision criterion.

In addition to the problems already described, there was yet another key decision in this mission that has not been properly described to the American public, namely, who was in charge of making the abort decision. Most people believed it was the president—that he erringly forced himself into the tactical decision process. This is incorrect. It was not the president. It was not the chairman of the Joint Chiefs. It was not commander in chief, Atlantic Command. It was the operational commander, the one out there on the scene, the one confronted with the real situation, who made the decisions. He was the person given the authority and responsibility to make that final decision to abort. It was agreed, in advance, that he would not be overruled. Whatever the outcome, the on-scene commander's judgment was to prevail—and it did. In this instance, we had no problem accepting this decision.

Here is where experience and good judgment paid off. The decision-making process owed its overall smoothness to the prior experience of Admiral Tom Moorer, experience that was gained from his handling of the attempted rescue operation in Vietnam. This experience was used to provide a guideline for the Iranian mission. During the Vietnam war, we all know of the tremendous frustration and tension created by the bureaucratic organization, which was managed in such a way that the Washington civilian hierarchy attempted to control virtually every detail of the war. But in the execution of the Son Tay rescue attempt, Admiral Moorer succeeded in blocking any civilian intrusion. As the chairman of the Joint Chiefs of Staff, he quelled the influence of the civilian hierarchy, thereby allowing the on-scene commander to execute his plan without interference. In accomplishing this maneuver, Moorer encountered enormous problems and surmounted numerous difficulties. In contrast, the "Tree Cut Down" episode in Korea, which had the same characteristics of civilian influence as Vietnam—was almost a fiasco. I remember listening in on the circuit during the very moment of execution, to hear the people in Washington in the situation room literally attempt to talk to the lieutenant colonel at the Demilitarized Zone (DMZ). In the case of the Iranian operation, we insisted that these bureaucratic difficulties not occur. We were fortunate. The secretary of defense committed himself not to interfere, and the president likewise committed himself not to interfere, once he had initially approved the plan. That was the way the mission was conducted.

The types of decision-making processes I have discussed so far, with crisis examples from Libya and Iran, are not unique, one-of-a-kind events. We are likely to face similar crises again and again in other parts of the world, as with, for example, Grenada and Lebanon. Fortunately, the military, probably better than any other organization in the nation, is organized to deal with such events, even though, with the benefit of hindsight, in each instance there are many flaws one can point to in the decision execution process.

BUREAUCRATIC BUDGETARY ISSUES IN PEACETIME

The bureaucratic force-level decision-making process has no comparability to the tactical situation. The former is lengthy, enormously complex and very time consuming, even for the Unified commander in chief (CINC). The bureaucratic process primarily involves interaction with the organizational structure of the Department of Defense (DoD), its interface with the Office of Management and Budget (OMB), the White House and the congressional staffs, the combination of which almost defies the application of any decision-making theory. Here I want to focus on, and limit my discussion to, the bureaucratic decision process as it continually confronts the service chiefs— that is, in the prioritization of investment strategies. For the last six to eight years, our investment strategy has been prioritized across four basic categories: (1) *force levels*—i.e., the size of the army, air force and navy; (2) the *modern-*

ization of those forces—i.e., new radars, new equipment, Tactical Flag Command Centers (TFCCs), and the like; (3) the *readiness* of the force on any given day; and (4) the combat *sustainability*, its endurance under fire or in times of tension.

The service chiefs and the chairman of the Joint Chiefs of Staff work extremely hard to prioritize intelligently, both across and within these four major areas, using all the analytical techniques at their disposal. However, in the final analysis, it often comes down to a "gut feel" and "experience," at least for the military leaders. We all recall, with some disdain, the days when the "systems analysis" process gained such stature as to be thought the only sensible way to arrive at a force level trade-off decision. After over 20 years of personal observation of the process in operation, in my opinion, the system has become subject to extreme abuse. This abuse can mainly be attributed to an overfamiliarity with, and concentration on, the technical details of the process. The process can too easily be manipulated to deliver a "conclusion."

This is not to say that the analytical techniques involved in the systems analysis process have no intrinsic value; in fact, such techniques can be very helpful. But a good decision involves more than technique. In the context of the military, in my judgment, "experience" is the most important of all criteria that will lead to better decision making. Unfortunately, such "experience" must encounter and deal with our inefficient bureaucracy and its distorted concept of authority and responsibility. A service chief is far more likely than a technocrat to judge "a proper investment strategy," since the service chief, in reaching his opinion, relies on a prudent blending of analytical support, coupled with his personal experience and the support of a vast array of true "professionals." Such a combination of skills far exceeds the respective advice of the Office of Secretary of Defense (OSD) minions, the General Accounting Office (GAO), Office of Management and Budget (OMB) and the White House and congressional staffs combined.

For example, the fundamental defense policy of the Carter Administration, as I understood it, was one of "detente." By definition, this policy embodied the notion that the Soviets were not a global threat and that they were not malevolent in intent. The interpretation of this policy by the bureaucracy meant that it repeatedly was caused to rationalize our defense as being "adequate" and "sufficient" for our needs, without due regard for the "threat" or the budget level required to meet it. This placed an enormous burden of policy implementation on the services. They were left to execute the budget, while being in the unenviable position of increasingly having to "do more with less." This phrase became a byword. Funds were always inadequate for the demands made on the commanders, but the expectation was still there that we would proceed as if "all was well." In Washington, this state of affairs created a major conflict between the various entities responsible to the decision process. No doubt the Carter Administration sincerely thought that we did have adequate funds; but the widespread professional feeling was that they fell far short of our real requirements.

Reflecting on the whole Joint Chiefs of Staff planning process, despite the criticism directed at it by both the Office of the Secretary of Defense and the congress, in reality the process has produced advice and recommendations far closer to our real needs than any other planning document from any other bureaucratic entity. In terms of what is required, in order for us to be able to do what the country expects of the military, the current JCS planning process is remarkably accurate. However, the strategy-force mismatch remains, and it is a real issue. It is not another "missile gap."

Another example where professional "experience" outweighs technical advice is the issue of "readiness," the number one priority of the JCS but one which was consistently rejected by the civilian leadership on account of the perceived high cost involved. However, when the Soviets invaded Afghanistan, this priority suddenly became acceptable. At that point, it was indisputable that we were unable to sustain our forces in the Indian Ocean without stealing heavily from other theaters. Recognition of this, in turn, dismantled our long-term strategy that had been oriented heavily toward Europe. For years we have labored under a "short war" strategy, rationalized by its supporters as not requiring a large number of combat consumables and spare parts. On this basis, if our Allies saw a need to purchase only 15 or 20 days worth of ammunition it made no sense for the United States to buy more than 30 to 60 days worth of consumables, regardless of the unified commander in chiefs' (CINCS) and Joint Chiefs' opinion that anything less than 180 days worth of supplies was a high-risk strategy.

To return to the discussion of prioritization of investment strategies in peacetime decision making, soon after the Afghanistan invasion, Salt II collapsed, and the nation elected a new president. Defense investment strategy shifted dramatically, and prioritization was no longer a pressing issue. The naval force was to be expanded to a 600-ship navy in a state of total preparedness. The strategic forces were to be remodernized. The service chiefs were more than satisfied with this new strategic philosophy. However, despite the promise of a seven percent real growth over the next five years, even an increase of this magnitude could not solve the prevalent strategy-force imbalance. Regrettably, the seven percent real growth target has not come close to being implemented, despite the most determined effort on the part of the president. So, in 1984, we were facing a potential conflict in strategies—between the navy's secretariat, whose policy was "force levels first," and the service chiefs, who still hold "readiness" as their highest priority. On the practical level, most of us believe that the risks generated by imminent crises compel us to strive to keep our forces in the highest possible state of readiness. Those forces that are forward deployed must be ready for whatever might be required of them. They cannot say, "Wait a minute, we're going to have to delay 30 to 45 days for our consumables to be shipped in before we can move between theaters." A more acceptable solution to this conflict must be sought. But the process is not easy.

In order to implement our national strategy successfully, the central question is where does the overall responsibility lie? The answer is, on many shoulders. But, ultimately, all investment decisions lie in the hands of the appropriations committees of the House and the Senate, and it is to them that we must turn. Despite the decision influencers and think tanks that we possess, and the plethora of ideas that emanate from them, defense budget decisions ultimately can be reduced to a single focal point: what do these two committees judge to be best to meet our needs? When these staffs enter the decision tree, a whole different set of inputs enter—inputs that have almost no relationship to the prioritization among the four fundamental investment strategy categories that are the heart and soul of the service chiefs' beliefs. Unfortunately, the issue often becomes one of politics—for example, employment levels in various regions of the country, or a wide variety of other interests. Given the nature of the present system, one that allows nonelected staff assistants, who have no legitimate responsibility for implementing the consequences of their decision making, to have so much authority, it is remarkable how well the process, works. Nevertheless, this "locus of authority" issue is one of the biggest weaknesses in our entire decision making process. Yet it is almost never confronted, and if the issue were challenged, it would be vehemently resisted.

CONCLUSIONS

Throughout this paper, I have tried to make the point, through the use of practical examples, that there are three basic decision categories that we must recognize before we can evaluate the applicability and efficacy of the garbage can theory of decision making. First, there is a major wartime decision-making process. Second, there is a tactical decision-making process for crises and limited engagements. Third, there is the bureaucratic, technocratic process, which is an entirely different arena of decision making, where military judgment finds difficulty residing. The examples used to illustrate these individual styles of decision making in operation—Libya, Iran, Washington and elsewhere—will hopefully serve us all as lessons for future reference.

Within the Department of Defense, at this time, there is a renewed awareness that mistakes have been made in the past and a willingness to rethink the major issues involved in crisis decision making.

From the Vietnam experience, it is now much better understood, by both the military and civilians, that the way the war was managed from Washington was wrong. We have also learned from recent crises that the political leadership must be involved and must be kept informed throughout. But, in crisis execution we have found that people on the scene must be left alone—we must select them right, train them right and have total confidence in their judgment and performance.

On the issue of prioritization of a suitable investment strategy and its implementation, we still need to make further progress. The bureaucracy remains highly complex and unwieldy in terms of implementing change.

However, the final question remains: how can a better understanding of the garbage can theory of decision making in military affairs help to bring about a significant improvement in future challenges facing the civilian and military leadership? Given the current "state of the art" in decision-making theory, it is too soon to be able to answer this question. From my own viewpoint, I can say that the theory appears to have a great deal of relevance to the examples I have discussed in this paper, but there are still a number of problems to be worked out and refinements to be made in the "translation" of "theory" to "practice" and in the precise interrelationship of the two in military contexts.

13

Sixth Fleet Operations:
June 1981 to July 1983

WILLIAM H. ROWDEN

As commander of the navy's Sixth Fleet from June 1981 to July 1983, I was intimately involved with U.S. military operations in the Mediterranean during a critical period in that region. A tenuous state of affairs existed in the eastern Mediterranean well before my arrival and continues through this writing, but three key events unfolded during my tour of duty there. These were the shooting down of two Libyan fighter planes over the Gulf of Sidra, the assassination of Anwar Sadat and the tragic bombing of the U.S. Embassy in Beirut, Lebanon.

Each of these incidents involved operational decisions at the fleet level and policy decisions through the chain of command to the highest levels of government. While none of these events can be considered in a vacuum—each is part of the mosaic of international events that has been laid over many years—I can describe them from my on-scene perspective as Sixth Fleet Commander. There is some overlap, but I will discuss them generally in chronological order.

Our forces had already been committed in the eastern Mediterranean near Lebanon when I arrived at the Sixth Fleet in June 1981. My first major responsibility there was to effect a disengagement of these forces and return the fleet to the more normal pursuits of training and maintaining readiness. How-

Vice Admiral William H. Rowden, USN, is the commander of the Naval Sea Systems Command and a former commander of the Sixth Fleet.

ever, I quickly found that one of the most difficult tasks of a commander is to achieve an agreement to terminate a crisis.

Once a force has been energized for a conflict, or possible conflict, it is difficult to make the transition (operationally and psychologically) back to more routine activities. The crisis seems to take on a life of its own, and its sheer weight gives it considerable momentum. In addition, the on-scene commander cannot see the broader picture available to policymakers both up the chain and in Washington, D.C. The subtle pressures and sticking points, particularly concerning international relations, are not as obvious to us. So a decision to "stand down" from a crisis is complex, at best, and involves numerous factors, both "seen" and "unseen."

However, in the case of the Sixth Fleet, we needed to get on with other business in the region, and did just that by the middle of July.

THE LIBYAN CHALLENGE

It is important to understand the basis of our disagreement with the Libyans. Several years ago, they claimed as internal waters the area south of latitude 32°30' in the Gulf of Sidra. Their claim was based on two points: first, that this area had been an indivisible part of Libya since the time of the Barbary States; and second, that the Gulf of Sidra is a closed bay, similar to Canada's Hudson Bay. The United States consistently has rejected both arguments. The United States policy is to respect territorial sea claims up to 12 miles, and we do not recognize those claims that exceed this distance. At its greatest point, the distance from latitude 32°30' to the Libyan coast to the south is about 150 miles.

Despite the Libyan claim, the United States decided to exercise its right to use the area. To accomplish this, an exercise was planned for August, 1981. This would occur coincidentally with the turnover of our aircraft carriers in the Mediteranean. The U.S.S. *Nimitz* was scheduled to relieve the U.S.S. *Forrestal*, and both carriers would be available to us during an overlap period.

The exercise planned was an open-ocean missile exercise in which ships and aircraft of the force engage drones employed as air targets. Such exercises require considerable assets to stage and evaluate properly, so we naturally wished to provide as many participating units as possible. Accordingly, during the Sixth Fleet battle force turnover, we could expect the combatant force level to be twice that of normal operating times, and we would, therefore, achieve the most effective exercise.

We planned the operation, and Rear Admiral James E. Service, then commander of the Battle Force Sixth Fleet and an operational subordinate of mine (now president of the Naval War College in Newport, Rhode Island), briefed the exercise through the entire chain of command, including the National Security Council. Meanwhile, in early August, I met in Naples with a high-ranking Department of Defense official, who asked what he might do to support our plans. I asked for full support, without second-guessing, provided we complied fully with the rules of engagement that had been established.

These rules provided for the right of self-defense; specifically, if fired upon, we had the right, indeed the obligation, to meet force with force. Execution of these rules provided that if we were to fire at any enemy target in self-defense we intended to hit that target. When the issue was joined, and we were required to act within the rules of engagement, I received the complete support of my superiors.

We had emphasized this point—that as a consequence of hostile action, casualties would likely be inflicted—in our briefings up the chain of command. In so doing, we explored many "what-ifs" dealing with our reaction to a demonstrated hostile act. The purpose was to exercise our own thought processes and responses to these situations for sound applicability to the rules of engagement we had derived, as well as to demonstrate a breadth of understanding and reaction to our superiors. This was intended to reinforce the soundness of our plan and gain the confidence of our superiors in our ability to execute it. In my judgment, we succeeded on both these counts.

The exercise firing area was in the Gulf of Sidra—above and below 32°30'. We placed surface combatants around the firing area to warn intruders out of the danger zone. Two U.S. Navy destroyers, U.S.S. *Pratt* and U.S.S. *Caron*, were placed south of 32°30'; a cruiser and a destroyer were placed to the east, a cruiser and two destroyers to the west and the two carriers to the north with all remaining forces. The *Pratt* and the *Caron* remained below latitude 32° for about a day and a half.

We also flew combat air patrol (CAP) and maintained air surveillance to warn off air intruders. During the first day of the operation, the Libyans flew a number (as I recall, about 36) of two-aircraft sorties toward and into the area of the danger zone. All were closed by our aircraft and turned away without incident. One of these flights originated from Girda Bya in the extreme south of the Gulf of Sidra; all the rest were from either Benina, near Bengazi, or Tripoli.

On the second day of the operation, August 19, Libyan flight operations began at sunrise, and we were again in place to intercept and warn them off. As on the previous day, several Libyan flights were closed without incident. But at about 0700 hours, two Libyan Fitters left Girda Bya and flew northward over water; two of our F-14s on the southern-most CAP station were directed to close them. At the point of interception—in a head-on situation, with a relative closing speed in excess of 1,000 miles per hour, the lead Fitter fired one missile at the F-14s. Both our planes did precisely what they were supposed to do under the rules of engagement: they engaged and shot down the two Libyan jets.

There is another very important point about this engagement that is frequently overlooked. At the same time the shoot-down occurred, two other intercepts were in progress. All flight leaders were able to monitor the engagement on their radios, but no one else sought to engage the Libyans with whom they were in contact because, beyond the local F-14/Fitter incident, there had been no provocation. The rules of engagement called only for engagement in self-defense, where firing had actually occurred. This Libyan incident demonstrates the superb discipline of our naval aviators, even when the adrenaline is flowing in a crisis situation, and also refutes the notion that we are "trigger-happy gunmen" on the lookout to start an incident.

After this shoot-down, the Libyans conducted a successful search-and-rescue for their downed aviators. We subsequently recommenced and completed the missile exercise. The next problem was one of disengagement. The *Pratt* and the *Caron* had been in contact off and on with several Libyan patrol boats and a surfaced submarine. Now my concern was how to make a clean break; we did not want it to appear that we had been chased out, and we certainly did not want to take them with us.

Therefore, we decided that at a given time, with air cover in the area, we would move our forces northward in a resolute fashion and see how the Libyans responded. They did nothing and seemed to be relieved as we left. We were fully prepared to respond had their reaction been otherwise.

ASSASSINATION IN CAIRO

A few weeks after the Libyan incident, we were confronted with an unexpected event that threatened to spark new turmoil in the Middle East. This was the assassination of Egyptian President Anwar Sadat on October 6, 1981. When the news first broke of the bloodshed at a military parade near Cairo, there was uncertainty about who was involved in the shooting, how the Egyptian people would react and whether the country's leadership would change hands smoothly.

The Joint Chiefs of Staff directed us to place our amphibious forces off Alexandria. We had two amphibious forces in the Mediterranean at that time, and both of these took up station off Alexandria. They included ten amphibious ships, with two battalions of Marines aboard. During this unsettled period, we were to provide medical support and visible indication of U.S. presence.

Shortly thereafter, these amphibious forces were joined by the *Nimitz* battle group, which had been in Venice. We were on station for about ten days, and, fortunately, no unrest developed. Again, the challenge was to effect a return to more "normal" Sixth Fleet operations.

In times of normal operations, the fleet is obliged to conduct training constantly in order to maintain a well-rounded capability in all its functions. Additionally, there are substantial demands for, and benefits derived from, port visits to cities of friends and allies all around the Mediterranean. Not only do we accomplish needed maintenance during these port visits, but the American sailor, who is among the very best of our ambassadors of good will, gets a chance to go ashore.

So once we perceived that the crisis for which we had been placed on special alert had passed, we were strongly convinced that we needed to get on with normal operations. Naturally, we understood that other considerations in addition to our perception of why the Sixth Fleet was in the Mediterranean must enter into decisions to take the fleet off alert. But we felt that the job we did under normal operations was valuable and needed to be done. So we would work toward the assumption of normal operations.

WITHDRAWAL OF THE PLO FROM BEIRUT

The final and most enduring crisis of my time with the Sixth Fleet was associated with the Israeli invasion of Lebanon and our ultimate involvement with U.S. Marines ashore in Beirut. In the latter part of May 1982, against a background of escalating tension between Israel and the Palestine Liberation Organization (PLO) in Beirut and southern Lebanon, an assassination attempt was made in London on the Israeli ambassador to the United Kingdom. The Israelis blamed the Palestinians, or more specifically the PLO, and decided it was time to intercede militarily. This operation was called "Peace for Galilee."

On June 6, the Israelis invaded Lebanon and within several days pushed all the way to the outskirts of Beirut. I was told to move our amphibious force to the eastern Mediterranean. Unfortunately, we were turning over the force, and the incoming ships were in Rota, Spain, about 2,200 miles from Beirut. We sent them east, and they arrived off Beirut about mid-June. Along with ships of the Soviet navy, they maintained their positions in the eastern Mediterranean off Lebanon for about the next five weeks.

On June 23, 1982, we were called upon to evacuate U.S. citizens from the town of Juniyeh, which is about ten miles north of Beirut. With two ships of the amphibious force, we moved about 560 civilians to Cyprus. We evacuated all the United States citizens and green card holders who wanted to leave Lebanon, but, in total, there were very few U.S. citizens evacuated. However, there were a great many citizens from Lebanon and many other nationalities who were represented, including the Soviet Union.

In July, the Israelis conducted an intensive bombing campaign in Beirut with the declared purpose of driving the PLO out of the city. The cost of achieving this by direct military ground action probably was deemed too high by the Israelis. By that time, they had suffered a death toll of about 300. (On a relative scale of national populations, this would equate to about 30,000 to 40,000 U.S. casualties.) So the invasion had been costly to the Israelis. But their declared purpose in Beirut was to dislodge the PLO from both Beirut and Lebanon.

Meanwhile, the U.S. and other parties entered negotiations to end the bombing and settle the PLO issue, in a way that would provide security for Israel's northern border. By the middle of August, it was agreed that the PLO would leave Beirut, and the Sixth Fleet was directed to help facilitate an orderly withdrawal. The U.S. Marines of the Sixth Fleet Marine Amphibious Unit (MAU) were to become part of a multinational force, which also would include Italy and France (a small contingent from Great Britain would be added later).

One of our greatest challenges with the landing of the U.S. troops in Beirut was to establish workable rules of engagement. These rules had to be simple and understandable. It does not make any difference if we write a rule that can be understood by a colonel if it cannot be understood, remembered and executed by a private. There were two basic rules. First, if you are shot at, you should defend yourself. The second rule was more complicated. It dealt with intent on the part of an adversary to harm our troops. If an opponent demonstrated intent to commit a hostile act, the decision could be made to engage the offending individual or organization. It was a very difficult rule to apply, and fortunately it was never called into use. But the soldier on the ground *did* have the authority to defend himself. This was a clear rule and was understood by everyone.

The introduction of troops in the Beirut port was accompanied by the clear understanding that they would be there no longer than 30 days. And if the job could be done more quickly, so much the better. Our orders also enjoined us, should the situation turn hostile, to be prepared to withdraw troops. But there was no definition of "turn hostile."

We landed the marines in port in the latter part of August—the 25th as I remember—and the withdrawal of the PLO began simultaneously. With that withdrawal, the Sixth Fleet had the responsibility of escorting every PLO-carrying ship leaving Beirut to its destination. In all, about 15,000 armed personnel, mostly members of the PLO, were evacuated. Roughly half, including some Syrian troops, went overland to Syria. The rest departed through the port on some twelve to fifteen ships. They sailed to North Yemen, South Yemen, Sudan, Tunisia, Crete and Cyprus, and to Syria by sea through Tartūs. This evacuation took five or six days, and on September 1, I met with Secretary of Defense Weinberger in Beirut. We observed the departure of the last shipload of PLO members and agreed that the marines could be withdrawn by September 10. They left on that date, some 16 days after we placed them ashore.

BACK TO LEBANON

Unfortunately, the situation deteriorated rapidly again. On September 14, Lebanon's president-elect, Bashir Gemayel, was assassinated. This event was followed quickly by the occupation of West Beirut by Israeli defense forces. On September 18, 1982, just over a week after our withdrawal, there was a massacre in the Lebanese refugee camps of Sabra and Shatilla. A few days later, the decision was made to reinsert our troops as part of the multinational force. I believe that decision felt the impetus of a requirement for stability, following as it did in the wake of the Sabra-Shatilla massacre. The rules of engagement were the same. Absent this time, however, were the strong indicators that we would only be there 30 days. There was mention of a 60-day limit, but in my recollection, the emphasis for limited duration was not the same as before.

Provisions remained to remove our troops should the situation turn hostile. This time, we were not held to 800 troops ashore. The number 1,200 was suggested, but I objected to this figure on the grounds that we should have the full authority to land our total force if the situation so demanded. We were told that the number ashore would be about 1,200, but we landed a properly constituted force of about 1,500 and held back those who operated and maintained marine aircraft. The marines occupied positions in the vicinity of the Beirut International Airport.

After this, our presence in Beirut became more or less permanent. But over the subsequent months, the indigenous situation changed radically. The most significant event that occurred between the relanding of the troops on September 29, 1982, and the day I left on July 8, 1983, was the bombing of the U.S. Embassy on April 18, 1983. The Embassy, a concrete building which was characteristic of many in Beirut, was hit by a pickup truck loaded with explosives—probably on the order of 3,000 to 4,000 pounds. It was gutted from the front wall to the rear wall. Every floor was heavily damaged, except the eighth floor, where the ambassador's office was located. It was the most devastating employment of explosives I had seen in that war-torn city. The massive explosion took the lives of 17 U.S. citizens and over 40 other persons.

BEIRUT RETROSPECTIVE

Our performance subsequent to this bombing has been called into question. I would like to offer a few personal views on this issue. First, it is important to bear in mind that our entire presence in Beirut could be characterized by one word—restraint. We had constantly been reminded of an obligation not to become involved in Lebanese affairs but rather, in situations requiring force, to enjoin the Lebanese Army to employ whatever force necessary to stabilize the situation. The order of the day: keep the rifle slung on the shoulder, and ammunition in the belt. Do not be provocative.

After the U.S. Embassy was bombed, we provided security troops for the temporary Embassy. (Our diplomatic activities were then being carried out in the British Embassy and another nearby building.) Heretofore, we had not provided security at the Embassy. We revised the rules of engagement, reasoning that we needed the authority to defend against the threat of our security being breached. We established fences and fortifications around the temporary Embassy buildings, because direct threats to these buildings would have to be challenged at a distance. This may seem a curious thought process, but remember that in establishing ourselves at the airport we were not considered to be occupying territory. We had a "presence" encampment there, from which we showed daily visibility.

In guarding the temporary Embassy, we reasoned that the rules should permit a more active self-defense than merely responding to attacks. We convinced our superiors of this need for change and ordered the new, tougher rules into effect.

During this period of unrest, we all sensed that there was a change coming over the populace of Beirut. When we first arrived there, we were well received by the people. (I used to drive through city and towns in a Jeep and encountered no problems.) The marines were welcomed as people who had brought stability to the city.

Things started to change. The number of young males increased; there were more pro-Khomeini posters; the people in some places became sullen. We started to vary our routes and to take precautions against hazarding our people in what appeared to be a changing environment. During most of this time, we were provided daily intelligence with numerous reports on such threats as car bombs. (There were several incidents of car bombings against the

Israelis.) However, there was little indication of actual increased violence against our troops, although there was one incident where a hand grenade was thrown at a patrol of five marines.

The tension continued to mount in Beirut during the remainder of the period I was associated with the Sixth Fleet and our operation there. We felt compelled to balance the dangers of this situation against our ongoing mission of maintaining a "presence" in Beirut. But in order to establish presence, visibility is necessary. So although the marines had dug in at individual company areas, they manned sentry posts and functioned in plain view of the people. We were constantly apprehensive about taking casualties. While we enjoyed good support in our efforts there, we felt that this support would dwindle rapidly should we take any casualties.

I handed over the situation to Vice Admiral Edward H. Martin on July 8, but I continued to have the situation foremost on my mind throughout the summer and fall of 1983. I have agonized greatly over the events of October 23, 1983, in which 241 U.S. men lost their lives when a truck laden with the equivalent of 12,000 pounds of TNT penetrated the marine's Battalion Landing Team Headquarters building at Beirut and detonated. I have often wondered if I might have done something differently if my responsibilities in Beirut had been extended beyond July 8, 1983. I do not know really, if I would have done anything differently or not. I do not know if I would have been alarmed by the concentration of the marines in that building or not.

I do know it was an enormously substantial building—the most substantial building, in my estimation, in that compound. The MAU commander certainly had good reason to put his marines, who were being sniped at, in that substantial building. I do not know if I would have countermanded his order; we believe strongly in allowing the commander on the ground to make on-scene decisions. Perhaps the only certainty to emerge from this tragedy is that the events of October 23, 1983, will weigh heavily on our hearts and minds for a long time to come.

As to the situation now—what should we do?[1] Certainly, we should not change the rules of engagement, because if we allow more active military involvement, that certainly bespeaks involvement in the internal issues of Lebanon. This then is the dilemma: we must avoid becoming involved in internal issues, but we *must* effectively protect the hostage force that is there now. We have taken some steps to do that by digging in our forces, but this has directly affected our "presence" role.

In short, our mission has to change. Since we cannot become more involved, then obviously we have to find a way, with honor, to get out. I think the situation, by any measure, including the order I received when we first landed troops in 1982, has "turned hostile." That being the case, in my opinion, we have little alternative but to withdraw.

NOTES

1. This chapter was completed by Admiral Rowden on January 27, 1984. On March 30, 1984, President Reagan announced that the United States would terminate its participation in the multinational force in Lebanon. In the preceding weeks, the marines had been redeployed to Sixth Fleet ships off shore.

14

Decision Making and the Grenada Rescue Operation

JOSEPH METCALF III

My comments will focus on decision making and the Grenada rescue operation, hopefully within the context of the "garbage can" model. The Grenada operation is an excellent example of operational decision making, as this crisis involved not only the military aspects of the decision process but also political, interservice and intraservice decision making. Grenada is also an appropriate case study because it is a "bounded problem"; it took place over a limited period of time, with a clear beginning and end.

Looking back to October 1983, and reflecting on the operation, it is clear that many decisions just "happened," and it is this indeterminate, disoriented decision process that will be difficult to represent in model form. Throughout the crisis, decisions were made because they had to be made, regardless of individual choice, and they involved a broad spectrum of different decision-making processes.

At the outset of the Grenada operation, we began, in military tradition, with a logo. All good military organizations worth their salt have either a logo or an incomprehensible acronym. For Grenada, we had both. "Urgent Fury" was the mission's code name, and my staff, showing an immense amount of

Vice Admiral Joseph Metcalf III, USN, is the deputy chief of Naval Operations for Surface Warfare and a former commander of the Second Fleet.

cleverness, put together a logo that emphasized the participation of all services in the operation. This sense of "participation" was one of the key operational objectives. Another important objective was to run the operation with the minimum of bureaucratic intervention and interservice wrangling. To a large extent, we succeeded. However, there were exceptions that I will address later.

At this point, it is useful to examine the roots of the Grenada operation, that is, why the United States intervened militarily. A good summary of the underlying problems that touched off this incident appeared in the January 1984 issue of the *Atlantic Monthly*. According to this source, it appears that the military action was the result of the failure of United States policy toward Grenada over a period of years. This diplomatic failure was a complex mixture of national pride, poor judgment and simple things like the development of airports. In this context, the "garbage can theory" fitted United States policy prior to the rescue operation in that the policy was plagued by a lack of clearly articulated goals.

But contrary to past diplomatic policy, when the United States decided to go into Grenada, the invasion goals were articulated very quickly and clearly. This decision-making process appears to fit the garbage can theory. However, regardless of whether the Grenada operation perfectly fits a garbage can model, the issue here is, how can we utilize this example for the improvement of decision-making models at the theoretical level?

In examining the process of decision making in military operations, another important variable is the decision maker's background. But it is difficult to put the background of a commander into a computer or a theoretical model. Yet it was a specific event in my own background, namely, my role in the evacuation of Saigon, that prepared me, in a unique way, to command the Grenada operation. During the Saigon mission, I was in charge of naval surface forces covering the evacuation and, thus, had the unparalleled opportunity to watch very closely the interaction between the National Command Authority and the on-scene commanders, principally, the commander of the Seventh Fleet and the commander of the evacuation forces.

What I observed was a classic example of what I term "the six thousand mile screwdriver"—the minute direction of the day-to-day operations of a field commander by higher and remote authority. In Grenada I found myself politically in an almost identical situation, in terms of actual operation control. What was different was that I was, in a way, on square "A" with latitude to work the problem of maintaining control. The process I evolved was simple. I assigned a section of my staff to deal specifically with matters "up" the chain of command. As the operation evolved, I spent almost half my time dealing with higher authority. It was a deliberate decision, on my part, to ensure that the people "up" the chain of command knew what was happening. I organized my staff to influence the Joint Chiefs of Staff and the commander in chief, Atlantic Command. I wanted explicitly to influence what they were telling me to do. This mode of organization coincides with the notion that decision makers like delegation of authority down to their own level of command, but below that level they strive for centralized control. However, I am not in total agreement with this concept. In the Grenada operation, I organized the structure of decision making in a way that, I thought, would maximize the delegation of authority down to me, whereas below me, I delegated "what" to do to my subordinates, and they were responsible for the "how."

From the outset of the operation, I recognized that the major participants would have different operational styles. The Marine Corps, the 82nd Airborne, the Rangers, the Joint Chiefs of Staff and the commander in chief, Atlantic Fleet, all had different perspectives and opinions. But, as I stated earlier, I wanted to make sure that the interservice disagreements were kept to a minimum, at least at our level, in the field. I was particularly concerned with the Marine Corps and the 82nd Airborne, where, I was sure, different operational procedures would come into play. Again, this is an area where "model fit" is an issue.

The organization chart shown in Figure 14.1 illustrates the chain of command under discussion. Normally, as commander, Second Fleet, I work for the commander in chief, Atlantic Fleet (CINCLANTFLT), but in the Grenada operation I reported to the commander in chief, Atlantic Command (CINCLANT), who, in turn, was under the Joint Chiefs of Staff (JCS). For Grenada operations, I was the commander of Joint Task Force 120 (CJTF 120) and was on the same line of authority as commander in chief, Atlantic Fleet, and the army and air force component commanders. In theory, the Task Force 120 organization is always in a "ready for action" status. People are tentatively assigned from all services. The Grenada operation was a joint endeavor, and I had assigned to it elements from all the services; army, navy, air force and marines (see Figure 14.2). My task was to direct and coordinate these forces, tell them "what to do," and not "how to do it." I dealt with the commanders of all services as "professionals" who knew their jobs. I also had the Caribbean Peacekeeping Force in a "support" status, but not directly in my command. This force was made up of policemen from Barbados, Jamaica and other eastern Caribbean nations. I also had in "support" the U.S.S. *Independence* Battle Group, elements of Military Airlift Command (MAC), Tactical Air Command, Strategic Air Command and the U.S. Readiness Command. The

Figure 14.1

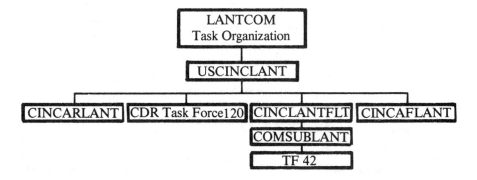

decision process worked well, and the subordinate commanders worked the problem.

My first important (and perhaps key) decision was the organization of the Commander Task Force 120 staff (see Figure 14.3). The normal task organization for CJTF 120 has 88 people assigned. Unfortunately, except for the biannual exercise, "Solid Shield," most of the time Joint Task Force 120 is a paper organization. When the Joint Chiefs of Staff activated the 120 Task Force, there was no time to call in the 88, nor would I have wished to do so. I selected my chief of staff and fifteen officers from my Second Fleet organization, to which were added augmentees from the air force, army, Central Intelligence Agency, and the State Department. Together, they filled out what I called a "battle staff" tactical decision team.

Early on, the army expressed mild consternation. As a joint commander, I was to command significant army forces, both Rangers and the 82nd Airborne. To allay their own uneasiness, they sent me one of their top division command-

Figure 14.2   Task organization.

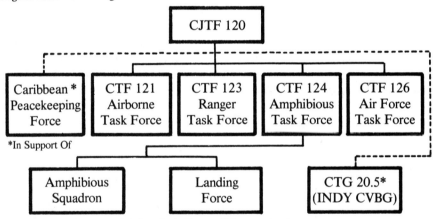

Figure 14.3   Command Joint Task Force 120 organization.

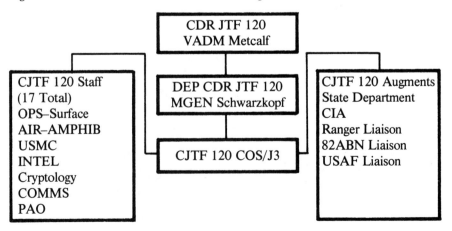

ers, Major General Norm Schwarzkopf. He came to me as a "liaison officer." Eventually, I made him my deputy commander. There were a number of reasons for this, one was that we developed a common synergism of ideas and objectives. This all may sound logical, but it raised the question, "By what authority did you do that, Admiral?" My response was that I needed a deputy commander, which to me was sufficient authority. Execution of the decision was simple. I assembled my subordinate commanders and told them that Major General Schwarzkopf was my deputy and that his authority emanated from me.[1] Sometimes, in the decision process, there are clear-cut actions that work out particularly well, and Major General Schwarzkopf's appointment as a deputy was one such instance. He was a principal element of the command and a key to both the decision process and the ultimate success of the mission.

Turning now to the mission itself, the following is a summary of the Grenada mission statement from higher command:

- Conduct military operations to protect and evacuate U.S. and designated foreign nationals from Grenada
- Neutralize Grenadian forces
- Stabilize the internal situation
- Maintain the peace

The formal version was only slightly more elaborate. Both versions, however, outline a clear set of goals, priorities and directives. The "how" of implementation was left to my own judgment.

In addition to the initial mission itself, I was also given the rules of engagement (ROE):

- Use force and weapons as may be essential to the accomplishment of the mission
- Minimize the disruptive influence of military operations on the local economy commensurate with the accomplishment of the mission
- Execute initial tasks readily with minimum damage and casualties

These, along with the mission statement, formed the critical direction for the accomplishments of the mission. In military terms, these rules were both difficult and restrictive. They presented the toughest challenge to the accomplishment of the mission, since they directed that we use only the essential force and weapons required to carry out the mission. What that meant was, do not use one more bullet, bomb or whatever than is necessary to accomplish the mission. Minimize the use of destructive forces. Implied was, act quickly. In my mind, the most important words were "minimum casualties." To me, this was the operative ROE. No matter what I did, minimum casualties was the important consideration. "Do it fast and minimize casualties."

In a sense, however, the rules of engagement were a nonsequitur. U.S. forces are trained and equipped to minimize their own casualties by the use of superior firepower. Therefore, I decided that if I was to ensure minimum damage to both sides, then I had to control the release of highly destructive weapons that might inflict significant damage on Grenada. Here was the one area where I specifically made selective decisions as to "how" the operation was to be conducted, that is, the control of force required to accomplish a task. The objective was to reduce any tendency toward the overzealous use of firepower. But, where appropriate, I granted permission to use superior fire-power (principally naval air, naval gunfire and army artillery). In each authorization decision, however, I kept the rules of engagement foremost in my mind, particularly *minimum casualties*. Nevertheless, as the fight unfolded, I was involved in some difficult decision making.

To reiterate, throughout the mission I had clear guidance. Overall, the mission statement and the rules of engagement were unambiguous; the problems lay in their execution.

From the time I was officially notified that I would lead the Grenada operation to H-hour was 39 hours. I call this period *the thirty-nine hours*. The first stage can be summarized as follows:

- What is the mission?
- What is the plan?
- What forces are assigned?
- What are the rules of engagement?
- Is the plan executable?

I needed a clear understanding of these points if I was to understand how the mission was to be carried out. The actual operation went on for 11 days, not including a Joint Chiefs of Staff warning order issued five days prior to D-day, to the appropriate commands. This Warning Order was straightforward and instructed the commander-in-chief, Atlantic Command, to prepare for operations in Grenada. The commander-in-chief, Atlantic Command, through the commander-in-chief, Atlantic Fleet, in turn directed me as commander of the Second Fleet to move forces. I was not in the warning order chain and did not participate in the initial planning process, nor was I asked to. I am sure I could have participated, but it was a deliberate decision on my part not to. My rationale was that I wanted to avoid being wedded to, or emotionally identified with, the development of a particular plan. However, I felt the need to stay informed, so I sent a few specific members of the staff over to the CINCLANT headquarters. I knew there were any number of options and much uncertainty about the selection of one over another. By not participating personally, at this early stage, I thought I would be in a better position to make an independent judgment about plan implementation, if any, when the time came.

When it came to my *thirty-nine hours*, and I was officially notified that I was to be in command, I was aware, in general terms, what CINCLANT had proposed. I felt there were holes and pitfalls in the plan as submitted to the JCS. But, as sometimes happens, this initial CINCLANT plan was significantly changed by the Joint Chiefs of Staff. In fact, the assignment of forces, as proposed by USCINCLANT, was turned around. The mission roles of the marines and army units were reversed. In my judgment, with the benefit of hindsight, either plan would have worked. My responsibility in the short time available was to determine if, in my judgment, the plan as approved was executable. Did it match the mission? Did it make sense? Did I understand it? Would my subordinates understand it? Could the forces assigned execute the mission within the restrictions of the rules of engagement?

My first task was to decide whether the planned operation could be executed successfully. I had reservations about certain high-risk aspects of the plan, particularly those involving Rangers parachuting at night. This reservation was diffused by talking with experienced and knowledgeable people who persuaded me that the Rangers really could, with acceptable risk, execute the assigned night parachute drop. Pragmatically working through these issues, I came to the conclusion that the plan as approved by the Joint Chiefs of Staff was executable with acceptable risk.

One aspect of the approved plan that had great appeal was the mission assignment of forces. Forces were assigned tasks that closely paralleled service training. It was the tactical key to the success of the operation. The JCS assignment of tasks to the army and marines utilized their specialized, individual training. And critically important, a deliberate planning effort was made to keep the units separate. We wanted to make sure that marines would not accidentally shoot at the army, and vice versa. The most essential lesson that emerged from this operation was to reaffirm the old lesson that units should fight as they have been trained to fight. It was this initial delegation of tasks that was the genius of the operation and that persuaded me of the plan's executability and compatibility with the mission.

In dealing with a military operation of this nature, there are many things to be taken into consideration. The second stage of my *thirty-nine hours* included the following considerations:

- What is the command and control structure?
- Where will Commander Joint Task Force 120 staff be located?
- What staff is needed?
  a. Commander Joint Task Force 120
  b. Commander Second Fleet
- Is staff augmentation required?
- Is the communications plan workable?

Obviously, the command and control structure was critical. One of the first things that must be established, particularly in a joint operation, is the structure of authority, that is, who is in charge. As force commander, I wanted it to be understood from the outset that I would coordinate forces. I also wanted it understood that I would tell commanders "what" to do rather than "how" to do it. I believe in the Nelsonian principle of *know your commanders*. To get across the point of who is in charge and meet eyeball to eyeball, I arranged for the available commanders[2] to come to Norfolk to meet with me at seven o'clock Monday morning, October 24, 1983—less than 24 hours before the operation was to take place.

At this session, we went over the plan for the operation. Each commander explained how he was going to carry out his assignments. They were all extremely confident about the mission and its accomplishment. However, in this type of operation, where it appears that all the cards are with you, there is a tendency to underestimate precisely what it will take to get the job done. I would not say we were "overconfident," but there was a distinct air of "bravado." We went over the intelligence estimates and how we would react to that intelligence. The intelligence estimates were very optimistic. Intelligence had suggested that the indigenous Grenada force, the People's Republican Army (PRA), was going to "cut and run" and that the Cubans were a "rag-tag outfit" that really was going to be a "piece of cake." Such a simplistic scenario is one that should automatically raise the skepticism of those in command. In order to gauge the level of suspicion in my commanders, we discussed issues such as the following: What would happen if we did not get an airfield reconnaissance? What if the intelligence estimates of the defenders' capabilities were wrong? This was a very useful discussion, which both clarified a number of issues and introduced the principals to each other. We worried and became sensitized to a possible weakness in the intelligence reports. We gauged each other's reactions, and we clarified the chain of command. I made the point that my command philosophy was to direct "what," not "how," to my subordinate commanders. So in summary, this meeting was for me to make sure they understood how I would react, for me to gauge how they would react, and, most important, to establish who was in charge.

The third set of the *thirty-nine hours* involved the following set of challenges:

- How will operations be run?
- Who constitutes the tactical decision team?
- How will the operation be coordinated?
  a. Nationally
  b. Locally
- How did the operation work?

From my experience with the Saigon evacuation, I knew that my success in controlling the Grenada operation at the scene of the fight would depend, in large measure, on how well I kept higher authority informed of my intentions and the progress of events. Therefore, as part of my battle organization, four of my staff were solely assigned this task of dealing up the chain of command to National Command Authority. This group, under the direction of a captain, was charged by me to send no less than two situation reports (SITREPs) an hour. My exact words were, "I don't care if we are talking about hangnails—we will put out two SITREPS an hour." The concept was not only to inform my seniors but to keep their staffs busy. I knew there were a lot of good energetic people in both the JCS and USCINCLANT who would like to be where we were; I wanted to channel their energies into reading my messages, not telling me what to do.

I assigned my operations officer, a captain with a lot of experience working with the USCINCLANT staff, to the "secure phone" to the Norfolk headquarters. He was the "Voice of Urgent Fury"; he was the CTF-120 voice on the circuit during all active combat operations. His first stint was 17 hours. The impact of this scheme was significant. The commander in chief and his staff always heard the same voice, a voice they knew and could relate to. The object was to create the impression that, in fact, we were in control and knew what was going on. I emphasize this point because I think both the system of *situation reports* and the *command voice* were the main reasons that higher authority permitted me to retain control over the military action at the local level (Grenada). I understand that General Vessey told the JCS, the president and Secretary Weinberger that it was his decision that I was going to run the operation.

I knew from experience that this was a very fragile situation. I was absolutely correct. And I do not blame them. From their standpoint, the operation could have gone one way or the other. I knew the Grenada operation represented tremendous political risks. Because of the risks, particularly in peacetime, there is a natural tendency for higher authority to move down and attempt to control local actions from afar. In this day of instant communications from and to anywhere in the world, combined with the high stakes involved, the local command has an obligation to communicate information up if he expects to retain control. Higher command authority must always have information, or they will remove control from the local commander. In the Grenada operation, the key to our success in retaining local control was to keep higher command fully informed, on an ongoing basis, throughout the entire mission.

In addition to this continuous information flow up the chain, I established an additional goal—that by five o'clock each day[3] our operation plans were to be set for the following day. This information was relayed to higher authority, and it enabled them to review it, in the context of my ongoing needs and estimates. Usually they turned around my "intentions" into a directive telling me to do what I told them I was going to do. This aspect of decision making was very successful, both in terms of getting the job done and in terms of ensuring that I, the commander on scene, continued to retain control over how the battle was to be fought.

A final aspect of preoperation planning was my decision to keep records of the entire "Urgent Fury" operation, since I realized that it would be a highly visible issue, long after the events had taken place, and that there would be examinations of our actions and reactions which at the time we had not even thought about.

During the first two days of the Grenada operation, there were many crucial and interesting decisions made, which provide good examples of the anatomy of practical decision making in a crisis situation. As previously mentioned, there was a basic operational plan to separate the marines and the army. The marines were to assault the northern end of the island, while responsibility for the lower, southern half was assigned to the army. The army area contained St. Georges, the principal town, the seat of government and economic activity. There were two airports on the island, one on the southwestern tip, known as Salines, and the other a smaller strip called Pearls. The Salines strip was a new airport, being built by the Cubans, while the Pearls airfield, I believe, was built by the U.S. Navy during World War II, as part of the Caribbean chain of bases to watch for German submarines. It is in comparing these two airports that one finds the seeds of the Grenada invasion.

The Pearls airport is a very short strip, located at the opposite end of the island, away from the principal city and tourist facilities. The normal amenities of a tourist entry point were nonexistent. A mountain range had to be crossed in order to reach the city. As a tourist, one had to ride for an hour and a half on a bus from this north island airport to the tourist facilities. The Cubans obtained a foothold in Grenada by agreeing and beginning to build the Salines airport, a modern 10,000-foot (in length) facility. In a sense, the United States went into Grenada with armed forces because in the 1970s the U.S. Government had failed to recognize the importance of Pearls airport in relation to the aspirations and economic well-being of the Grenadian people and their government. By the 1980s, it was too late.

The operations to secure the island were planned to begin at five o'clock on the morning of October 25, 1983. The plan was a simultaneous assault by the Rangers on Salines airport and by the marines on Pearls. However, as is often the case with even the simplest operation, unforeseen complications developed with the Grenada invasion. Despite these last-minute complications, the ability and training of the participants enabled them to deal with uncertainty and made the final outcome a success.

Looking at the stages that led up to these problems, one of the things that did break down was the intelligence on how the Cubans would fight. It turned out that in the days before the United States went in, the Cubans had sent a high-ranking military officer to inspect the island defenses. In the one or two days he had to prepare, he made an amazing turnaround of basic defenses, particularly at the Salines airport. We believe that the day before the invasion, an antiaircraft gun was installed to cover the airstrip. Fortunately, this antiaircraft gun, a ZU-23, was not properly sighted and could only depress to about 600 feet above the runway. The C-130s planes (which dropped the Rangers) flew at 500 feet. Correctly placed, this gun would either have destroyed these airplanes or, certainly, have raised havoc with the paratroopers. We were very lucky. Perhaps given another day to prepare, the Cuban colonel would have run his trap lines again and fixed the gun so that it would have raked the airfield. Yet even though this gun did not work properly, the Cubans had constructed bunkers all around the airfield, and small-arms fire did create chaos. We had expected to control the airport area in the initial hours of the invasion. As it turned out, however, we did not have the area fully under our control until well into the next day. Even though we only controlled one end of the airstrip, we inserted the 82nd Airborne into the island using this strip. We did it by keeping the defenders' heads down with "Spectre" gunships and navy aircraft.

One of the most important aspects of the operation, which went awry almost immediately, was the rescue of Governor-General Schoon. The United States needed to deal with a legitimate government in Grenada, and the governor-general was a key figure to its accomplishment. However, the defenders appeared to have had intelligence as to our intentions, because when our helicopters were sent in to rescue the governor-general, the Cubans and Grenadians were waiting for them. Essentially, they beat back our attack. We did manage to get 22 Seals into the governor-general's house, but they were trapped. The house was surrounded.

The defenders only had small arms and were being assaulted by Cubans and Grenadians in armored personnel carriers (APCs). This situation precipitated one of my first critical decisions—should we allow "Spectre" gunships to fire into built-up and potentially populated areas around the governor-general's house? Should we use marine "Hueys" and "Cobra" gunship helicopters to protect the governor-general? At that time, it is important to note that I was on the U.S.S. *Guam* off the Pearls airport. The marines and their helicopters were also in this area. When the call for help came, I instantly turned to the commander of the landing force and asked if he could get his gunships to the southern end of the island—could he help? His response was "affirmative," since the marines were encountering no problems around Pearls. Essentially, it was undefended.

Two of the "Cobra" gunships that went to support the Seals in the governor-general's house were promptly shot down, and it became immediately apparent that the Cubans had installed a significant means of defending the harbor of St. Georges. They had installed an antiaircraft defense system.

I was faced with a tough problem. We had obviously run into more than we expected. The Cubans were apparently "dug in." The governor-general was surrounded. Although the final outcome was never in doubt, I was very worried about the basic rule of engagement, *minimum casualties*. By eight o'clock in the morning of October 25, the northern part of the island was essentially secure, and in the south the Rangers were making progress at the Salines Airport. But the situation at the governor-general's mansion I considered to be very serious.

Through tactical intelligence, mainly by monitoring Cuban radio broadcasts, we determined that the defense was being directed from a place called Fort Frederick. Fort Frederick was an old British fort, set on high ground overlooking the town. Since we had already lost two aircraft trying to support the force trapped in the governor-general's house, we concluded that the antiaircraft fire must be coming from Fort Frederick, so we had to destroy this command post. Unfortunately, Fort Frederick was surrounded by a residential area, and the governor-general's house was not far away. Therefore, in carrying out our military objective, there would be a clear risk to the surrounding countryside. However, it was equally clear that if we did not deny the use of Fort Frederick to the Cubans, we were going to lose United States soldiers and airmen. The decision was easily and quickly made; I ordered A-7s [a light attack aircraft] on the hill. The attack took place at 1:40 in the morning, and, in hindsight, the battle was won right there. From that time on, everything was local action. All coordination of Cuban forces ended. In destroying Fort Frederick, we had destroyed their "nerve center." We did not know it at the time, but this "center" was the only one on the island.

In addition to the fort itself, a hospital also received damage in this attack. However, since the hospital buildings were part of the Cuban headquarters complex, such damage was an inevitable necessity, despite the tragic loss of life in the hospital. But given the strength of the Fort Frederick complex, despite the damage that was done to the fort itself, I believe that the Cubans could have held out against us. It was the psychological impact of one large concentrated attack that ended their will to fight.

The rescue of the governor-general had not been included in any of my earlier instructions. But it soon became apparent, through talks with my State Department representatives, that his rescue was of paramount importance. In a political sense the success of the entire operation now hung on the rescue of the governor-general. So at this point, Major General Schwarzkopf suggested that in order to take the pressure off the governor's house, St. Georges should be flanked to the north. At the time, it looked as if the main body of Cubans was oriented south, toward the Salines airport. General Schwarzkopf suggested that we land the marines north of the city itself. This plan presented an immediate problem; there were no surveyed beaches north of St. Georges. We selected what appeared to be a satisfactory beach, called Grand Mal. It was located near a fuel farm and appeared to have in the vicinity a small, but adequate, landing zone (LZ).

At this juncture in decision making, the conventional wisdom would have been not to attempt the landing. Among other things, this plan meant complete commitment of our reserve forces, as by that time I had come to consider the marines as my reserve. To use the remaining rifle company to flank St. Georges meant to commit them without having a complete understanding of the situation on the island. There was no intelligence available as to what they might run up against on this unsurveyed beach. They would be totally exposed. In addition, these forces were on the other side of the island from the proposed landing site. In fact, the marine rifle company, supporting tanks and LVTs were either aboard ship or swimming about the LSTs. However, regardless of these problems, and despite the lack of supporting intelligence, I felt that the Cuban and PRA strength was south of the city of St. Georges and that landing north of the city would be a better and more viable option. So weighing all the pros and cons, I decided a landing was worth the risks involved. As events turned out, this was the absolutely correct decision.

But because of the uncertainties involved in executing the plan, I wanted the marines to make a daylight landing at Grand Mal Beach. I gave the order to go at about 10:00 in the morning (darkness fell about 7:30 in the evening). Compliance with this order required extraordinary effort on the part of both the marines and the navy ships. The LVTs had to be backloaded on the LSTs, and the ships moved around the island. It was an extraordinary military evolution, which reflected the superb state of preparedness and the training of all involved.

The next problem in operational decision making was how to ensure the safety of the university students. The university campus, code named "True Blue" in the mission plan, was located at the eastern end of the Salines airstrip. The Rangers landed on the western end of the airstrip but were initially unable to reach the campus, due to opposition by, primarily, small arms and other weapons. Since our mission rule of engagement was to sustain "minimum casualties" throughout the rescue, the ground commanders proceeded slowly, in order to avoid any frontal assaults on defended positions. Nevertheless, despite the problems, they succeeded in their mission and the campus was finally relieved at 7:15 on the evening of the first day.

So, in summary, by the end of that first day we had rescued the university students and secured the airstrip but not the area immediately to the north of the airstrip. We also had a force in the governor-general's house, but it was surrounded and besieged. The marines were proceeding to land LVTs and tanks to flank the town of St. Georges to the north. Large elements of the 82nd Airborne were landed at the Salines airport and were preparing to move inland.[4]

By 7:10 on the morning of D-day plus one, the marines, who had landed on Grand Mal, moved down and entered the area called Queens Park Race Course, just north of St. Georges. As soon as the marine tanks arrived, they fired a couple of ranging rounds into a gun emplacement that had opened fire on the hillside. The people manning the guns in that area just "faded away." It was all over. The marines went on up the hillside and rescued the governor-general and secured the immediate area. We had secured the mission objective with "no-loss of life."

One thing that the Cubans and PRA forces learned to respect was navy air and "Spectre" gunships. The Cubans had never seen these in Angola or in other places where they had operated. Early on day two, just north of the airfield, the 82nd Airborne found a concentration of Cubans and PRA. They had made the mistake of concentrating where we could fire at them. As a result of our A-7s attack, 250 simultaneously gave up.

This attack was an example of the selective use of fire power. In this instance, the Cubans were in an area, close to the airport, where I was not concerned about "damage." The requirement for approval of close air support from carrier aircraft and "Spectre" gunships was "solid communications with a qualified spotter." Again, it was on a case-by-case basis that I allowed a commander, in a specific area, to use maximum force.

Let us return to the second day of the rescue of the students in the Grand Anse Beach area. This was a very interesting joint operation with a number of issues and challenges involving all the services. The Grand Anse Beach area was in the responsibility zone of the 82nd Airborne. My orders were to get the students out by the end of the second day. We were in telephone contact with students, who were "holed up" in a beach hotel. We had decided that despite the different kinds of communications apparatus available to us, in this instance the local telephone was most effective. As sailors say, "any port in a storm."

The commanding general of the 82nd Airborne assessed the situation in light of the rules of engagement and decided that it might be necessary to ravage the countryside in order to get into the area where the students were located. From his position at Salines he was separated from the Grand Anse Beach area by hilly terrain, with ridges and saddlebacks, which could easily be defended. It was his assessment that the Cubans were blocking the way. So, the general suggested a well laid-out plan to use marine helicopters, Rangers, navy air and naval gunfire support and artillery. Five hours later, our mission was successfully accomplished, despite the initial problems in execution mentioned earlier. The entire operation had required split-second timing, close air support strikes, and artillery, in order to surround an area in which we had only a rough idea where the students were located. Nevertheless, the total operation was completed, as specified by the rules of engagement, "without excessive damage to property."

In its execution, the operation was a classic military envelopment. The marine helicopters landed the Rangers on the beach, to the seaward side of the hotel. The artillery and 82nd Airborne moved in, from the land side. Tactical air "softened up" the area on the land side. And when the helicopters landed, the students ran out of their hotel and into the waiting aircraft. The operation was over 26 minutes from start-up, and the students were safe on the Salines air strip. It was a masterpiece of command and control.

On the fourth day of the mission, the Rangers left Grenada. By this time, all that remained to be done was the matter of physically securing the island. In this, the marines were very aggressive, and by the fifth day they had taken the northern part of the island.

On the third day, the press arrived. From about noon on D+2, USCINCLANT had encouraged me to allow the media onto the island. Initially, I had been ambivalent about this issue. There were other priorities to be dealt with. So, when I asked the authorities for the numbers involved and found out it was 400, I became more concerned. In terms of completing our own operations, we had finally entered St. Georges. Even by the third day, there was no water or electricity in the town. The townspeople were off the streets in their homes. St. Georges was a ghost town. Because of this, I agreed to an initial press pool of 25, on the second day, 50. Once we had a place to house them, I planned to allow them all in. But, there was no way to provide them with transport, and there was no way to accommodate the large numbers that we expected would eventually show up. They had to make the best of the situation.

I have not discussed one of the most important aspects of command and control and the decision process, the commander's daily conference. During every day of the mission, either the commanders came out to the flagship or I went ashore to decide on the next day's itinerary. This meeting took place, regardless of our progress. Even on that hectic first afternoon, with only half of the Salines airport under control and the students still not rescued, the commander of the 82 Airborne joined me on the U.S.S. *Guam*. The outcome of each of these meetings was a hard copy evening message that was sent up the chain of command to the USCINCLANT and the Joint Chiefs of Staff, outlining our military objectives for the following day.

I mentioned earlier that throughout this mission I established a situation-report system. This, I insisted, was to provide two situation reports per hour to higher command, no matter what happened. On the first day, we averaged three messages per hour "up the line." The first message brought to me for release was written in computer format—the format that computers can read but people cannot. I made the decision to scratch this style of message in favor of a format of factual, serialized messages, messages written in plain English for people, not computers. This format was far preferable and, as I mentioned earlier, these messages were instrumental in our successful retention of local control throughout the mission. Not only congressional committees, but even the president himself, read these messages to keep abreast of events. All along, we managed to anticipate and also to answer their queries before they had time to become issues.

This reporting system had yet another positive communication advantage. It created trust and credibility in the face of any conflicting reports from other sources. The main reason for this was that I made a deliberate decision, at the outset, to allow free communications by service commanders to their home bases. I knew that the army and air force had communication channels to their home bases, which I could not, and did not want, to control. Naturally, information as to "how things were going" was reported up these separate communications lines. Such information was frequently at odds with my own reports of the situation, and all this varied information was being passed on to the Pentagon. I knew this would happen and was not concerned. Through the fog of battle, the same event can take on many different hues. However, as we had established our own simple system of situation reports "up the chain of command," it was our situation reports, rather than those miscellaneous reports from other sources, that were relied upon and taken to be the "true" state of affairs. It was a credit to both the JCS and the USCINCLANT; they turned to me for clarification whenever doubts were raised. This way, rumors were contained before they ever had a chance to get out of hand.

I would like to tell a story about an incident that happened the first night that I believe had a great deal to do with our ability to retain control of our destiny. As we all know, staffs are responsible for briefing their bosses. And these briefings always take place first thing in the morning. Further, staff officers are bright and energetic and all of them would have liked to be with us—in the action so to speak. The first night of the "Urgent Fury" operation, about midnight, my staff started to be bugged with questions from USCINCLANT; questions that had already been answered in numerous messages. They wanted numbers, estimates of the situation, and so on. It was a classic staff doing its thing. At about four o'clock in the morning, the chief of staff woke me up and said, "we can't take this anymore." So I went to flag plot, got on the radio, and asked for the USCINCLANT watch officer. I gave him a few sharp words about what was available and what was not. This was a three-star telling a four-star staff, please get off my back. I knew this would work. I knew the commander in chief was not going to be in the command center at four o'clock in the morning, and besides I was in the right. So the leadership up the line and I came to an agreement. At least, I was going to run the show and not the staffs. From that point on we did not have a problem. In fact, to control the situation, USCINCLANT, to their credit, set up a special staff officer who screened everything that went out to us. I am told they had an enormous reject bin.

A final element of command and control, which helped to unify our communications system, happened by accident and was due to the limitations of our communications equipment. We only had one secure voice channel, and this was a task force common circuit. The usual operating practice is for commanders to set up a private circuit. But we only had one channel available, so when Admiral McDonald wanted to talk to me, we had to use the party line. We have all had experience, in the past, with such multiuse circuits, and they are known to have a tendency to overload and break down. However, in this particular instance, when either my call sign or Admiral Mcdonald's went out over the circuit, the line was instantly cleared. Captains of the ships huddled around the CIC to listen in, and so this particular party line came to serve a very useful function. It conveyed our intentions to those commanders, without my having to go over them again individually with each captain. In this way, whenever pressing problems built up, we were able to work them out over the circuit. But, if there were things that could not be worked out over the public line, then I would put them on the hard copy. So, all in all, despite its traditional disadvantages, for us the "party line" worked out very well. Everyone involved in the mission decision making knew the intended plans and the pressures on local command. It was particularly useful for the army commander to be able to understand some of these pressures and to know that the desire to move out was not just my own personal decision but a policy directive "down the line." Throughout the entire mission, this communication system remained central to our operating strategy.

Under "command and control" issues were also included the following elements:

- Staff requirements
  a. Fly away battle staff
  b. Augments
  c. Tactical decision team
  d. Commander Second Fleet duties
- Daily force commander conferences, intentions MSGS
- Reporting
  a. Command voice
  b. Frequent narrative SITREPS
  c. Constant dialogue up and down the chain

d. Commander Joint Task Force 120/commander-in-chief, Atlantic Command Conferences on common circuit

The efficiency of "command and control" was a function of flagship capabilities and limitations. In the Grenada mission, the number of decision makers was limited by the physical size of the U.S.S. *Guam*'s flag plot. Half of that space was taken up with tables, a computer terminal, radar scopes and so forth, so key decision makers were grouped very closely together. All in all, it was a "tight fit," but this did not impede close coordination.

Nevertheless, there was one intelligence failure, namely the lack of a common chart. On the U.S.S. *Guam*, I had a chart of Grenada dated 1895. The army had another version of this chart, and the marines yet another. So we had no common grid to work from, either to call targets or to develop operations. Initially, this created an immense problem.

However, we finally resolved the issue by means of a captured tourist chart, printed by the Office of Tourism in London. This became the "common chart" for all the forces involved. It was a good map, because it showed elevations over which a grid could be drawn. On November 2, after the initial assault, we received a new set of charts from the U.S. Defense Mapping Agency.

This map deficiency problem is an example of a precombat decision, a garbage can decision, made by a decision maker without clear goals. If the Defense Mapping Agency did have mapping goals, then Grenada was not a sufficient priority, ahead of time, for the Agency to have been persuaded that there was a pressing need to reproduce and update island maps. The decision was a nonoperational, priority decision, and before the Grenada crisis erupted it was understandable that the area was not a top priority with the Agency. In other words, no one felt that Grenada would be a place for combat operations. In terms of mapping priorities, Cuba, Nicaragua and other places in the Caribbean Basin were far ahead. So, despite the fact that it would have been extremely helpful to have had up-to-date maps at the beginning of our mission, the fact that we did not cannot be blamed on this Agency. In the circumstances, given their system of prioritization, they did the best they could.

In conclusion, having reviewed the more critical issues involved in the Grenada operation and described how we coped with them on an ongoing basis, I would now like to generalize the lessons learned from this mission and the ways in which we might capitalize on them in the future.

Under the general category *joint operations*, we demonstrated the following:

- You can carry out an operation of this nature, in *minimum planning time*, if the plan is kept simple. The Grenada operation plan was simple. Most important, the heart of the command and control unit was a core group of people who had operated together.
- *"Come-as-you-are" forces can* work together.
- The term *capitalizing on inherent strengths* refers to the way we train. In this operation, there were some notable exceptions to this

dictum. But where we deviated from it, we did not do as well. For example, Rangers are trained to operate in the dark, but we inserted them in daylight. Probably, if we had made the assault in the dark, we would have secured the airport and the governor-general's residence, rescued him and avoided the situation we eventually found ourselves in.

- The lesson here is, use forces as they are *trained to fight*. Do not try to invent something different for them to do.
- *Command and control:* keep it simple; face-to-face contact where possible.
- *Minimum direction* from the national command authority: clearly, this was of enormous importance to me as the on-scene commander.
- What I wanted and got from higher authority was a "what," not a "how." This system worked best. I tried to use the same command policy for the forces doing the fighting.
- Finally *unhampered logistics flow* was also important. Looking back, the 82nd Airborne ended up with over 5000 people on the island. I left the decision of whether or not to reinforce to the commanding general of the 82nd Rangers. Probably, I should have had more input on that issue, because we ended up with far more people than needed, but I stuck to the principle that the commander was to determine the "how." On reflection, I probably would have made the same decision again, as it reflected my philosophy of command. If a commander thought he needed additional troops, then it was my philosophy not to second-guess him.

In summarizing the lessons learned from *operations coordination*, I think that in any mission it is understanding of operational coordination that is often the most important lesson of all.

- The joint task force commander must be on the scene.
- Joint exercises are not currently structured for short-notice operations
- A noncrisis environment liaison is required

However, those issues are currently under discussion with the Joint Chiefs of Staff. In Grenada, we demonstrated to all concerned that the joint command system works. But we have not yet succeeded in driving home my main point, namely, that if the system is going to work, you must have a trained staff that has previously worked together, one that can make operational decisions, and one that can make them quickly. These staff characteristics are the key to success, in all short-notice, fast-reaction situations. Within the navy, the Commander Task Force 120 organization is unique to the Second Fleet. It is my impression that a similar operating staff does not exist in the army. The army has staffs that can operate their own forces, but Commander Joint Task Force 120 exercises as a joint staff.

In summarizing *communications*, I will not rehash those areas that I have already discussed. In brief, the lessons are as follows:

- Communications must be reliable, available, secure, interoperable and flexible.
- Flyaway packages are needed.
- Hard copy communications are required.
- One must test often to verify interoperability.

We do conduct communications exercises in the navy, but in these exercises, we give our communicators about 12 months preparation. Therefore, it should not be surprising that when the exercises start, communications work. However, after Grenada, when I went before the Congress, I was asked why we had so much trouble with the communications, despite all the money that has been put into the area.

Before the Congress, Admiral McDonald took up the issue. He pointed out that the problem was to operationally verify interoperability. The communicators may not be so much at fault. Our failure in preparatory exercises to uncover and anticipate problems similar to those we faced in Grenada may have been because our exercises are overprepared. Given enough time, anyone can make communications work. And if the objective of an exercise is to make things work, then the conduct of the exercise will be optimized to show that the exercise will work. Unfortunately, in a crisis situation—a "come-as-you-are" situation—they did not work.

In the Second Fleet, we are currently working to have joint exercises that can be structured on short notice. However, as a practical matter this may not be possible. We must figure out a way to structure exercises so that communicators have only a limited amount of time to set themselves up, make their communication plans and act. "No-notice" communication drills are needed, because this is what happens in a live situation like Grenada.

In Grenada we did not have interoperability with the army and the air force, even though we had been assured at the outset that we did. So, consequently, we could not make the installed communications work. Part of the problem was the U.S.S. *Guam*. She is an old ship with an old communications suite. However, when I returned to the U.S.S. *Mount Whitney*, our most modern and best flagship, and asked if such a suite had been available would the communication system have succeeded, the answer was no. So we are not realistic on this issue of interoperability. It is a very significant lesson that has emerged from the Grenada operation.

The lessons learned from the *intelligence* aspect of the operation can be summarized as follows:

- Indications and warning were adequate.
- Tactical support was excellent.
- Strength and disposition were good.
- Characterization of resistance was a failure.
- Maps and charts were inadequate.

- National emphasis is needed on the third world, including human intelligence.

Public affairs lessons can be summarized in a similar fashion. All the points must be included in military decision making. In the Grenada mission

- The media entry was properly timed.
- The operational commander must have control over these events.

In this paper, I have examined the elements of military decision making that underlay the Grenada mission, including an outline of the practical problems encountered in the field and the solutions we arrived at. The purpose of this presentation has been to provide the decision-making theorist with a practical example of the problems that present themselves in a specific crisis situation. Whether or not all these practical problems can be modeled in a garbage can decision model, or whether the theoretical model making process is still too underdeveloped at this stage is not my brief. However, in order to be of practical assistance in military decision making at the applied level, such models need to take account of all the elements discussed here.

NOTES

1. The decision was actually executed on October 26 and confirmed with commanders at daily meetings on October 27, 1983.

2. Actually, only the commander of the 82nd Airborne Rangers, Major General Trabau, the commander of the Special Forces, Major General Shultie, and Major General Schwarzkopf were present. I was not concerned about the absence of navy and marine commanders; I knew how they operated.

3. In reality, the time tended to vary. Once we were as late as nine o'clock.

4. At three o'clock in the morning of October 26, a second marine company was helicopter-lifted from Pearls to join up with marine forces at Grand Mal.

GLOSSARY

ABN	Airborne
AIR-AMPHIB	Air Warfare—Amphibious Warfare
CDR	Commander
CINCAFLANT	Commander in Chief, U.S. Air Force, Atlantic
CINCARLANT	Commander in Chief, U.S. Army, Atlantic
CINCLANTFLT	Commander in Chief, Atlantic Fleet
CJTF	Commander, Joint Task Force
COMMS	Communications
COMSUBLANT	Commander, Submarine Forces, Atlantic
COS/J3	Chief of Staff/Operations Officer

CTF	Commander, Task Force
CTG	Commander, Task Group
DEP CDR	Deputy Commander
INDY CVBG	U.S.S. *Independence* Battle Group
INTEL	Intelligence
LANTCOM	Atlantic Command
LVT	Landing Vehicle Track
LST	Landing Ship Tank
MAC	Military Airlift Command
OPS-SURFACE	Operations-Surface Warfare
PAO	Public Affairs Officer
USAF	U.S. Air Force
USCINCLANT	U.S. Commander in Chief, Atlantic Command
USMC	U.S. Marine Corps

15

Decision Making and Managing Ambiguity in Politico-Military Crisis

HARRY D. TRAIN II

Discussions about crisis management—past, present and future—generally fall into one of two camps. First, there is the perspective of the operators, those who are, or who have been, in the position of accountable authorities, responsible for carrying out a crisis management operation. Second, there is the perspective of the theoreticians, that is, those authorities who are not accountable for the management of any operation. While both these groups address the problems involved in decision making, they do so from very different perspectives, and there is very little interplay between them. This chapter sets out to explore the nature of these differences.

In so doing, it will draw on a number of crises, such as Grenada and Iran, together with my own personal experience, first as the executive assistant to the chairman of the Joint Chiefs of Staff during the Son Tay Prison raid and the Jordanian crisis, and second as director of the Joint Staff during the Cyprus crisis, the Phnom Penh evacuation, the Saigon evacuation, the Mayaguez crisis and two Beirut evacuations.

While I was commander of the Sixth Fleet, there was a collision between a Soviet Echo II class submarine and our frigate U.S.S. *Voge*. This potential

Admiral Harry D. Train II, USN (ret.), is a former commander in chief of the Atlantic Command and Supreme Allied Commander, Atlantic.

crisis was "managed" early enough to avoid becoming full-blown. During the four years I was commander in chief, U.S. Atlantic Command and Commander in Chief, U.S. Atlantic Fleet, the crises I was called on to manage were (1) the Cuban refugee exodus, (2) the revelation that there was a Soviet combat brigade in Cuba, and (3) a portion of the Iranian Crisis—the portion that was dealt with by putting forces in the Indian Ocean. I was not personally involved, nor did I know in advance, about the Iranian hostage rescue operation, even though I provided some of the forces for that raid.

PROBLEM RECOGNITION

In crisis management, the first step, and sometimes the most elusive step, is to recognize the problem. And in examining the decision-making process in a crisis management environment, this vital step should not be ignored. Occasionally, this first step is a very complex one. In the Grenada crisis, recognition of the problem occurred somewhere between the time that Maurice Bishop was deposed and the time it became known there were American students on the island of Grenada whose safety was not assured. Somewhere between those two points, there occurred, in another part of the world, the attack on the marine barracks in Lebanon. The role that particular attack played in the U.S. government's recognition of Grenada as a problem that had to be dealt with, I am not prepared to say. But I am confident it was significant in formulating the basic decision by the National Command Authority to take forceful action.

CRISIS AVOIDANCE

Related to the need for problem recognition is the need to recognize when a potential crisis can be avoided, and taking the necessary steps to achieve that objective. For example, in the collision between the Soviet and U.S. ships mentioned earlier, events were managed so that it was possible to avoid a major crisis.

In this situation, there was a squadron of five antisubmarine warfare frigates deployed to the Mediterranean for the specific purpose of keeping track of Soviet submarines. The frigates had maintained contact on the Echo II submarine for ten days. Each time the submarine came to periscope depth, the commander saw only the U.S.S. *Voge*, and none of the other ships of the squadron. Ironically, U.S.S. *Voge* was a command-and-control configured ship, not one of the ships equipped with the sensors that were doing the tracking. We think that the submarine commander, knowing that he was being tracked, assumed U.S.S. *Voge* was the sensor ship.

On the day of the collision, the submarine came up to communicate and saw U.S.S. *Moinester*, one of the sensor-equipped ships. The commander did not see anything remarkable about U.S.S. *Moinester*, but he did see U.S.S. *Voge* on the horizon and, being somewhat frustrated, moved over at high speed and came up alongside U.S.S. *Voge*, probably to take a look at the sensor equipment he suspected *Voge* carried. U.S.S. *Voge* tried to turn away and maintain its distance. But the submarine came up alongside about 400 yards away, stayed with the *Voge* for about 10 minutes, then turned right and ran into the side of *Voge*. The submarine rolled over about 75 degrees after hitting *Voge* and then went down and was not seen again for about 25 minutes. Our squadron commander reported the incident in a very articulate message that was paralleled by a voice report. I decided that I had better tell the Soviet Mediterranean fleet commander what had happened. It looked like he had lost his submarine.

Another ship in the antisubmarine warfare squadron was in the anchorage off Kithira, Greece in proximity to the Soviet flagship. I instructed our ship to tell the Soviet admiral that one of his ships had collided with one of mine, where the collision occurred, and that his submarine had not surfaced. He might want to get there to investigate for himself and ascertain what had happened to his submarine. His response was, "Thank you very much—what happened?" I was about to explain what had happened—since by then I had received the details—when the National Command Authority, who had been fully informed of the incident, directed that I not answer the question.

We spent the next four or five months trying to decide how to tell the Soviets what happened, since our leadership agreed that the Soviets' seamanship infraction was so gross that in order to avoid overreaction on their part, we had better explain what we knew about the incident from our perspective. Eventually, we decided to release pictures of the incident to the press, and the Soviets saw that it was clearly their fault. We later learned (I do not know how we learned) that the commanding officer of the Soviet submarine was drunk. In any event, the incident did not escalate to a crisis, and it was never treated in a crisis management mode. We did a lot of things on our own initiative at the beginning of the crisis, simply because we had to. Often a crisis situation becomes a real crisis because the people in the field do not do things that they really ought to do. And they do not assume authority which, technically, they do not have under normal circumstances. In the *Voge* situation, I did not have the authority to send the message to the Soviet admiral, Admiral Akimov, but I did so, nevertheless, and I am glad that I did. If the situation happened again, I would still do the same thing. This is an example of the types of unusual decisions that the nation expects us to make in crisis situations.

CRISIS DENIAL

In addition to recognizing or avoiding crises, crisis decision making can also involve denying the fact that there really is a crisis at hand. The problem may be recognized as a potential problem, but immediately "shorted to ground" because there is no energy left over to do something about it. For example, in the case of events in Angola in the mid-1970s, the U.S. government could have addressed them as a crisis. It could have attempted to do something about what was happening there. But because, in my view, the government had insufficient energy left over from other crisis management efforts in progress to address it, it decided the problem would go away. It would not be a problem, and it certainly would not be addressed as a crisis. In these types of situations, sometimes the recognition of the problem lies with the political arena, sometimes with the military, or sometimes with both.

An example of political recognition of a problem that the military did not initially recognize or address as such was the Jordanian crisis of 1970. In other examples, the problem has had military recognition. It has come up first through the military chain of command and then been presented to the political leadership—that is, the government—as a situation that needed to be addressed. However, it does not really matter which way a problem occurs or who recognizes it first, as long as the National Command Authority recognizes problems, addresses the issues and makes decisions to organize to do something about them.

PROBLEM DEFINITION

It is often very useful if higher authority, such as, for example, the National Command Authority and the people helping them do business, define the problem. For example, in the case of Grenada, Vice Admiral Metcalf had the advantage of having higher authority define the problem very well. As a result of that definition, he was given a clear, concise and understandable political and military objective that he was to pursue. However, in the absence of such clearly stated political objectives, it is very difficult—for the military authorities in particular—to function. A further complication is created when the stated political objective given to the military leadership by the government is not the real political objective but rather a "displayed" political objective, one that will bear the scrutiny of the public as opposed to one that is really in the minds of the duly-elected and accountable political leadership.

"Displayed" Objective

One example of a "displayed" objective might be found in the recent U.S. military presence in Lebanon. Here the question arises, did the people on the scene in Lebanon have the benefit of the real political objectives, or were they working with "displayed" political objectives? This question has yet to be publicly addressed. However, in time the true answers may emerge.

Another example is the case of the Iranian hostage raid. In this, I could be considered to have been the victim of a "displayed" political objective. In this context, when I was asked for my RH-53 helicopters, I was told they were to be deployed to the Indian Ocean to support a possible mine-laying operation. I was not told that they were to fly thousands of miles over uncharted desert, through sandstorms, and then land in hostile territory at the end of the flight. Therefore, in making my own decisions in response to that "displayed" military objective, which derived from the "displayed" political objective, I decided it would best to send an intact squadron. Included in that intact squadron, as would normally be expected, were three helicopters with a very high number of operating hours. Under our planned maintenance system, these helicopters were still within operating limits, based on accumulated flight hours, but they were approaching the point where they would be taken "off-line" for maintenance. I chose to send those helicopters anyway because they allowed squadron integrity. Had I been told what those helicopters were really going to do, I would not have sent the three helicopters with the high hours. It turned out, however, due perhaps to good fortune, that those three helicopters with the high flight hours made it through the operation.

Vital Interests

As well as knowing the real political objectives, it is also useful for the military authorities to know what vital interests have been identified by the political leadership as the interests we are defending or protecting. If there is a consistent breakdown, historically, in communication between the National Command Authority level and the military commander in the field (the accountable commanders'), it lies in the military's not being told what are the true American vital interests. It is a problem that plagued us throughout the course of the Vietnam War. In that situation, it was extremely difficult, if not impossible, for a military commander, charged with leading men, to tell those men what vital U.S. interests were at risk that caused them to be there in the first place.

An essential part of leadership is to be able to tell your people why they are there, and why they are doing what they are doing. When we deployed the U.S.S. *Nimitz* and the U.S.S. *Eisenhower* carrier battlegroups to the Indian Ocean (deployments that lasted eight months and four days in one case, and eight months and seven days in the other, during which there were virtually no port calls for those ships), the crews were kept reasonably satisfied because they knew what they were doing and what vital U.S. interests they were protecting. The entire chain of command functioned very well in being able to present an articulate case to their people and to lead them into maintaining a high state of morale and effectiveness during the course of a very challenging and traumatic deployment.

However, if the political objectives are withheld by Washington, and not shared with the command that is doing the planning, then those political objectives are relatively worthless, in terms of translating them into military objectives and operations to achieve the required outcomes.

MICRO MANAGEMENT

Having the objectives defined by higher authority is useful, but for military commanders to be told, in detail, by the political leadership precisely how to achieve an objective is quite a different issue. The political leadership should assume that the people to whom they give the "what-to-do" assignment can, within the limits of their assets, successfully carry out the "how" aspect of such assignments. In addition, the political leadership should not go into a great amount of detail, like the National Command Authority did, for example, in the late 1970s during the early evacuations of Beirut.

Then, the administration was so concerned that the United States was likely to become involved in hostilities during the evacuation that a decision was made in the White House Situation Room, to keep the Amphibious Task Force over the horizon—not to let it be seen from the beach. Instead, the National Command Authority sent an LCU (an extremely large landing craft) onto the beach at Beirut and instructed that there were to be no weapons on board and no flack jackets or helmets in evidence on the crew. General George Brown, the chairman of the Joint Chiefs of Staff, was so concerned that this was an unwise decision that he wanted the commanders in the field to protest. He had personally tried to protest, but his opinion did not prevail, so he requested that I, as the director of the Joint Staff, send the execute message to the operating authorities and include a large number of information addresses. He thought that if the execute message originated from the director, as opposed to the chairman, the operating authorities would feel freer to challenge it. I met his request, but no one in the field objected.

However, several months later, when I went to relieve as commander of the Sixth Fleet, the incumbent commented on the inadequacies of the Beirut evacuation plan. I asked him why he had not spoken up at the time. His response was that he thought the message was from valid authority and was reluctant to object. Here, the whole point of the issue is that sometimes when you play games, the games do not work. In this instance, the National Command Authority erred by telling us not only what to do ("get American citizens out") but also *how* to do it. The shortcomings of this approach were also noted by George Brown, in one of his speeches, where he observed that the military establishment in the United States had no separate life of its own. It was not an end in itself, but simply a means to the end of protecting and preserving our national security. In the final analysis, he noted, it is the American people who determine our national goals and objectives, including the defense and security of our nation. The armed forces are the instruments of the people. They are constituted and supported by elected representatives of the people and serve to achieve national goals. And what that service shall consist of is decided by the people and their elected representatives. He concluded by emphasizing that *how* we perform that service, on the other hand, has always been and must always be a matter of pride, professionalism and integrity for the individual military man and for the entire fraternity of arms he represents.

Therefore, in light of our past experiences, it is clear that objectives, once defined, are best left to the individual commands and their leaders to be implemented.

"WHAT IF" DRILLS

Identifying a political objective, and then developing a plan to achieve it, presents a number of political problems, unrelated to the original objective. More often than not, the initial plan is developed in Washington (in the National Military Command Center or in the White House) and is based on a series of hypothetical questions. These are what military commanders often call the "what if" drills and academicians call the "ambiguities of preference." The Washington staffs begin with questions such as, "How long would it take to move a carrier task force from point A to point B?", and "How long would it take a marine amphibious brigade from, say Camp Lejeune to reach such and such a place?" However, commanders are rarely informed why these questions are being asked—that is, what is their purpose, or their objective.

A good illustration of a "what if" drill occurred during the Jordanian Crisis when Admiral Tom Moorer, then chairman of the Joint Chiefs of Staff, was in the president's office at the White House. He called me on the phone and said, "Harry, get Charlie Duncan [who was then commander in chief, U.S. Atlantic Command] on the phone, and keep this line open." When I got Admiral Duncan on the other phone, Admiral Moorer said, "Now ask him how long it would take to get a carrier battlegroup from the Atlantic to the Levant Coast—or how long would it take before you could sail a carrier battlegroup from the Atlantic to the Levant Coast."

Admiral Duncan replied, "Well, we happen to have U.S.S. *John F. Kennedy* and two cruisers at sea in the Caribbean. The carrier has its air group aboard, they are in the final stages of training, and they could sail at any time." I gave that answer to Admiral Moorer. I heard him talking to President Nixon, and I heard President Nixon say, "I said how long would it take to sail it!" I conveyed that message to Admiral Duncan, and, in one of his rare moments of levity, his answer was, "As soon as we can get the bows pointed east!"

During the entire period, Admiral Duncan was not told what we were really doing—that is, that we were responding to a crisis, or that we had a situation in Jordan that required the commitment of his force. It was not until three or four days later that we finally got around to telling the commander in chief, Atlantic Command what was really going on. Personally, I do not agree with this philosophy, but it is customary procedure in these situations. The "what if" drill consistently forms (1) the basis for response to crises and (2) the development of plans, by the accountable military authorities, in response to crises. Rarely is the true political objective transmitted to the accountable commander, so that he can have the opportunity to comment on how best to achieve the required political objective and to offer his considerable expertise from the field. It ought to be possible to develop better plans and better communication with the commander in the field, to convey to him the overall political objective, and let him come back with a supporting plan.

There used to be another problem that compounded those of the "what if" drill, namely, the propensity to put acting chairman of the Joint Chiefs of Staff into the loop in the middle of the planning process. Then, the whole "drill" had to be repeated again, as the acting chairman, whose viewpoint and background often differed from that of the chairman, was briefed. This problem has been eliminated for now. Under the new policy, a single service chief functions as acting chairman whenever the chairman is absent, for a three-month period, thereby maintaining some continuity. However, this policy is set by the current chairman, and may not necessarily endure beyond his term.

ALLOCATION OF SCARCE RESOURCES

The next problem that must be solved when a decision is made to respond to a crisis with military force is to establish a reasonable set of priorities. Due to the limited resources, force composition must be decided not only on the basis of numbers required to do the job but also on the need for continuing operations versus the option to cancel. For example, when we deployed the two carrier battlegroups to the Indian Ocean, we had to decide what we would stop doing in order to be able to free up the forces to send to the Indian Ocean. That was a fairly important decision, and one in which the National Command Authority had to concur. Ultimately, we decided that we would take a carrier battlegroup each from the western Pacific and the Mediterranean and put them into the Indian Ocean. However, in order to be able to do this, we had to deal first with the issue of prioritization.

UNDERSTANDING PRINCIPLES

In addressing a crisis, there is frequently a point at which the political leadership lacks sufficient background in the issues to be able to make an intelligent military decision. There has to be some tutoring on the part of the military authorities so that inadvertent mistakes are avoided. Specifically, the civilian decision makers must understand the basic principles that govern the employment of military units in the course of employing military presence as a tool to influence events somewhere in the world.

If the political leadership is allowed to make decisions without an understanding of these basic military principles, then serious errors can result. For example, if a decision is made to use the smallest military presence, at the least possible cost—political or economic—then, in military terms, this is a decision to opt for a "hostage force" rather than a "dominant force." And, according to military principles, the use of a hostage force as a military presence means that the deployer is confident that none of the competing parties want to attack, embarrass or otherwise involve that hostage force. This understanding is the basis for the United Nations peacekeeping forces that have been used over the years. In these and other types of peacekeeping efforts, there has been a conscious decision to use a hostage force, knowing that neither side wants to attack it.

If, however, you have a situation where one of the competing parties wants to attack or embarrass the United States, wants to involve that force and to harm it, then a hostage force ought not to be used. It must be a dominant force. Alternatively, a hostage force can be used in a way that makes it essentially dominant. For example, the marines that were used recently in Lebanon were a hostage force when ashore. But, when embarked on their amphibious ships off the coast of Lebanon they were a dominant force. We actually created their hostage nature when we put them ashore. However, it is not clear that the entire breadth of the problem was fully understood, or that a conscious decision was made to put a hostage force in harm's way, or that it was liable to become involved.

From this, it is clear that intuition alone cannot be relied upon to provide "good" decisions—the basic military principles have to be addressed. And, dealing with crisis situations, over their duration, also means dealing with the problems of feedback and definition. If necessary, goals may have to be redefined as the crisis develops, and decisions made to change the initial game plans.

TRANSITION AND WARTIME POSTURING

When the point of transition from crisis management to war-fighting is reached, one of the major problems is the posturing of forces to make that transition. In the Jordanian crisis, there was clearly the danger that we were going to cross the threshold from crisis management to war. At the national level, the following question should have been addressed: When do you stop managing the crisis and start positioning the Sixth Fleet to best absorb what we describe today as the "D-Day Shootout," or to best absorb those preemptive actions that will result in crossing the threshold to active war-fighting? This question was not addressed. Instead, the National Command Authority in Washington kept the force spread out over the eastern Mediterranean. That way, we were not gaining the advantage of mutual support between aircraft carriers. And had we been the victim of a preemptive attack by the Soviet naval forces on the scene, this positioning would have led to disaster.

RECOGNIZING CRISIS TERMINATION

Another important aspect of military decision making is to decide when the crisis is over. If this is not clear, then the situation results in an open-ended crisis management organization that becomes a nonremovable part of the bureaucratic organization. Sometimes, the decision is a simple one—the crisis is over. There is a clear-cut transition back to an everyday state of affairs. This clear-cut situation is characteristic of evacuation operations. For example, the evacuation of Saigon, the evacuation of Phnom Penh, the 1976 evacuation of Beirut—these were all operations with an objective, namely to move U.S. citizens out of harm's way. When this was accomplished, it was easy to decide that the crisis was over and to return to normal.

But in other situations, the crisis becomes open-ended, the crisis organization becomes permanent, and instead of crisis management, it becomes day-to-day business under the guise of crisis management. This type of situation wastes assets and creates a great deal of frustration within the military system. At the point when crisis termination is being addressed, be it short- or long-term, it is also useful to decide whether you have won or lost. In the past, the United States has not always been able to recognize this fact. But such recognition may be simplified by asking, "Have the political objectives been achieved?"

In the case of the Mayaguez crisis, for example, the answer was clear: the political goal was achieved. Unfortunately, 54 marines were lost in the process.

But on account of the public outcry which this loss of life brought about, the victory became overshadowed by the loss of life. The political objective was clearly achieved—with military force. But the cost of victory exceeded the threshold of tolerance of both the political authorities and the public.

In other instances, for example the Iranian hostage raid, the political goal was not achieved, and the United States clearly lost. However, to dwell too long on military gains and losses and postcrisis analyses has a hidden military disadvantage, namely, that of not being able to inspire people to perform well in the future at high levels of risk.

ACCOUNTABILITY AND AUTHORITY

Finally, there is the crucial link between accountability and authority. This issue pervades all stages of decision making in crisis situations and management. However, in considering this issue, it must be remembered that *authority* is often a "state of mind." Yet, in a crisis situation, the full burden of accountability is placed on the commander on the scene by his superiors, but they frequently withhold from him the authority he needs to react effectively, and in a timely way, to developments and opportunities as they are unfolding in the field.

In crisis contexts, it is crucial that the field commander be given authority and control of his mission and be allowed to make his own judgments, while keeping higher command fully informed at all stages of his decision making. In turn, the commander, once he has set the mission plan—the "what" that is to be done, should be equally flexible in delegating the "how" aspect of implementation to those below him. Only in this way can accountability be fully effective. But lacking authority, the field commander's position is untenable, since he lacks the power to make his leadership fully effective and his decision making carry weight.

CONCLUSION

In conclusion, it must be remembered that no two military or political situations are ever identical, and no two crises should ever be expected to be so similar that the elements and stages of decision making discussed in this chapter will also occur together in a crisis management context. What this chapter has attempted to do is to abstract and identify a number of key elements and principles, from my own practical experience in crisis management, that might have a wider application to operational decision making in crisis situations. However, regardless of the context of such decision making—be it theoretical or practical—the one thing decision makers can count on, 100 percent of the time, is that in any decision-making situation there will always be ambiguity. The problem for the military decision maker lies in how best to set about reducing such ambiguity by streamlining the process through which military decisions are reached, both in crisis and noncrisis situations. Applying the steps discussed herein may be helpful in managing that ambiguity and, therefore, in managing the crisis successfully.

APPENDIX

A Garbage Can Model of
Organizational Choice

MICHAEL D. COHEN, JAMES G. MARCH, and JOHAN P. OLSEN

Organized anarchies are organizations characterized by problematic preferences, unclear technology, and fluid participation. Recent studies of universities, a familiar form of organized anarchy, suggest that such organizations can be viewed for some purposes as collections of choices looking for problems, issues and feelings looking for decision situations in which they might be aired, solutions looking for issues to which they might be an answer, and decision makers looking for work. These ideas are translated into an explicit computer simulation model of a garbage can decision process. The general implications of such a model are described in terms of five major measures on the process. Possible applications of the model to more narrow predictions are illustrated by an examination of the model's predictions with respect to the effect of adversity on university decision making.

Consider organized anarchies. These are organizations—or decision situations—characterized by three general properties.[1] The first is problematic

Editor's Note: The following article is reprinted (in part) from Cohen, Michael D., March, James G., and Olsen, Johan P. "A Garbage Can Model of Organizational Choice." *Administrative Science Quarterly* 17 (1972):1–25.

[1]We are indebted to Nancy Block, Hilary Cohen, and James Glenn for computational, editorial, and intellectual help; to the Institute of Sociology, University of Bergen, and the Institute

preferences. In the organization it is difficult to impute a set of preferences to the decision situation that satisfies the standard consistency requirements for a theory of choice. The organization operates on the basis of a variety of inconsistent and ill-defined preferences. It can be described better as a loose collection of ideas than as a coherent structure; it discovers preferences through action more than it acts on the basis of preferences.

The second property is unclear technology. Although the organization manages to survive and even produce, its own processes are not understood by its members. It operates on the basis of simple trial-and-error procedures, the residue of learning from the accidents of past experience, and pragmatic inventions of necessity. The third property is fluid participation. Participants vary in the amount of time and effort they devote to different domains; involvement varies from one time to another. As a result, the boundaries of the organization are uncertain and changing; the audiences and decision makers for any particular kind of choice change capriciously.

These properties of organized anarchy have been identified often in studies of organizations. They are characteristic of any organization in part—part of the time. They are particularly conspicuous in public, educational, and illegitimate organizations. A theory of organized anarchy will describe a portion of almost any organization's activities, but will not describe all of them.

To build on current behavioral theories of organizations in order to accomodate the concept of organized anarchy, two major phenomena critical to an understanding of anarchy must be investigated. The first is the manner in which organizations make choices without consistent, shared goals. Situations of decision making under goal ambiguity are common in complex organizations. Often problems are resolved without recourse to explicit bargaining or to an explicit price system market—two common processes for decision making in the absence of consensus. The second phenomenon is the way members of an organization are activated. This entails the question of how occasional members become active and how attention is directed toward, or away from, a decision. It is important to understand the attention patterns within an organization, since not everyone is attending to everything all of the time.

Additional concepts are also needed in a normative theory of organizations dealing with organized anarchies. First, a normative theory of intelligent decision making under ambiguous circumstances (namely, in situations in which goals are unclear or unknown) should be developed. Can we provide some meaning for intelligence which does not depend on relating current action to known goals? Second, a normative theory of attention is needed. Participants within an organization are constrained by the amount of time they can devote to the various things demanding attention. Since variations in behavior in organized anarchies are due largely to questions of who is attending

of Organization and Industrial Sociology, Copenhagen School of Economics, for institutional hospitality and useful discussions of organizational behavior; and to the Ford Foundation for the financial support that made our collaboration feasible. We also wish to acknowledge the helpful comments and suggestions of Søren Christensen, James S. Coleman, Harald Enderud, Kåre Rommetveit, and William H. Starbuck.

to what, decisions concerning the allocation of attention are prime ones. Third, organized anarchies require a revised theory of management. Significant parts of contemporary theories of management introduce mechanisms for control and coordination which assume the existence of well-defined goals and a well-defined technology, as well as substantial participant involvement in the affairs of the organization. Where goals and technology are hazy and participation is fluid, many of the axioms and standard procedures of management collapse.

This article is directed to a behavioral theory of organized anarchy. On the basis of several recent studies, some elaborations and modifications of existing theories of choice are proposed. A model for describing decision making within organized anarchies is developed, and the impact of some aspects of organizational structure on the process of choice within such a model is examined.

THE BASIC IDEAS

Decision opportunities are fundamentally ambiguous stimuli. This theme runs through several recent studies of organizational choice.[2] Although organizations can often be viewed conveniently as vehicles for solving well-defined problems or structures within which conflict is resolved through bargaining, they also provide sets of procedures through which participants arrive at an interpretation of what they are doing and what they have done while in the process of doing it. From this point of view, an organization is a collection of choices looking for problems, issues and feelings looking for decision situations in which they might be aired, solutions looking for issues to which they might be the answer, and decision makers looking for work.

Such a view of organizational choice focuses attention on the way the meaning of a choice changes over time. It calls attention to the strategic effects of timing, through the introduction of choices and problems, the time pattern of available energy, and the impact of organizational structure.

To understand processes within organizations, one can view a choice opportunity as a garbage can into which various kinds of problems and solutions are dumped by participants as they are generated. The mix of garbage in a single can depends on the mix of cans available, on the labels attached to the alternative cans, on what garbage is currently being produced, and on the speed with which garbage is collected and removed from the scene.

Such a theory of organizational decision making must concern itself with a relatively complicated interplay among the generation of problems in an organization, the deployment of personnel, the production of solutions, and the opportunities for choice. Although it may be convenient to imagine that choice opportunities lead first to the generation of decision alternatives, then to an examination of their consequences, then to an evaluation of those conse-

[2]We have based the model heavily on seven recent studies of universities: Christensen (1971), Cohen and March (1972), Enderud (1971), Mood (1971), Olsen (1970, 1971), and Rommetveit (1971). The ideas, however, have a broader parentage. In particular, they obviously owe a debt to Allison (1969), Coleman (1957), Cyert and March (1963), Lindblom (1965), Long (1958), March and Simon (1958), Schilling (1968), Thompson (1967), and Vickers (1965).

quences in terms of objectives, and finally to a decision, this type of model is often a poor description of what actually happens. In the garbage can model, on the other hand, a decision is an outcome or interpretation of several relatively independent streams within an organization.

Attention is limited here to interrelations among four such streams.

Problems. Problems are the concern of people inside and outside the organization. They might arise over issues of lifestyle; family; frustrations of work; careers; group relations within the organization; distribution of status, jobs, and money; ideology; or current crises of mankind as interpreted by the mass media or the nextdoor neighbor. All of these require attention.

Solutions. A solution is somebody's product. A computer is not just a solution to a problem in payroll management, discovered when needed. It is an answer actively looking for a question. The creation of need is not a curiosity of the market in consumer products; it is a general phenomenon of processes of choice. Despite the dictum that you cannot find the answer until you have formulated the question well, you often do not know what the question is in organizational problem solving until you know the answer.

Participants. Participants come and go. Since every entrance is an exit somewhere else, the distribution of "entrances" depends on the attributes of the choice being left as much as it does on the attributes of the new choice. Substantial variation in participation stems from other demands on the participants' time (rather than from features of the decision under study).

Choice opportunities. These are occasions when an organization is expected to produce behavior that can be called a decision. Opportunities arise regularly and any organization has ways of declaring an occasion for choice. Contracts must be signed; people hired, promoted, or fired; money spent; and responsibilities allocated.

Although not completely independent of each other, each of the streams can be viewed as independent and exogenous to the system. Attention will be concentrated here on examining the consequences of different rates and patterns of flows in each of the streams and different procedures for relating them.

THE GARBAGE CAN

A simple simulation model can be specified in terms of the four streams and a set of garbage processing assumptions.

Four basic variables are considered; each is a function of time.

A stream of choices. Some fixed number, m, of choices is assumed. Each choice is characterized by (a) an entry time, the calendar time at which that choice is activated for decision, and (b) a decision structure, a list of participants eligible to participate in making that choice.

A stream of problems. Some number, w, of problems is assumed. Each problem is characterized by (a) an entry time, the calendar time at which the problem becomes visible, (b) an energy requirement, the energy required to resolve a choice to which the problem is attached (if the solution stream is as high as possible), and (c) an access structure, a list of choices to which the problem has access.

A rate of flow of solutions. The verbal theory assumes a stream of solutions and a matching of specific solutions with specific problems and choices. A simpler set of assumptions is made and focus is on the rate at which solutions are flowing into the system. It is assumed that either because of variations in the stream of solutions or because of variations in the efficiency of search procedures withi the organization, different energies are required to solve the same problem at different times. It is further assumed that these variations are consistent for different problems. Thus, a solution coefficient, ranging between 0 and 1, which operates on the potential decision energies to determine the problem solving output (effective energy) actually realized during any given time period is specified.

A stream of energy from participants. It is assumed that there is some number, v, of participants. Each participant is characterized by a time series of energy available for organizational decision making. Thus, in each time period, each participant can provide some specified amount of potential energy to the organization.

Two varieties of organizational segmentation are reflected in the model. The first is the mapping of choices onto decision makers, the decision structure. The decision structure of the organization is described by D, a v-by-m array in which d_{ij} is 1 if the ith participant is eligible to participate in the making of the jth choice. Otherwise, d_{ij} is 0. The second is the mapping of problems onto choices, the access structure. The access structure of the organization is described by A, a w-by-m array in which a_{ij} is 1 if the jth choice is accessible to the ith problem. Otherwise, a_{ij} is 0.

In order to connect these variables, three key behavioral assumptions are specified. The first is an assumption about the additivity of energy requirements, the second specifies the way in which energy is allocated to choices, and the third describes the way in which problems are attached to choices.

Energy additivity assumption. In order to be made, each choice requires as much effective energy as the sum of all requirements of the several problems attached to it. The effective energy devoted to a choice is the sum of the energies of decision makers attached to that choice, deflated, in each time period, by the solution coefficient. As soon as the total effective energy that has been expended on a choice equals or exceeds the requirements at a particular point in time, a decision is made.

Energy allocation assumption. The energy of each participant is allocated to no more than one choice during each time period. Each participant allocates his energy among the choices for which he is eligible to the one closest to decision, that is the one with the smallest energy deficit at the end of the previous time period in terms of the energies contributed by other participants.

Problem allocation assumption. Each problem is attached to no more than one choice each time period, choosing from among those accessible by calculating the apparent energy deficits (in terms of the energy requirements of other problems) at the end of the previous time period and selecting the choice closest to decision. Except to the extent that priorities enter in the organizational structure, there is no priority ranking of problems.

These assumptions capture key features of the processes observed. They might be modified in a number of ways without doing violence to the empirical observations on which they are based. The consequences of these modifications, however, are not pursued here. Rather, attention is focused on the implications of the simple version described. The interaction of organizational structure and a garbage can form of choice will be examined.

ORGANIZATIONAL STRUCTURE

Elements of organizational structure influence outcomes of a garbage can decision process (a) by affecting the time pattern of the arrival of problems, choices, solutions, or decision makers, (b) by determining the allocation of energy by potential participants in the decision, and (c) by establishing linkages among the various streams.

The organizational factors to be considered are some that have real-world interpretations and implications and are applicable to the theory of organized anarchy. They are familiar features of organizations, resulting from a mixture of deliberate managerial planning, individual and collective learning, and imitation. Organizational structure changes as a response to such factors as market demand for personnel and the heterogeneity of values, which are external to the model presented here. Attention will be limited to the comparative statics of the model, rather than to the dynamics produced by organizational learning.

To exercise the model, the following are specified: (a) a set of fixed parameters which do not change from one variation to another, (b) the entry times for choices, (c) the entry times for problems, (d) the net energy load on the organization, (e) the access structure of the organization, (f) the decision structure of the organization, and (g) the energy distribution among decision makers in the organization.

Some relatively pure structural variations will be identified in each and examples of how variations in such structures might be related systematically to key exogenous variables will be given. It will then be shown how such factors of organizational structure affect important characteristics of the decisions in a garbage can decision process.

Fixed Parameters

Within the variations reported, the following are fixed: (a) number of time periods—twenty, (b) number of choice opportunities—ten, (c) number of decision makers—ten, (d) number of problems—twenty, and (e) the solution coefficients for the 20 time periods—0.6 for each period.[3]

---

[3]The model has also been exercised under conditions of a set of solution coefficients that varies over the time periods. Specifically, the following series has been used: 1, 0.9, 0.7, 0.3, 0.1, 0.1, 0.3,

Entry Times

Two different randomly generated sequences of entry times for choices are considered. It is assumed that one choice enters per time period over the first ten time periods in one of the following orders: (a) 10, 7, 9, 5, 2, 3, 4, 1, 6, 8, or (b) 6, 5, 2, 10, 8, 9, 7, 4, 1, 3.

Similarly, two different randomly generated sequences of entry times for problems are considered. It is assumed that two problems enter per time period over the first ten time periods in one of the following orders: (a) 8, 20, 14, 16, 6, 7, 15, 17, 2, 13, 11, 19, 4, 9, 3, 12, 1, 10, 5, 18, or (b) 4, 14, 11, 20, 3, 5, 2, 12, 1, 6, 8, 19, 7, 15, 16, 17, 10, 18, 9, 13.

Net Energy Load

The total energy available to the organization in each time period is 5.5 units. Thus, the total energy available over twenty time periods is $20 \times 5.5 = 110$. This is reduced by the solution coefficients to 66. These figures hold across all other variations of the model. The net energy load on the organization is defined as the difference between the total energy required to solve all problems and the total effective energy available to the organization over all time periods. When this is negative, there is, in principle, enough energy available. Since the total effective energy available is fixed at 66, the net load is varied by varying the total energy requirements for problems. It is assumed that each problem has the same energy requirement under a given load. Three different energy load situations are considered.

Net energy load 0: light load. Under this condition the energy required to make a choice is 1.1 times the number of problems attached to that choice. That is, the energy required for each problem is 1.1. Thus, the minimum total effective energy required to resolve all problems is 22, and the net energy load is $22 - 66 = -44$.

Net energy load 1: moderate load. Under this condition, the energy required for each problem is 2.2. Thus, the energy required to make a choice is 2.2 times the number of problems attached to that choice, and the minimum effective energy required to resolve all problems is 44. The net energy load is $44 - 66 = -22$.

Net energy load 2: heavy load. Under this condition, each problem requires energy of 3.3. The energy required to make a choice is 3.3 times the number of problems attached to that choice. The minimum effective energy required to resolve all problems is 66, and the net energy load is $66 - 66 = 0$.

Although it is possible from the total energy point of view for all problems to be resolved in any load condition, the difficulty of accomplishing that result where the net energy load is zero—a heavy load—is obviously substantial.

0.7, 0.9, 1, 0.6, 0.6, 0.6, 0.6, 0.6, 0.6, 0.6, 0.6, 0.6, 0.6. This simulation, using only one combination of choice and problem entry times, gives results consistent with all of the conclusions reported in the present article.

Access Structure

Three pure types of organizational arrangements are considered in the access structure (the relation between problems and choices).

Access structure 0: unsegmented access. This structure is represented by an access array in which any active problem has access to any active choice.

$$A_0 = \begin{array}{l} 1111111111 \\ 1111111111 \\ 1111111111 \\ 1111111111 \\ 1111111111 \\ 1111111111 \\ 1111111111 \\ 1111111111 \\ 1111111111 \\ 1111111111 \\ 1111111111 \\ 1111111111 \\ 1111111111 \\ 1111111111 \\ 1111111111 \\ 1111111111 \\ 1111111111 \\ 1111111111 \\ 1111111111 \\ 1111111111 \end{array}$$

Access structure 1: hierarchical access. In this structure both choices and problems are arranged in a hierarchy such that important problems—those with relatively low numbers—have access to many choices, and important choices—those with relatively low numbers—are accessible only to important problems. The structure is represented by the following access array:

$$A_1 = \begin{array}{l} 1111111111 \\ 1111111111 \\ 0111111111 \\ 0111111111 \\ 0011111111 \\ 0011111111 \\ 0001111111 \\ 0001111111 \\ 0000111111 \\ 0000111111 \\ 0000011111 \\ 0000011111 \\ 0000001111 \\ 0000001111 \\ 0000000111 \\ 0000000111 \\ 0000000011 \end{array}$$

0000000011
0000000001
0000000001

Access structure 2: specialized access. In this structure each problem has access to only one choice and each choice is accessible to only two problems, that is, choices specialize in the kinds of problems that can be associated to them. The structure is represented by the following access array:

$$A_2 =$$

1000000000
1000000000
0100000000
0100000000
0010000000
0010000000
0001000000
0001000000
0000100000
0000100000
0000010000
0000010000
0000001000
0000001000
0000000100
0000000100
0000000010
0000000010
0000000001
0000000001

Actual organizations will exhibit a more complex mix of access rules. Any such combination could be represented by an appropriate access array. The three pure structures considered here represent three classic alternative approaches to the problem of organizing the legitimate access of problems to decision situations.

Decision Structure

Three similar pure types are considered in the decision structure (the relation between decision makers and choices).

Decision structure 0: unsegmented decisions. In this structure any decision maker can participate in any active choice opportunity. Thus, the structure is represented by the following array:

$$D_0 =$$

1111111111
1111111111
1111111111
1111111111
1111111111
1111111111

```
1111111111
1111111111
1111111111
1111111111
```

Decision structure 1: hierarchical decisions. In this structure both decision makers and choices are arranged in a hierarchy such that important choices—low numbered choices—must be made by important decision makers—low numbered decision makers—and important decision makers can participate in many choices. The structure is represented by the following array:

$$D_1 = \begin{array}{l} 1111111111 \\ 0111111111 \\ 0011111111 \\ 0001111111 \\ 0000111111 \\ 0000011111 \\ 0000001111 \\ 0000000111 \\ 0000000011 \\ 0000000001 \end{array}$$

Decision structure 2: specialized decisions. In this structure each decision maker is associated with a single choice and each choice has a single decision maker. Decision makers specialize in the choices to which they attend. Thus, we have the following array:

$$D_2 = \begin{array}{l} 1000000000 \\ 0100000000 \\ 0010000000 \\ 0001000000 \\ 0000100000 \\ 0000010000 \\ 0000001000 \\ 0000000100 \\ 0000000010 \\ 0000000001 \end{array}$$

As in the case of the access structure, actual decision structures will require a more complicated array. Most organizations have a mix of rules for defining the legitimacy of participation in decisions. The three pure cases are, however, familiar models of such rules and can be used to understand some consequences of decision structure for decision processes.

Energy Distribution

The distribution of energy among decision makers reflects possible variations in the amount of time spent on organizational problems by different decision makers. The solution coefficients and variations in the energy requirement for problems affect the overall relation between energy available and energy required. Three different variations in the distribution of energy are considered.

Energy distribution 0: important people—less energy. In this distribution important people, that is people defined as important in a hierarchical decision structure, have less energy. This might reflect variations in the combination of outside demands and motivation to participate within the organization. The specific energy distribution is indicated as follows:

Decision maker	Energy	
1	0.1	
2	0.2	
3	0.3	
4	0.4	
5	0.5	$= E_0$
6	0.6	
7	0.7	
8	0.8	
9	0.9	
10	1.0	

The total energy available to the organization each time period (before deflation by the solution coefficients) is 5.5.

Energy distribution 1: equal energy. In this distribution there is no internal differentiation among decision makers with respect to energy. Each decision maker has the same energy (0.55) each time period. Thus, there is the following distribution:

Decision maker	Energy	
1	0.55	
2	0.55	
3	0.55	
4	0.55	
5	0.55	$= E_1$
6	0.55	
7	0.55	
8	0.55	
9	0.55	
10	0.55	

The total energy available to the organization each time period (before deflation by the solution coefficients) is 5.5.

Energy distribution 2: important people—more energy. In this distribution energy is distributed unequally but in a direction opposite to that in E_0. Here the people defined as important by the hierarchical decision structure have more energy. The distribution is indicated by the following:

Decision maker	Energy	
1	1.0	
2	0.9	
3	0.8	
4	0.7	
5	0.6	$= E_2$
6	0.5	
7	0.4	
8	0.3	
9	0.2	
10	0.1	

As in the previous organizations, the total energy available to the organization each time period (before deflation by the solution coefficients) is 5.5.

Where the organization has a hierarchical decision structure, the distinction between important and unimportant decision makers is clear. Where the decision structure is unsegmented or specialized, the variations in energy distribution are defined in terms of the same numbered decision makers (lower numbers are more important than higher numbers) to reflect possible status differences which are not necessarily captured by the decision structure.

Simulation Design

The simulation design is simple. A Fortran version of the garbage can model is given in the appendix, along with documentation and an explanation. The $3^4 = 81$ types of organizational situations obtained by taking the possible combinations of the values of the four dimensions of an organization (access structure, decision structure, energy distribution, and net energy load) are studied here under the four combinations of choice and problem entry times. The result is 324 simulation situations.

SUMMARY STATISTICS

The garbage can model operates under each of the possible organizational structures to assign problems and decision makers to choices, to determine the energy required and effective energy applied to choices, to make such choices and resolve such problems as the assignments and energies indicate are feasible. It does this for each of the twenty time periods in a twenty-period simulation of organizational decision making.

For each of the 324 situations, some set of simple summary statistics on the process is required. These are limited to five.

Decision Style

Within the kind of organization postulated, decisions are made in three different ways.

By resolution. Some choices resolve problems after some period of working on them. The length of time may vary, depending on the number of problems. This is the familiar case that is implicit in most discussions of choice within organizations.

By oversight. If a choice is activated when problems are attached to other choices and if there is energy available to make the new choice quickly, it will be made without any attention to existing problems and with a minimum of time and energy.

By flight. In some cases choices are associated with problems (unsuccessfully) for some time until a choice more attractive to the problems comes along. The problems leave the choice, and thus it is now possible to make the decision. The decision resolves no problems; they have now attached themselves to a new choice.

Some choices involve both flight and resolution—some problems leave, the remainder are solved. These have been defined as resolution, thus slightly exaggerating the importance of that style. As a result of that convention, the three styles are mutually exclusive and exhaustive with respect to any one choice. The same organization, however, may use any one of them in different choices. Thus, the decision style of any particular variation of the model can be described by specifying the proportion of completed choices which are made in each of these three ways.

Problem Activity

Any measure of the degree to which problems are active within the organization should reflect the degree of conflict within the organization or the degree of articulation of problems. Three closely related statistics of problem activity are considered. The first is the total number of problems not solved at the end of the twenty time periods; the second is the total number of times that any problem shifts from one choice to another, while the third is the total number of time periods that a problem is active and attached to some choice, summed over all problems. These measures are strongly correlated with each other. The third is used as the measure of problem activity primarily because it has a relatively large variance; essentially the same results would have been obtained with either of the other two measures.

Problem Latency

A problem may be active, but not attached to any choice. The situation is one in which a problem is recognized and accepted by some part of the organization, but is not considered germane to any available choice. Presumably, an organization with relatively high problem latency will exhibit somewhat different symptoms from one with low latency. Problem latency has been measured by the total number of periods a problem is active, but not attached to a choice, summed over all problems.

Decision-Maker Activity

To measure the degree of decision-maker activity in the system, some measure which reflects decision maker energy expenditure, movement, and persistence is required. Four are considered: (a) the total number of time periods a decision maker is attached to a choice, summed over all decision makers, (b) the total number of times that any decision maker shifts from one choice to another, (c) the total amount of effective energy available and used, and (d) the total effective energy used on choices in excess of that required to make them at the time they are made. These four measures are highly intercorrelated. The second was used primarily because of its relatively large variance; any of the others would have served as well.

Decision Difficulty

Because of the way in which decisions can be made in the system, decision difficulty is not the same as the level of problem activity. Two alternative measures are considered: the total number of choices not made by the end of the twenty time periods and the total number of periods that a choice is active, summed over all choices. These are highly correlated. The second is used, primarily because of its higher variance; the conclusions would be unchanged if the first were used.

IMPLICATIONS OF THE MODEL

An analysis of the individual histories of the simulations shows eight major properties of garbage can decision processes.

First, resolution of problems as a style for making decisions is not the most common style, except under conditions where flight is severely restricted (for instance, specialized access) or a few conditions under light load. Decision making by flight and oversight is a major feature of the process in general. In each of the simulation trials there were twenty problems and ten choices. Although the mean number of choices not made was 1.0, the mean number of problems not solved was 12.3. The results are detailed in Table 1. The behavioral and normative implications of a decision process which appears to make choices in large part by flight or by oversight must be examined. A possible explanation of the behavior of organizations that seem to make decisions

Table 1: Proportion of Choices That Resolve Problems Under Four Conditions of Choice and Problem Entry Times, by Load and Access Structure

		Access structure			
		All	*Unsegmented*	*Hierarchical*	*Specialized*
	Light	0.55	0.38	0.61	0.65
Load	Moderate	0.30	0.04	0.27	0.60
	Heavy	0.36	0.35	0.23	0.50
	All	0.40	0.26	0.37	0.58

without apparently making progress in resolving the problems that appear to be related to the decisions may be emerging.

Second, the process is quite thoroughly and quite generally sensitive to variations in load. As Table 2 shows, an increase in the net energy load on the system generally increases problem activity, decision-maker activity, decision difficulty, and the uses of flight and oversight. Problems are less likely to be solved, decision makers are likely to shift from one problem to another more frequently, choices are likely to take longer to make and are less likely to resolve problems. Although it is possible to specify an organization that is relatively stable with changes in load, it is not possible to have an organization that is stable in behavior and also has other desirable attributes. As load changes, an organization that has an unsegmented access structure with a specialized decision structure stays quite stable. It exhibits relatively low decision difficulty and decision maker activity, very low problem latency, and maximum problem activity. It makes virtually all decisions placed before it, uses little energy from decision makers, and solves virtually no problems.

Third, a typical feature of the model is the tendency of decision makers and problems to track each other through choices. Subject to structural restrictions on the tracking, decision makers work on active problems in connection with active choices; both decision makers and problems tend to move together from choice to choice. Thus, one would expect decision makers who have a feeling that they are always working on the same problems in somewhat different contexts, mostly without results. Problems, in a similar fashion, meet the same people wherever they go with the same result.

Fourth, there are some important interconnections among three key aspects of the efficiency of the decision processes specified. The first is problem activity, the amount of time unresolved problems are actively attached to choice situations. Problem activity is a rough measure of the potential for decision conflict in the organization. The second aspect is problem latency, the amount of time problems spend activated but not linked to choices. The third aspect is decision time, the persistence of choices. Presumably, a good organizational structure would keep both problem activity and problem latency low through rapid problem solution in its choices. In the garbage can process such a result was never observed. Segmentation of the access structure tends to reduce the number of unresolved problems active in the organization but at the cost of increasing the latency period of problems and, in most cases, the time

Table 2: Effects of Variations in Load Under Four Conditions of Choice and Problem Entry Times

		Mean problem activity	*Mean decision maker activity*	*Mean decision difficulty*	*Proportion of choices by flight or oversight*
	Light	114.9	60.9	19.5	.45
Load	Moderate	204.3	63.8	32.9	.70
	Heavy	211.1	76.6	46.1	.64

326

Decision Making in Military Organizations

devoted to reaching decisions. On the other hand, segmentation of the decision structure tends to result in decreasing problem latency, but at the cost of increasing problem activity and decision time.

Fifth, the process is frequently sharply interactive. Although some phenomena associated with the garbage can are regular and flow through nearly all of the cases, for example, the effect of overall load, other phenomena are much more dependent on the particular combination of structures involved. Although high segmentation of access structure generally produces slow decision time, for instance, a specialized access structure, in combination with an unsegmented decision structure, produces quick decisions.

Sixth, important problems are more likely to be solved than unimportant ones. Problems which appear early are more likely to be resolved than later ones. Considering only those cases involving access hierarchy where importance is defined for problems, the relation between problem importance and order of arrival is shown in Table 3. The system, in effect, produces a queue of problems in terms of their importance, to the disadvantage of late-arriving, relatively unimportant problems, and particularly so when load is heavy. This queue is the result of the operation of the model. It was not imposed as a direct assumption.

Seventh, important choices are less likely to resolve problems than unimportant choices. Important choices are made by oversight and flight. Unimportant choices are made by resolution. These differences are observed under both of the choice entry sequences but are sharpest where important choices enter relatively early. Table 4 shows the results. This property of important choices in a garbage can decision process can be naturally and directly related

Table 3: Proportion of Problems Resolved under Four Conditions of Choice and Problem Entry Times, by Importance of Problem and Order of Arrival of Problem (for Hierarchical Access)

		Time of arrival of problem	
		Early, first 10	Late, last 10
Importance of problem	High, first 10	0.46	0.44
	Low, last 10	0.48	0.25

Table 4: Proportion of Choices That Are Made by Flight or Oversight under Four Conditions of Choice and Problem Entry Times, by Time of Arrival and Importance of Choice (for Hierarchical Access or Decision Structure)

		Time of arrival of choice	
		Early, first 5	Late, last 5
Importance of choice	High, first 5	0.86	0.65
	Low, last 5	0.54	0.60

to the phenomenon in complex organizations of important choices which often appear to just happen.

Eighth, although a large proportion of the choices are made, the choice failures that do occur are concentrated among the most important and least important choices. Choices of intermediate importance are virtually always made. The proportion of choice failures, under conditions of hierarchical access or decision structures is as follows:

Three most important choices	0.14
Four middle choices	0.05
Three least important choices	0.12

In a broad sense, these features of the process provide some clues to how organizations survive when they do not know what they are doing. Much of the process violates standard notions of how decisions ought to be made. But most of those notions are built on assumptions which cannot be met under the conditions specified. When objectives and technologies are unclear, organizations are charged to discover some alternative decision procedures which permit them to proceed without doing extraordinary violence to the domains of participants or to their model of what an organization should be. It is a hard charge, to which the process described is a partial response.

At the same time, the details of the outcomes clearly depend on features of the organizational structure. The same garbage can operation results in different behavioral symptoms under different levels of load on the system or different designs of the structure of the organization. Such differences raise the possibility of predicting variations in decision behavior in different organizations.

Editor's note: A section of the article has been removed here, since it is not relevant.

CONCLUSION

A set of observations made in the study of some university organizations has been translated into a model of decision making in organized anarchies, that is, in situations which do not meet the conditions for more classical models of decision making in some or all of three important ways: preferences are problematic, technology is unclear, or participation is fluid. The garbage can process is one in which problems, solutions, and participants move from one choice opportunity to another in such a way that the nature of the choice, the time it takes, and the problems it solves all depend on a relatively complicated intermeshing of elements. These include the mix of choices available at any one time, the mix of problems that have access to the organization, the mix of solutions looking for problems, and the outside demands on the decision makers.

A major feature of the garbage can process is the partial uncoupling of problems and choices. Although decision making is thought of as a process for solving problems, that is often not what happens. Problems are worked upon in the context of some choice, but choices are made only when the shifting combinations of problems, solutions, and decision makers happen to make action possible. Quite commonly this is after problems have left a given choice arena or before they have discovered it (decisions by flight or oversight).

Four factors were specified which could be expected to have substantial effects on the operation of the garbage can process: the organization's net energy load and energy distribution, its decision structure, and problem access structure. Though the specifications are quite simple their interaction is extremely complex, so that investigation of the probable behavior of a system fully characterized by the garbage can process and previous specifications requires computer simulation. No real system can be fully characterized in this way. Nonetheless, the simulated organization exhibits behaviors which can be observed some of the time in almost all organizations and frequently in some, such as universities. The garbage can model is a first step toward seeing the systematic interrelatedness of organizational phenomena which are familiar, even common, but which have previously been regarded as isolated and pathological. Measured against a conventional normative model of rational choice, the garbage can process does appear pathological, but such standards are not really appropriate. The process occurs precisely when the preconditions of more normal rational models are not met.

It is clear that the garbage can process does not resolve problems well. But it does enable choices to be made and problems resolved, even when the organization is plagued with goal ambiguity and conflict, with poorly understood problems that wander in and out of the system, with a variable environment, and with decision makers who may have other things on their minds.

There is a large class of significant situations in which the preconditions of the garbage can process cannot be eliminated. In some, such as pure research, or the family, they should not be eliminated. The great advantage of trying to see garbage can phenomena together as a process is the possibility that that process can be understood, that organizational design and decision making can take account of its existence and that, to some extent, it can be managed.

APPENDIX

Version five of the Fortran program for the garbage can model reads in entry times for choices, solution coefficients, entry times for problems, and two control variables, NA and IO. NA controls various combinations of freedom of movement for decision makers and problems. All results are based on runs in which NA is 1. Comment cards included in the program describe other possibilities. The latter variable, IO, controls output. At the value 1, only summary statistics are printed. At the value 2, full histories of the decision process are printed for each organizational variant.

The following are ten summary statistics:

   1. (KT) Problem persistence, the total number of time periods a problem is activated and attached to a choice, summed over all problems.

2. (KU) Problem latency, the total number of time periods a problem is activated, but not attached to a choice, summed over all problems.

3. (KV) Problem velocity, the total number of times any problem shifts from one choice to another.

4. (KW) Problem failures, the total number of problems not solved at the end of the twenty time periods.

5. (KX) Decision-maker velocity, the total number of times any decision maker shifts from one choice to another.

6. (KS) Decision-maker inactivity, the total number of time periods a decision maker is not attached to a choice, summed over all decision makers.

7. (KY) Choice persistence, the total number of time periods a choice is activated, summed over all choices.

8. (KZ) Choice failures, the total number of choices not made by the end of the twenty time periods.

9. (XR) Energy reserve, the total amount of effective energy available to the system but not used because decision makers are not attached to any choice.

10. (XS) Energy wastage, the total effective energy used on choices in excess of that required to make them at the time they are made.

In its current form the program generates both the problem access structure and the decision structure internally. In order to examine the performance of the model under other structures, modification of the code or its elimination in favor of Read statements to take the structures from cards will be necessary.

Under IO = 2, total output will be about ninety pages. Running time is about two minutes under a Watfor compiler.

APPENDIX TABLE: Fortran Program for Garbage Can Model, Version Five

```
C       THE GARBAGE CAN MODEL. VERSION 5
C          ***
C       IO IS 1 FOR SUMMARY STATISTICS ONLY
C       IO IS 2 FOR SUMMARY STATISTICS PLUS HISTORIES
C          ***
C       NA IS 1 WHEN PROBS AND DMKRS BOTH MOVE
C       NA IS 2 WHEN DMKRS ONLY MOVE
C       NA IS 3 WHEN PROBS ONLY MOVE
C       NA IS 4 WHEN NEITHER PROBS NOR DMKRS MOVE
C          ***
C       IL IS A FACTOR DETERMINING PROB ENERGY REQ
C          ***
C       VARIABLES
C            ***
C            NUMBERS
```

```
C                  COUNTERS      UPPER LIMITS      NAME
C                  ***
C                    I               NCH           CHOICES
C                    J               NPR           PROBLEM
C                    K               NDM           DECMKRS
C                    LT              NTP           TIME
C            ***
C         ARRAYS
C                  CODE            DIMEN           NAME
C                  ***
C                  ICH             NCH             CHOICE ENTRY TIME
C                  ICS             NCH             CHOICE STATUS
C                  JET             NPR             PROB. ENTRY TIME
C                  JF              NPR             PROB. ATT. CHOICE
C                  JFF             NPR             WORKING COPY JF
C                  JPS             NPR             PROB. STATUS
C                  KDC             NDM             DMKR. ATT. CHOICE
C                  KDCW            NDM             WORKING COPY KDC
C                  XEF             MCH             ENERGY EXPENDED
C                  XERC            NCH             CHOICE EN. REQT.
C                  XERP            NPR             PROB. EN. REQT.
C                  XSC             NTP             SOLUTION
C                                                  COEFFICIENT
C            ***
C         2-DIMENSIONAL ARRAYS
C                  ***
C                  CODE            DIMEN           NAME
C                  ***
C                  IKA             NCH,NDM         DECISION STRUCTURE
C                  JIA             NPR,NCH         ACCESS STRUCTURE
C                  XEA             NDM,NTP         ENERGY MATRIX
C            ***
C            ***
C            ***
C         ***
C      SUMMARY STATISTICS FOR EACH VARIANT
C                  COL  1: KZ: TOTAL DECISIONS NOT MADE
C                  COL  2: KY: TOTAL NUMBER ACTIVE CHOICE PERIODS
C                  COL  3: KX: TOTAL NUMBER CHANGES BY DECISION
C                              MAKERS
C                  COL  4: KW: TOTAL PROBLEMS NOT SOLVED
C                  COL  5: KV: TOTAL NUMBER CHANGES BY PROBLEMS
C                  COL  6: KU: TOTAL NUMBER LATENT PROBLEM
C                              PERIODS
C                  COL  7: KT: TOTAL NUMBER ATTACHED PROBLEM
C                              PERIODS
C                  COL  8: KS: TOTAL NUMBER PERIODS DMKRS RESTING
C                  COL  9: XR: TOTAL AMOUNT OF UNUSED ENERGY
C                  COL 10: XS: TOTAL AMOUNT OF WASTED ENERGY
C         ***
C      INPUT BLOCK, READ-IN AND INITIALIZATIONS.
       DIMENSION ICH(20),JF(20),KERC(20),XEE(20),XSC(20),JFF(20),XERP(20
      *),JET(20),JPS(20),ICS(20),KDC(20),KDCW(20),JIA(20,20),IKA(20,20),
       CXEA(20,20),KABC(20,20),KBBC(20,20),KCBC(20,20)
1001   FORMAT(5(I3,1X))
1002   FORMAT(10(I3,1X))
1003   FORMAT(25(I1,1X))
```

```
1004      FORMAT(10F4,2)
          NTP=20
          NCH=10
          NPR=20
          NDM=10
   8      READ(5,1002)(ICH(I),I=1,NCH)
          READ(5,1004)(XSC(LT),LT=1,NTP)
          READ(5,1002)(JET(J),J=1,NPR)
          READ(5,1003) NA,IO
          WRITE(6,1050) NA
1050      FORMAT('1          DEC.MAKER MOVEMENT CONDITION (NA) IS ',I1/)
          DO 998 IL=1,3
          IB=IL-1
          DO 997 JAB=1,3
          JA=JAB-1
          DO 996 JDB=1,3
          JD=JDB-1
          DO 995 JEB=1,3
          JE=JEB-1
          XR=0.0
          XS=0.0
          KS=0
          DO 10 I=1,NCH
          XERC(I)=1.1
          XEE(I)=0.0
  10      ICS(I)=0
          DO 20 K=1,NDM
          KDC(K)=0
  20      KDCW(K)=KDC(K)
          DO 40 J=1,NPR
          XERP(J)=IL*1.1
          JF(J)=0
          JFF(J)=0
  40      JPS(J)=0
   C      SETTING UP THE DECISION MAKERS ACCESS TO CHOICES.
          DO 520 I=1,NCH
          DO 510 J=1,NDM
          IKA(I,J)=1
          IF(JD.EQ.1) GO TO 502
          IF(JD.EQ.2) GO TO 504
          GO TO 510
 502      IF(I,GE,J) GO TO 510
          IKA(I,J)=0
          GO TO 510
 504      IF(J.EQ.I) GO TO 510
          IKA(I,J)=0
 510      CONTINUE
 520      CONTINUE
   C      SETTING UP THE PROBLEMS ACCESS TO CHOICES.
          DO 560 I=1,NPR
          DO 550 J=1,NCH
          JIA(I,J)=0
          IF(JA.EQ.1) GO TO 532
          IF(JA.EQ.2) GO TO 534
          JIA(I,J)=1
          GO TO 550
 532      IF ((I-J).GT.(I/2)) GO TO 550
```

```
             JIA(I,J)=1
             GO TO 550
     534   IF(I.NE.(2*J)) GO TO 550
             JIA(I,J)=1
             JIA(I-1,J)=1
     550   CONTINUE
     560   CONTINUE
             DO 590 I=1,NDM
             DO 580 J=1,NTP
             XEA(I,J)=0.55
             IF(JF.EQ.1)GO TO 580
             XXA=I
             IF(JE.EQ.0) GO TO 570
             XEA(I,J)=(11.0-XXA)/10.0
             GO TO 580
     570   XEA(I,J)=XXA/10.0
     580   CONTINUE
     590   CONTINUE
C          *** FINISH READ      INITIALIZATION
             DO 994 LT=1,NTP
    1006   FORMAT(2X,6HCHOICE,2X,I3,2X,6HACTIVE )
C          CHOICE ACTIVATION
C          DO 101 I=1,NCH
             IF(ICH(I).NE.LT)GO TO 101
             ICS(I)=1
     101   CONTINUE
C          PROB. ACTIVATION
             DO 110 J=1,NPR
             IF(JET(J).NE.LT)GO TO 110
             JPS(J)=1
     110   CONTINUE
C          FIND MOST ATTRACTIVE CHOICE FOR PROBLEM J
             DO 120 J=1,NPR
             IF (JPS(J).NE.1) GO TO 120
             IF(NA.EQ.2)GO TO 125
             IF(NA.EQ.4)GO TO 125
             GO TO 126
     125   IF(JF(J).NE.0) GO TO 127
     126   S=1000000
             DO 121 I=1,NCH
             IF (ICS(I).NE.1) GO TO 121
             IF(JIA(J,I).EQ.0)GO TO 121
             IF(JF(J).EQ.0)GO TO 122
             IF(JF(J).EQ.I)GO TO 122
             IF((XERP(J)+XERC(I)-XEE(I)).GE.S)GO TO 121
             GO TO 123
     122   IF ((XERC(I)-XEE(I)).GE.S)GO TO 121
             S=XERC(I)-XEE(I)
             GO TO 124
     123   S=XERP(J)+XERC(I)-XEE(I)
     124   JFF(J)=I
     121   CONTINUE
             GO TO 120
     127   JFF(J)=JF(J)
     120   CONTINUE
             DO 130 J=1,NPR
```

```
131     JF(J)=JFF(J)
130     JFF(J)=0
        LTT=LT-1
        IF(LT.EQ.1)LTT=1
C       FIND MOST ATTRACTIVE CHOICE FOR DMKR K
        DO 140 K=1,NDM
        IF(NA.EQ.3)GO TO 145
        IF(NA.EQ.4) GO TO 145
        GO TO 146
145     IF(KDC(K),NE.0)GO TO 147
146     S=1000000
        DO 141 I=1,NCH
        IF (ICS(I).NE.1) GO TO 141
        IF (IKA(I,K).EQ.0)GO TO 141
        IF (KDC(K).EQ.0)GO TO 142
        IF (KDC(K).EQ.I)GO TO 142
148     IF((XFRC(I)-XEE(I)-(XEA(K.LTT)*XSC(LTT))).GE.S)GO TO 141
        GO TO 143
142     IF((XERC(I)-XEE(I)).GE.S)GO TO 141
        S=XERC(I)-XEE(I)
        GO TO 144
143     S=XERC(I)-XEE(I)-XEA(K,LTT)*XSC(LTT)
144     KDCW(K)=I
141     CONTINUE
        GO TO 140
147     KDCW(K)=KDC(K)
140     CONTINUE
        DO 150 K=1,NDM
151     KDC(K)=XDCW(K)
        IF(KDC(K).NE.0)GO TO 150
        XR=XR+(XEA(K,LT)*XSC(LT))
        KS=KS+1
150     KDCW(K)=0
C       ESTABLISHING THE ENERGY REQUIRED TO MAKE EACH CHOICE.
        DO 199 I=1,NCH
        IF(ICS(I).EQ.0)GO TO 199
        XERC(I)=0.0
        DO 160 J=1,NPR
        IF(JPS(J).NE.1) GO TO 160
        IF(JF(J).NE.I)GO TO 160
        XERC(I)=XERC(I)+XERP(J)
160     CONTINUE
        DO 170 K=1,NDM
        IF(IKA(I,K).EQ.0)GO TO 170
        IF(KDC(K).NE.I)GO TO 170
        XEE(I)=XEE(I)+XSC(LT)*XEA(K,LT)
170     CONTINUE
199     CONTINUE
C       MAKING DECISIONS
        DO 299 I=1,NCH
        IF (ICS(I).NE.1) GO TO 299
        IF(XERC(I).GT.XEE(I))GO TO 299
        XS=XS+XEE(I)-XERC(I)
        ICS(I)=2
        DO 250 J=1,NPR
        IF(JF(J).NE.I)GO TO 250
```

```
         JPS(J)=2
250      CONTINUE
         IF(NA.EQ.3)GO TO 261
         IF(NA.EQ.4)GO TO 261
         GO TO 299
261      DO 262 K=1,NDM
         IF(KDCW(K).NE.I)GO TO 262
         KDCW(K)=1
262      CONTINUE
299      CONTINUE
         DO 200 I=1,NCH
200      KABC(LT,I)=ICS(I)
         DO 210 K=1,NDM
         KBBC(LT,K)=KDC(K)
         IF(KDCW(K).EQ.0)GO TO 210
         KDC(K)=0
210      KDCW(K)=0
         DO 220 J=1,NPR
         KCBC(LT,J)=JF(J)
         IF(JPS(J).EQ.0) GO TO 230
         IF(JPS(J).EQ.1) GO TO 220
         KCBC(LT,J)=1000
         GO TO 220
230      KCBC(LT,J)=-1
220      CONTINUE
994      CONTINUE
C        FINISH TIME PERIOD LOOP. BEGIN ACCUMULATION OF 10
         SUMMARY STATISTICS.
         KZ=0
         KY=0
         KX=0
         KW=0
         KV=0
         KU=0
         KT=0
         DO 310 I=1,NTP
         DO 320 J=1,NCH
         IF(KABC(I,J).NE.1)GO TO 320
         KY=KY+1
         IF(I.NE.NTP)GO TO 320
         KZ=KZ+1
320      CONTINUE
310      CONTINUE
         DO 330 I=2,NTP
         DO 340 J=1,NDM
         IF(KBBC(I,J).EQ.KBBC(I-1,J))GO TO 340
         KX=KX+1
340      CONTINUE
330      CONTINUE
         DO 350 I=1,NTP
         DO 360 J=1,NPR
         IF(KCBC(I,J).EQ.0)GO TO 351
         IF(KCBC(I,J).EQ.-1) GO TO 360
         IF(KCBC(I,J).EQ.1000) GO TO 352
         KT=KT+1
         GO TO 360
351      KU=KU+1
```

```
        GO TO 360
352     IF(I.NE.NTP)GO TO 360
        KW=KW+1
360     CONTINUE
350     CONTINUE
        KW=NPR−KW
        DO 370 I=2,NTP
        DO 380 J=1,NPR
        IF(KCBC(I,J).EQ.KCBC(I−1,J))GO TO 380
        KV=KV+1
380     CONTINUE
370     CONTINUE
C       BEGIN WRITEOUT OF MATERIALS FOR THIS ORGANIZATIONAL
VARIANT.
1000    FORMAT(1H1)
1019    FORMAT(2X,'LOAD=',I1,' PR.ACC.=',I1,' DEC.STR.=',I1,' EN.DIST.=',
        BI1,2X,'STATS 1−10',3X,8I5,1X,2F6.2/)
        WRITE(6,1019)IB,JA,JD,JE,KZ,KY,KX,KW,KV,KU,KT,KS,XR,XS
        IF(IO.EQ.1) GO TO 995
2000    FORMAT(' CHOICE ACTIVATION HISTORY',34X.'DEC.MAKER
        ACTIVITY HISTOR BY'/' 20 TIME PERIODS, 10 CHOICES',33X,'20
        TIME PERIODS, 10 DEC.MAKE CRS'/' 0=INACTIVE, 1=ACTIVE,
        C2=MADE',33X,'0=INACTIVE,X=WORKING ON CHO DICE X'//9X,'1 2 3 4 5
        6 7 8 9 10',30X,'1 2 3 4 5 6 7 8 9 10'/)
        WRITE(6,2000)
2001    FORMAT( 5X,I2,3X,10I2,25X,I2,3X,10I2)
        WRITE(6,2001)(LT,(KABC(LT,J),J=1,NCH),LT,( KBBC(LT,J),J=1,NDM),
        B LT=1,NTP )
2002    FORMAT(/' PROBLEM HISTORY:RO=S=TIME, COLS=PROBS., −1=
        NOT ENTERED., B0=UNATTACHED,X=ATT.TO CH.X,**SOLVED'/10x,
        C' 1 2 3 4 5 6 7 8 9 10 11 12 13 14 15 16 17 18  19 20'/)
        WRITE(6,2002)
2003    FORMAT(20(5X,I2,3X,20(IX,I2)/1))
        WRITE(6,2003)(LT,(KCBC(LT,J),J=1,NPR),LT=1,NTP)
        WRITE(6,1000)
995     CONTINUE
996     CONTINUE
997     CONTINUE
998     CONTINUE
        STOP
        END
```

*******   DATA AS FOLLOWS (AFTER GUIDE CARDS)   ***********

```
0         1         2         3         4         5         6         7         8
12345678901234567890123456789012345678901234567890123456789012345678901234567890

008.005.006.007.004.009.002.010.003.001
1.000.900.700.300.100.100.300.700.901.00
0.600.600.600.600.600.600.600.600.600.60
009.005.008.007.010.003.003.001.007.009
006.008.005.002.004.002.004.010.006.001
1 2
```

Michael D. Cohen is an NSF-SSRC postdoctoral fellow at Stanford University; James G. March is David Jacks Professor of Higher Education, Political Science, and Sociology at Stanford University; and Johan P. Olsen is an assistant professor of Political Science at the University of Bergen.

BIBLIOGRAPHY

Allison, Graham T. "Conceptual Models and the Cuban Missile Crises." *American Political Science Review* 63(1969): 689–718.

Christensen, Søren. Institut og laboratorieorganisation på Danmarks tekniske Højskole. Copenhagen: Copenhagen School of Economics, 1971.

Cohen, Michael D., and March, James G. *The American College President*. New York: McGraw-Hill, Carnegie Commission on the Future of Higher Education, 1972.

Coleman, James S. *Community Conflict*. Glencoe: Free Press, 1957.

Cyert, Richard M., and March, James G. *Behavioral Theory of the Firm*. Englewood Cliffs; Prentice-Hall, 1963.

Enderud, Harald. Rektoratet og den centrale administration på Danmarks tekniske Højskole. Copenhagen: Copenhagen School of Economics, 1971.

Lindblom, Charles E. *The Intelligence of Democracy*. New York: Macmillan, 1965.

Long, Norton. "The Local Community as an Ecology of Games." *American Journal of Sociology* 44 (1958): 251–261.

March, James G., and Simon, Herbert A. *Organizations*. New York: John Wiley, 1958.

Mood, Alexander (ed.). *More Scholars for the Dollar*. New York: McGraw-Hill, Carnegie Commision on the Future of Higher Education, 1971.

Olsen, Johan P. *A Study of Choice in an Academic Organization*. Bergen: University of Bergen, 1971.

Olsen, Johan P. *The Reorganization of Authority in an Academic Organization*. Bergen: University of Bergen, 1971.

Rommetveit, Kåre. Framveksten av det medisinske fakultet ved Universitet i Tromsø. Bergen: University of Bergen, 1971.

Schilling, Warner R. "The H-bomb Decision: How to Decide without Actually Choosing." In *The Politics of Science*, edited by W.R. Nelson. London: Oxford University Press, 1968.

Thompson, James D. *Organizations in Action*. New York: McGraw-Hill, 1967.

Vickers, Geoffrey. *The Art of Judgment*. New York: Basic Books, 1965.

Name Index

Subject Index

Access structures
  choice opportunities and, 146
  definition of, 18
  efficiency of, 173, 174, 177–179, 186–188
  hierarchical, 18
  in Monte Carlo model, 146, 147, 151
  organization classification by, 150
  program chief, 186–187, 208–210
  solutions and, 146
  types of
    quasi-specialized, 187, 200, 209
    random, 186, 209
    specialized, 146, 186–187, 200, 209
    total, 186, 209
    universal, 146
Accountability, 307
Administrative Behavior (Simon), 60
AEO. *See* Assistant executive officer
Afghanistan, Soviet invasion of, 261
Agency, theories of, 15
Ambiguity(ies), 1–2, 12. *See also* Participant
    ambiguity; Preference ambiguity;
    Technology ambiguity
Anarchy(ies), organized, 12. *See also*
    Ambiguity(ies)
  naval warfare as, 38, 40
  organizational intelligence in, 26
Angola, 300–301
"Architecture of complexity, The" (Simon),
    60
Artifical intelligence (AI), 66–69
  barriers to, 68–69
  limitations of, 68
  miniaturization of, 68–69
Aspiration levels, 129–131, 143, 148
Assistant executive officer (AEO), 168, 199
  access probability of, 178, 187–188
  efficiency measurement of, 173–174,
    178–179
  saliency, 174, 178–179, 188, 208

Atlantic Monthly, 278
Attention allocation, 5–6, 21, 85, 143
Authority structure, 60, 283–284. *See also*
    Hierarchical authority system
    (HAS)
  delegation of, 6
  mutual exchange relations and, 60–61

Bad spot syndrome, 213–215, 223
Behavioral decision theory, 121
Behavioral Theory of the Firm, A (Cyert and
    March), 80
Beirut. *See* Lebanon
Belief assignment, 148–149
Benevolence of technology
  decision style and, 156–157
  performance levels and, 154–156,
    157–159
Bottom-up planning, 125
Bounded rationality, 233. *See also* Rational
    choice model
Boxcar effect, 49–50
Budget. *See also* Office of Management and
    Budget (OMB)
  congressional role of, 135
  OSD function in, 136
  peacetime priorities, 264–267
  top-down focus of, 135–136

CEO. *See* Chief executive officer
Chief executive officer (CEO), 167, 199
  efficiency, 175
  saliency, 179, 188, 206–208
Choice, organizational, 80
Choice densities, 150, 159–160
Choice opportunities
  in C3I procurement, 108–109
  entry times, 149–150
  linkages between, 4
  in loosely coupled systems, 85